Contents

Identifying more able mathematicians

What characteristics might gifted mathematicians display?

More able mathematicians are likely to have good powers of logic, reasoning and deduction, and will be able to hypothesise, experiment and categorise. This list of questions may be useful in establishing mathematical ability:

- Do they enjoy number puzzles?
- Do they show a good awareness of patterns and sequences?
- Do they ask interesting mathematical questions?
- Do they give explanations you may not have thought of?
- Are they good at solving problems?
- Are they good at applying knowledge in unfamiliar contexts?
- Do they like to choose their own methods?

This list is by no means exhaustive; there are many more characteristics that may be observed in gifted mathematicians, and many gifted children will display only some of these qualities. For example, a child who you believe to be a high achiever may not show advanced problem-solving skills. This may be because they don't yet know how to set about solving a problem, because they haven't learned the strategies required. You may find children who are gifted in just one or two areas of maths. For example, they may excel at calculation and number, but may not do so well at shape and space.

What about children who don't show any of these traits?

There may be gifted mathematicians in your class who do not display any of these characteristics. This could be due to one or more of these factors:

- lack of confidence
- unwillingness to stand out from their peers
- the desire to avoid 'extra' work
- an insufficiently stimulating learning environment
- lack of challenging activities
- lack of familiarity with basic number facts and skills
- language barriers
- problems with reading and/or writing.

What can be done to identify gifted mathematicians?

Here are a few suggestions of practical steps that can be taken:

- Ask parents and carers to supply information about any mathematical abilities they have noticed at home.
- Conduct a brief interview with children at the beginning of the school year to find out about their interests and anything they think they are especially good at.
- Keep a portfolio of particularly good work completed either at home or in school. This will help to assess progress and spot patterns.
- Testing can provide evidence of high ability, but you should be aware that some more able or gifted children may not perform well in tests, and many factors can affect children's performance in a test environment.

The identification–provision cycle

A two-way process of identification and provision is needed. You will not be able to observe exceptional abilities in children unless they are given the opportunity to demonstrate them. Activities must be provided that challenge children and allow them the scope to show what they can do. In this way, appropriate provision leads to identification, which in turn allows you to make better provision.

Providing for more able mathematicians

How can a stimulating learning environment be created?

It is important that more able children are asked probing and open-ended questions. These will allow you to assess and extend their understanding, get them to think more deeply, and lead them to continue their explorations. Here are some examples of the types of question you might ask:

- What do you think will happen if …?
- How many different ways can you …?
- Is it always true that …?
- Why?
- What patterns can you see?
- Why did you choose to work it out like that?
- Why do you think this happens?
- How do you know that?
- Can you make up a rule?

It is also important to create an atmosphere in which children feel they are able to ask questions, and have access to resources to find the answers. One practical thing you can do is to create a 'Challenge corner': an area of the classroom where you can set out maths resources, puzzles, prompts and questions for children to explore. This should be accessible by all children in the class, giving everyone the opportunity to challenge themselves.

What are 'challenge' activities?

'Challenging' work can be defined as something difficult that requires the learner to learn something new. For children to enjoy a challenging activity there must be something about it that motivates them. For example, it could be about a subject that they are particularly interested in, or it could be placed in a meaningful context, with a goal that has nothing to do with completing a page of calculations. The level of challenge must be just right – it must stretch them without being so difficult that children are demotivated and want to give up. The best challenge activities will allow different levels of outcome, so that a wide range of children can succeed at them.

More able or gifted children need to be given opportunities to:

- exercise their curiosity and explore new ideas
- choose their own ways of working and representing their results
- ask questions and find the answers
- make conjectures and test them out
- discuss their ideas with adults and other children
- reflect on their own work.

What thinking skills should more able children be using?

More able children need to be given opportunities to access their higher-order thinking skills. Bloom's Taxonomy identifies six levels of thinking:

- knowledge – the acquisition and recall of facts
- comprehension – the ability to describe what you know in your own words
- application – the application of what you have learned in context
- analysis – for example, categorising things and identifying patterns
- synthesis – the creation of new ideas or products
- evaluation – the evaluation of ideas, processes and products.

The first three are generally thought of as lower-order skills, although application requires a deeper level of thinking than the first two. If you can plan activities that incorporate the three higher-order thinking skills, children will be challenged.

Introducing *Abacus Evolve Challenge*

What is *Abacus Evolve Challenge*?

Abacus Evolve Challenge is designed to stretch and motivate more able mathematicians. The activities are creative and engaging, and offer opportunities for written, verbal and practical work. Using and applying skills are practised throughout, with plenty of open-ended investigations and problem solving. Speaking and listening skills are promoted through the high proportion of paired and group work.

Which children is *Challenge* for?

Challenge is not just for those children who would be classed as 'gifted'. The activities have been written with the whole of the 'top table' in mind. Differentiation by outcome is often possible because of the open-ended nature of the activities, and the teacher notes accompanying the activities usually suggest ways to differentiate further.

What types of enrichment and extension are provided?

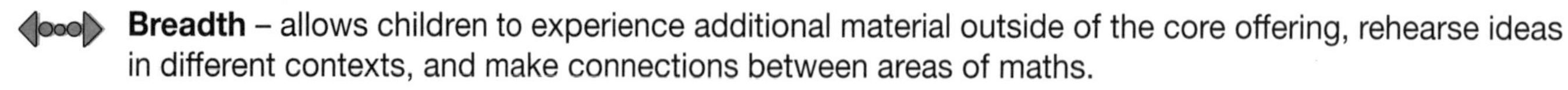

Breadth – allows children to experience additional material outside of the core offering, rehearse ideas in different contexts, and make connections between areas of maths.

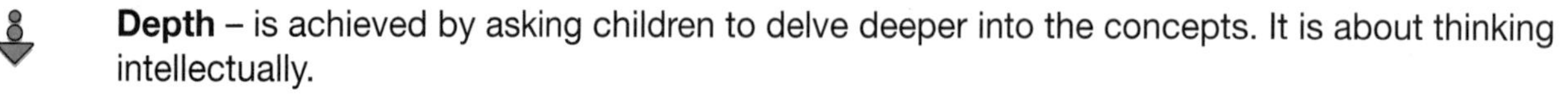

Depth – is achieved by asking children to delve deeper into the concepts. It is about thinking intellectually.

Pace – refers to speed in covering the curriculum and can result in achievement at a level exceptional for the age range.

What types of activity are provided?

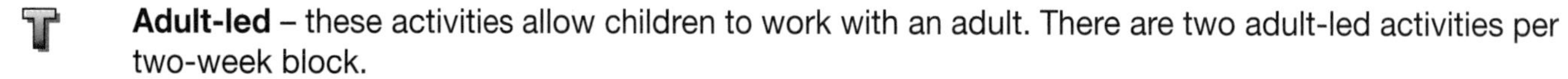

Adult-led – these activities allow children to work with an adult. There are two adult-led activities per two-week block.

Practise – these activities allow children to practise what they have learned with the rest of the class, at a higher level.

Discover – these activities allow children to learn about things like famous mathematicians and ancient number systems.

Investigate – these activities allow children to explore a concept freely, asking questions, looking for patterns and drawing conclusions.

When should the *Challenge* activities be used?

There are 90 activities per Year; six for every two-week block. They are intended to be used by small groups of children in the part of the maths lesson when the class is split into groups for differentiated work. This allows the more able children to be included in the whole-class parts of the lesson.

What level of adult support is needed?

The *Challenge* resources have been designed with effective classroom management in mind. Four of the activities in each two-week block can be carried out by children without adult support, allowing you to focus on the other groups. Some of these will require a couple of minutes to get the group started on the activity, but after this children should be able to continue unaided.

Two of the activities in each two-week block require adult support, so that your able and gifted children have the benefits of adult input.

How does *Challenge* fit alongside the *Abacus Evolve* maths scheme?

The *Challenge* activities are organised using the same blocked structure as *Abacus Evolve*. You can use the *Abacus Evolve* weekly plans, and fit the *Challenge* activities into these. *Abacus Evolve* objectives are referenced for each activity, and these will help you to decide which core activities to run them alongside. If you also have the *Challenge* Module of I-Planner Online, you will be able to see the *Challenge* activities allocated to suitable days in the weekly plans.

It is intended that the more able children join in with the whole-class parts of the lesson: the mental oral starter, the main teaching activity, and the plenary. When the rest of the class is split up into 1-dot, 2-dot and 3-dot groups to do Textbook activities or practical activities, you can give your top group a *Challenge* activity that fits in well with what the rest of the class are doing.

Can I use *Challenge* with another maths scheme or my own planning?

Although the *Challenge* activities complement *Abacus Evolve* activities, they are not specifically linked to them, so there is no dependence on any part of the *Abacus Evolve* scheme. The *Challenge* activities can be used to accompany any other maths scheme or your own planning. You can search for *Challenge* activities that fit your teaching by looking at the Renewed Framework objectives in the Teacher Guide. All of the Renewed Framework objectives are covered by the *Challenge* activities.

Using the *Challenge* resources

What resources are in the *Challenge* range?

Each Year includes:

- a Teacher Guide
- a Textbook
- an I-Planner Online Module.

Teacher Guide

The Teacher Guide contains detailed notes to accompany each activity. The information provided includes:

- Suggested group size and adult support
- Resources required (Textbook pages, Photocopy Masters and other resources)
- *Abacus Evolve* objectives
- Renewed Framework objectives
- A description of the activity
- 'Extra help': ideas for differentiating at a lower level
- 'Further extension': ideas for differentiating at a higher level
- 'If you have time': ideas for continuing the activity
- Background maths information for the non-specialist teacher
- 'Be aware': things to watch out for, such as common misconceptions
- Outcomes for the activity, given in child-friendly language
- Ideas for other resources to support the activity, such as useful websites.

Textbook

There are five Textbook pages per two-week block, so nearly every activity has an accompanying Textbook page. The pages are colourful and engaging, and they include the following features:

- speech bubbles to indicate opportunities for discussion
- an Extra activity at the bottom of each page for children who finish early.

The Textbook pages are not just intended for children to use individually. They are often suitable for paired or group work.

I-Planner Online

The *Abacus Evolve* I-Planner is a powerful online tool that provides ready-to-use weekly, medium-term and yearly plans that are completely flexible. It can save hours of planning time, but allows you to adapt the plans to meet the exact needs of your class. The Challenge module of I-Planner for each Year includes an extra column in the weekly plans in which you can see all the Challenge activities allocated to suitable days. This allows you to plan the Challenge activities seamlessly into your maths lessons.

What support is provided for assessing the children?

The adult-led activities are ideal for day-to-day observational assessment, as they provide plenty of opportunities to work closely with the children and ask probing questions to ascertain their level of understanding.

The charts on pages 8–11 of this book show the Assessment Foci from the Assessing Pupils' Progress guidelines, and the Challenge activities that can be used to provide evidence towards this type of assessment.

On pages 106–115 of this book you will find three end-of-term investigative activities. These will allow you to assess how well children use and apply the skills they have built up over the term.

Icon guide

Group size

 Children working individually, without an adult

 Children working in pairs, without an adult

 Children working in groups, without an adult

 Children working in groups, with an adult

Type of resource

 Textbook

 Photocopy Master

 Additional resources

Type of enrichment/extension

 Breadth

 Depth

 Pace

Type of activity

 Adult-led

 Practise

 Discover

 Investigate

Support for Assessing Pupils' Progress

If you are using Assessing Pupil's Progress to assess children, you may find this chart helpful when deciding which of the *Challenge* activities could be used to provide evidence towards each Assessment Focus.

We do not recommend that you use every activity to make an assessment. It is also important to recognise that a full assessment cannot be made on the basis of the *Challenge* activities alone; you will need to draw on other sources of information as well. We would advise that in each block of work you use this chart as guidance towards choosing one activity to assess against APP criteria, to complement other day-to-day or periodic assessments.

The Year 6 *Challenge* activities should give children the opportunity to work at a high Level 5, and in some cases at a low Level 6.

	Ma1 Using and applying mathematics		
	Problem solving	**Communicating**	**Reasoning**
Level 5	• A1.1 What are you worth? • A1.2 Let's cook • A1.3 Money for charity • B1.1 Consecutive numbers • D1.6 Viewing figures • E1.6 Tides • B2.2 Music maths • C2.5 Average word lengths • E2.3 Fill it up • E2.4 Magazine monthly • A3.5 Summer holiday • B3.2 Pop tour • B3.4 Making a bird table • C3.2 Probability game • C3.4 Fences • C3.5 Time zones • E3.1 Angel of the North • E3.2 Walking speeds • E3.3 Maps	• B1.1 Consecutive numbers • B1.2 Straw patterns • B1.4 Gate shapes • D1.5 Strange subtractions • B2.5 Bird's eye view • C2.5 Average word lengths • D2.3 Addition walls • E2.6 Square number patterns • A3.6 Well I never! • B3.3 Subtracting with a difference • C3.2 Probability game • C3.4 Fences • E3.5 Domino rectangles	• B1.2 Straw patterns • B1.3 Naming numbers • B1.6 Match the properties • D1.2 Angles in quadrilaterals • D1.3 More missing angles • D1.5 Strange subtractions • E1.1 Last digits • A2.2 Which calculation? • A2.4 Where does the number go? • A2.5 Exploring powers of numbers • A2.6 Horses in a field • B2.3 Approximate multiplications • C2.1 Compound shapes • C2.3 More compound shapes • D2.3 Addition walls • D2.4 Square roots • D2.5 Brackets • D2.6 Matchstick patterns • E2.6 Square number patterns • A3.6 Well I never! • B3.3 Subtracting with a difference • E3.5 Domino rectangles

Ma2 Number			
	Numbers and the number system	**Fractions, decimals, percentages, ratio and proportion**	**Operations, relationships between them**
Level 6		• E2.4 Magazine monthly	
Level 5	• A1.1 What are you worth? • A1.3 Money for charity • B1.3 Naming numbers • E1.1 Last digits • A2.1 Planets in our Solar System • A2.2 Which calculation? • A2.5 Exploring powers of numbers • E3.6 PINs	• A1.2 Let's cook • E1.6 Tides • A2.3 Posting a parcel • A2.4 Where does the number go? • E2.5 Decimal dominoes	• E1.3 Russian multiplication • B2.1 Where do the brackets go? • D2.1 Adding decimals • D2.5 Brackets • D3.5 Missing-number divisions

Ma2 Number			
	Mental, written and calculator methods	**Solving numerical problems**	**Algebra**
Level 6	• B2.3 Approximate multiplications • D2.4 Square roots	• E2.2 Food guidelines • A3.3 Stretching and shrinking • E3.4 Three ratios	
Level 5	• A1.5 Pay rise • D1.4 Finding differences • D1.5 Strange subtractions • D1.6 Viewing figures • B2.2 Music maths • D2.1 Adding decimals • D2.2 Dinner out • D2.3 Addition walls • E2.1 Bestselling books • A3.2 VAT • A3.4 Messy maths book • A3.5 Summer holiday • B3.1 More money • B3.2 Pop tour • B3.3 Subtracting with a difference • B3.4 Making a bird table • D3.4 Exploring division • D3.5 Missing-number divisions • D3.6 Long division	• A1.6 How many are needed? • C1.5 A pound of carrots • E1.4 Fair shares • D2.2 Dinner out • E2.1 Bestselling books • A3.1 Flying high • B3.1 More money • B3.5 How much juice? • B3.6 How much petrol? • D3.6 Long division • E3.1 Angel of the North • E3.2 Walking speeds • E3.3 Maps	• B1.1 Consecutive numbers • B1.2 Straw patterns • A2.6 Horses in a field • B2.4 Coordinates • D2.6 Matchstick patterns • D3.2 Rotating shapes

Ma3 Shape, space and measures			
	Properties of shape	**Properties of position and movement**	**Measures**
Level 6	• D1.3 More missing angles		• C2.2 Cuboid boxes
Level 5	• B1.4 Gate shapes • B1.6 Match the properties • D1.2 Angles in quadrilaterals • B2.6 Seeing shapes	• B2.5 Bird's eye view • D3.1 Reflecting 3D shapes • D3.2 Rotating shapes • D3.3 Transformations in patterns	• B1.5 Constructing triangles • C1.4 Metric lengths • C1.5 A pound of carrots • D1.1 Angles around a circle • A2.3 Posting a parcel • C2.1 Compound shapes • C2.3 More compound shapes • E2.3 Fill it up • B3.5 How much juice? • B3.6 How much petrol? • C3.4 Fences • C3.5 Time zones

Ma4 Handling data			
	Specifying the problem and planning, collecting data	**Processing and representing data**	**Interpreting data**
Level 5	• C1.3 Dice throws • C3.1 Dice probabilities • C3.2 Probability game	• C1.1 Science test • C1.2 Spelling scores • C1.3 Dice throws • C2.6 Conversion graphs	• C1.1 Science test • C1.2 Spelling scores • C2.4 Finding averages • C2.5 Average word lengths • C2.6 Conversion graphs • C3.3 Fruity pie charts

Talk Maths Extra pupil software

Abacus Evolve *Talk Maths Extra* will reinforce key maths skills and get children talking about maths.

1 Marble run

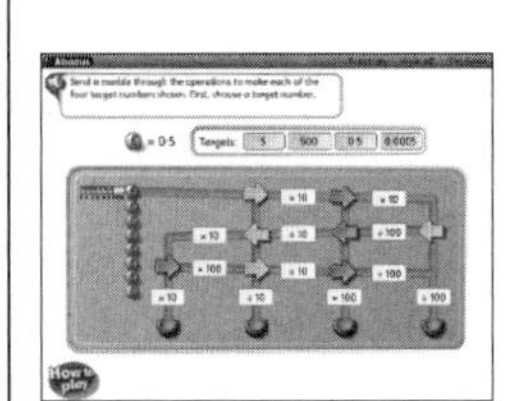

Make a number by selecting a path for a marble through various calculations.

2 Always, sometimes, never

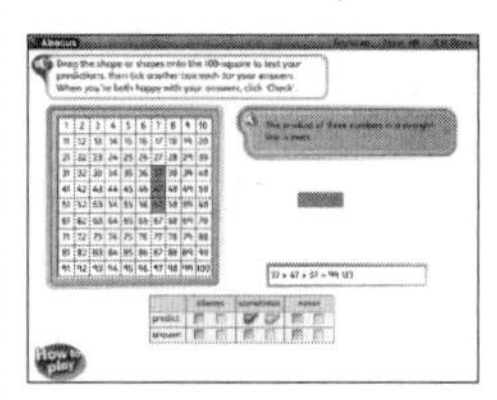

Investigate statements about products of consecutive and adjacent numbers.

3 Shape properties

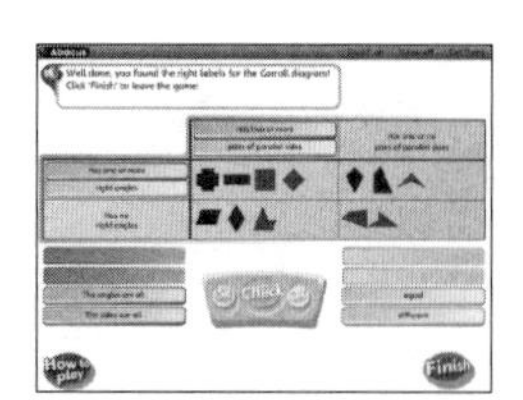

Place shapes onto a Carroll diagram, then choose labels to match.

4 Number triangle

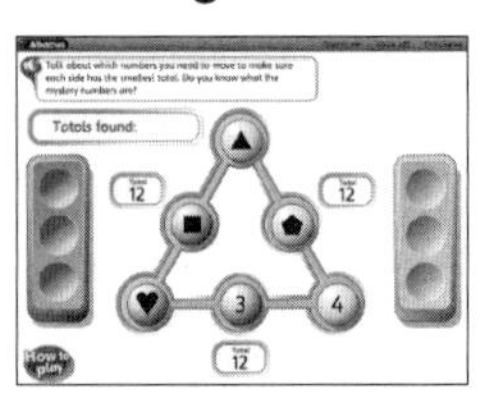

Place numbers around a triangle so that each side has the same total.

5 Function machine

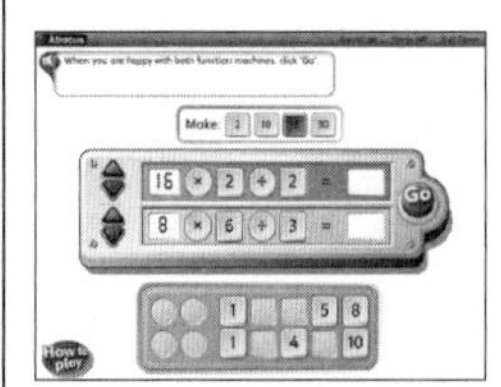

Make a number in two ways by forming number sentences involving × and ÷.

6 Mystery decimal

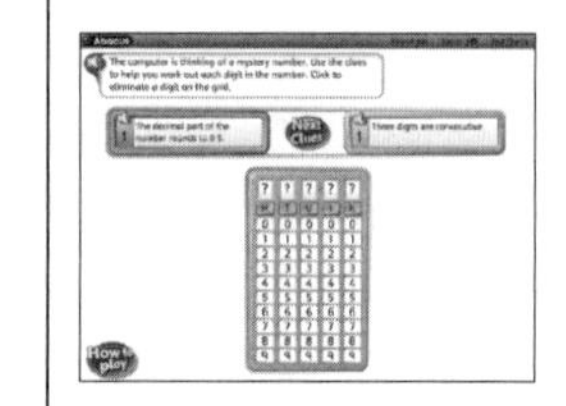

Find a mystery HTU·th number by eliminating digits based on clues.

7 Place-value puzzle

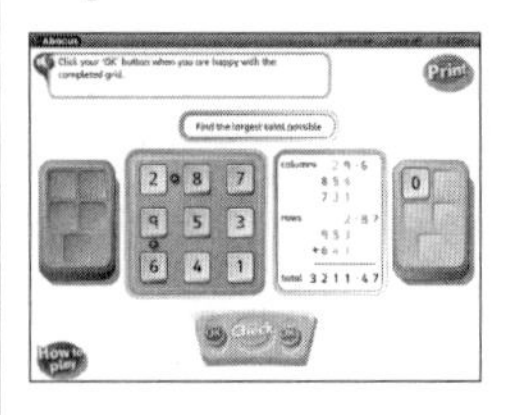

Create HTU, TU·t and U·th numbers to make the largest and smallest totals possible.

8 Visualising 3D shapes

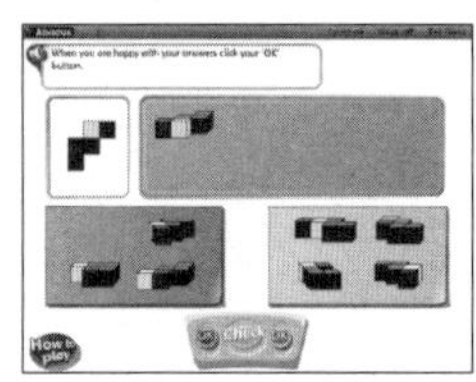

Work out which 3D images would have a given view from the top.

9 Line graphs

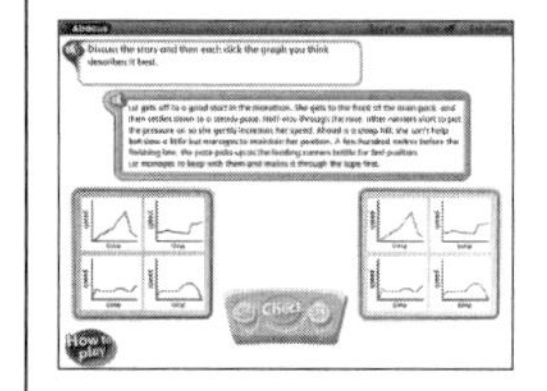

Choose the line graph that best represents what happens in a story.

10 Mystery number

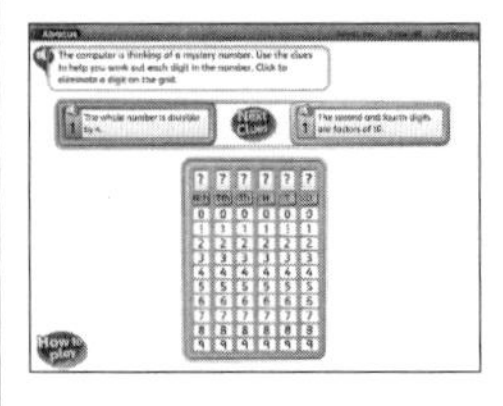

Find a mystery 6-digit number by eliminating digits based on clues.

11 Marble run

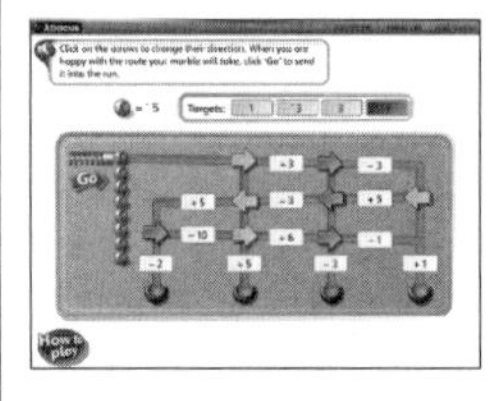

Make a number by selecting a path for a marble through various calculations.

12 Capacity dominoes

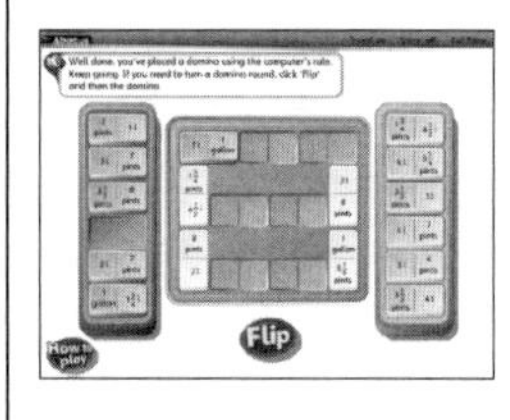

Place dominoes so that touching ends have roughly equivalent capacities.

13 Direction and distance

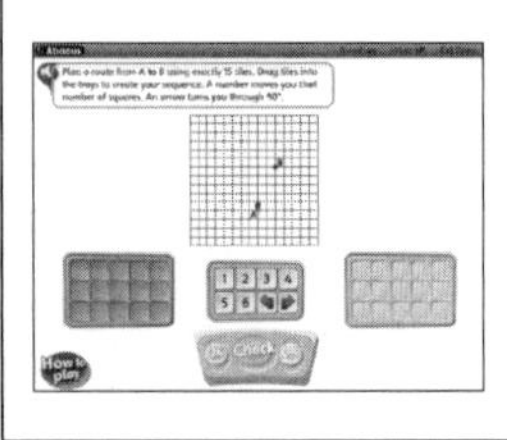

Describe a route to get from point A to point B, using a given number of instruction tiles.

14 Ordering currency amounts

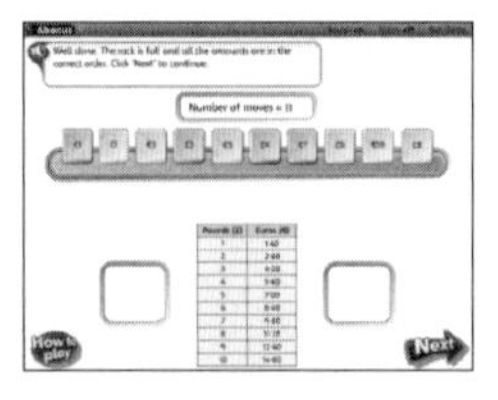

Place amounts in pounds and euros/dollars in order, using a conversion table to help.

15 Number properties

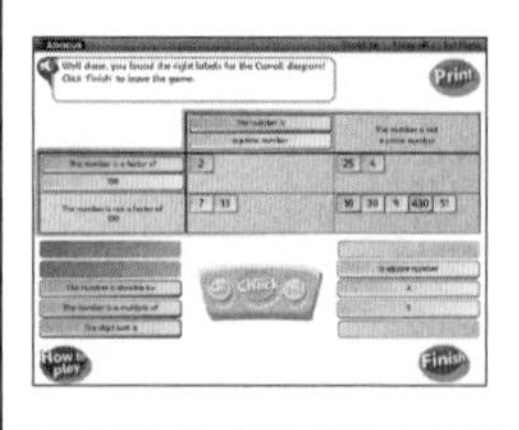

Create numbers and put them on a Carroll diagram, then choose labels to match.

16 Units of measurement

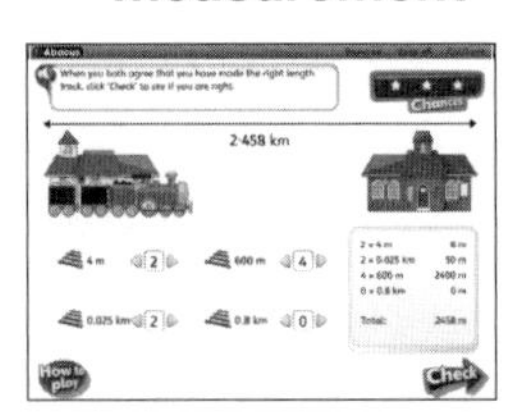

Select units of length, capacity and weight to make up a larger unit.

17 Measuring capacity

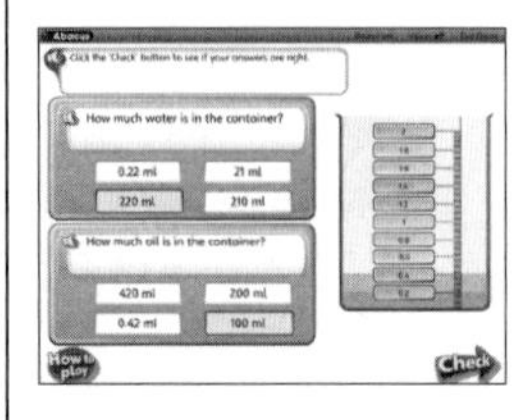

Complete the scale on a measuring beaker, then say how much water and oil is in the beaker.

18 Estimating an area

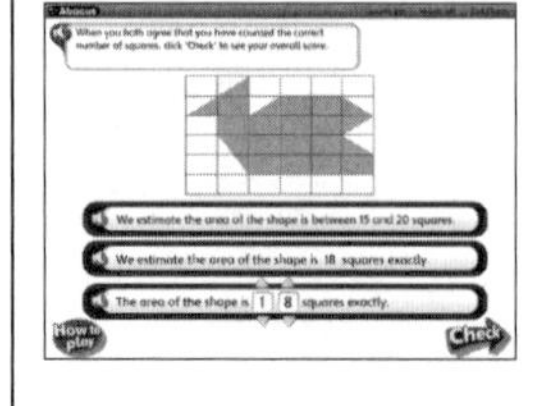

Look at an irregular shape laid over a grid and estimate the area in squares.

This chart shows which *Talk Maths Extra* activities could be used to extend some of the *Challenge* activities. The 4-dot version of each *Talk Maths Extra* activity is likely to be the most suitable for your children.

***Challenge* activity**	**Related *Talk Maths Extra* activities**
A1.1 What are you worth?	1 Marble run
A1.3 Money for charity	1 Marble run
A1.4 Casting out 9s	5 Function machine
B1.1 Consecutive numbers	2 Always, sometimes, never
B1.3 Naming numbers	2 Always, sometimes, never, 10 Mystery number, 15 Number properties
B1.4 Gate shapes	3 Shape properties
B1.6 Match the properties	3 Shape properties
C1.4 Metric lengths	1 Marble run, 16 Units of measurement
D1.2 Angles in quadrilaterals	3 Shape properties
D1.4 Finding differences	4 Number triangle
E1.3 Russian multiplication	5 Function machine
A2.1 Planets in our Solar System	6 Mystery decimal, 7 Place-value puzzle
A2.2 Which calculation?	1 Marble run, 7 Place-value puzzle
A2.3 Posting a parcel	16 Units of measurement
A2.4 Where does the number go?	7 Place-value puzzle
A2.5 Exploring powers of numbers	10 Mystery number
B2.2 Music maths	1 Marble run
B2.5 Bird's eye view	8 Visualising 3D shapes
B2.6 Seeing shapes	8 Visualising 3D shapes
C2.1 Compound shapes	18 Estimating an area
C2.3 More compound shapes	18 Estimating an area
C2.6 Conversion graphs	9 Line graphs
E2.1 Bestselling books	7 Place-value puzzle
E2.6 Square number patterns	10 Mystery number, 15 Number properties
A3.1 Flying high	11 Marble run
A3.6 Well I never!	1 Marble run
B3.1 More money	7 Place-value puzzle
B3.2 Pop tour	7 Place-value puzzle
B3.5 How much juice?	17 Measuring capacity
B3.6 How much petrol?	12 Capacity dominoes
D3.3 Transformations in patterns	13 Direction and distance
E3.1 Angel of the North	14 Ordering currency amounts
E3.2 Walking speeds	14 Ordering currency amounts
E3.6 PINs	10 Mystery number, 15 Number properties

Solve the Problem pupil software

Abacus Evolve *Solve the Problem* will challenge children with rich, open-ended problems that draw on a range of mathematical strategies.

Mystery Shopper

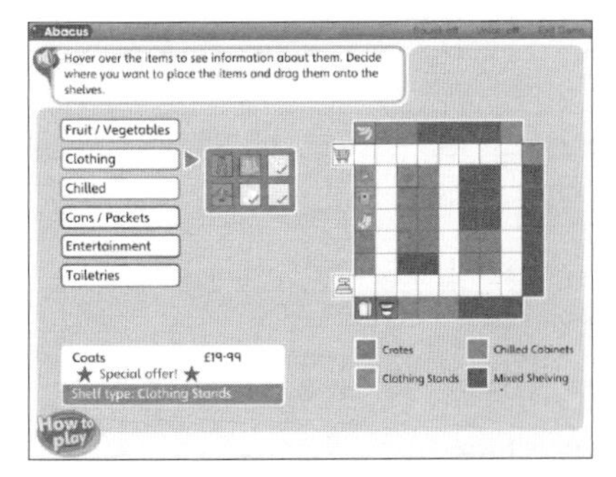

Children are in charge of a supermarket. They must arrange the layout of six types of item inside the shop so that it best appeals to customers. They watch a mystery shopper buy her goods and use the results to help them refine their layout.

Underwater Explorer

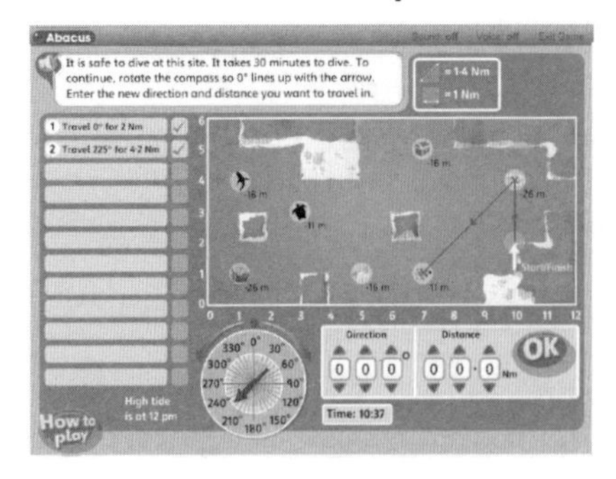

Children plan a route for a diving boat. They score points for each site visited and incur penalties for hitting land. They also need to watch out for the tide. Various challenges can be set, e.g. planning a route to see a set number of sites in a given time/ distance.

Antarctic Mission

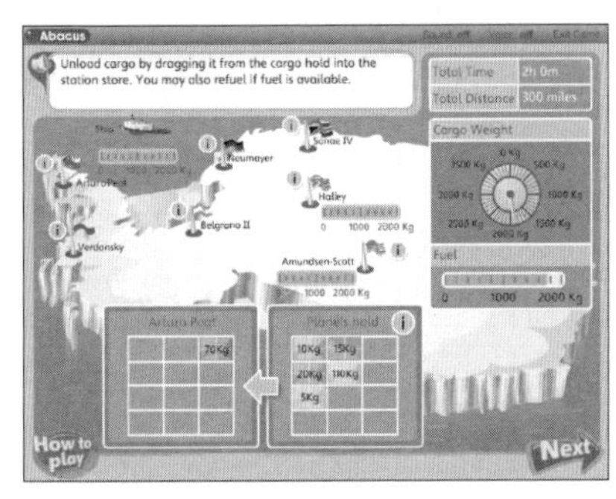

Children plan the routes for a plane to drop off and pick up supplies for research stations in the Antarctic. They must think about where they can refuel. Various challenges can be set, e.g. visiting as many stations as possible in a given time.

Apple Picking

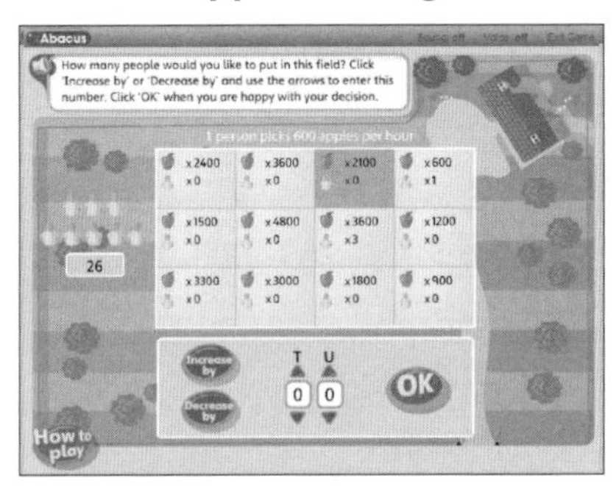

Children use fruit pickers to pick all the apples in an orchard. They must use a given number of people to pick all the apples in a set time, or as quickly as possible. Alternatively, they can be given a time and asked to find the minimum number of people required.

Cycle Race

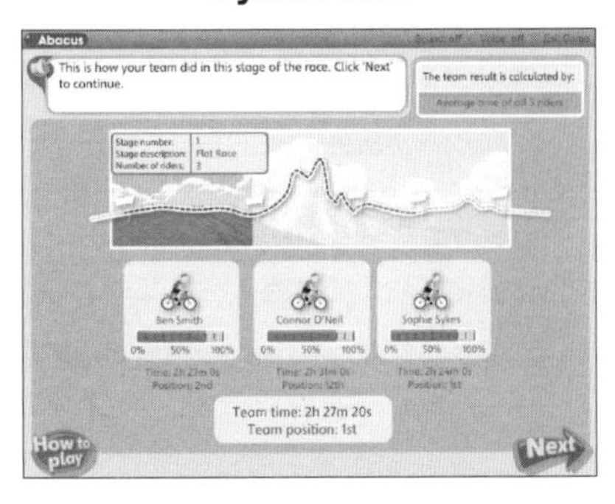

Children choose three riders from a team of six to compete in four stages of a cycle race. They use each rider's performance in previous races to inform their selections. Children will need to plan ahead to secure the best overall position for their team.

Setting the Stage

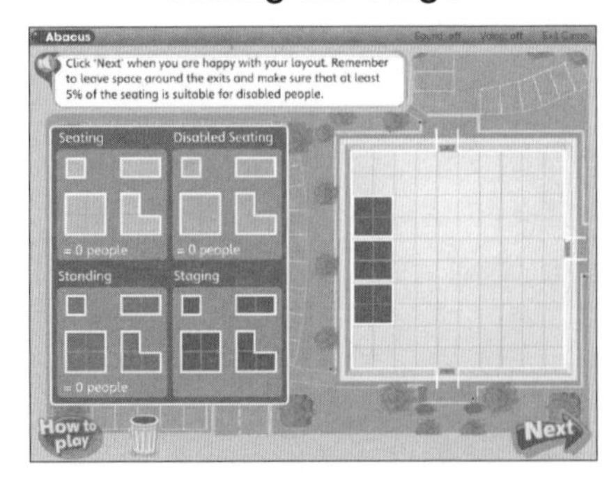

Children own a stadium, which is used for concerts, sports and shows. The layout can be adjusted for each event. They must design different layouts to satisfy individual event criteria, whilst meeting the requirements of the Health and Safety department.

This chart shows which *Solve the Problem* activities could be used to extend some of the *Challenge* activities. The *Solve the Problem* activities are suitable for all ability levels, as children can set their own problems.

***Challenge* activity**	**Related *Solve the Problem* activities**
A1.6 How many are needed?	Apple Picking
D1.1 Angles around a circle	Underwater Explorer
A2.3 Posting a parcel	Antarctic Mission
C2.4 Finding averages	Cycle Race
C2.5 Average word lengths	Cycle Race
D2.6 Matchstick patterns	Mystery Shopper
E2.2 Food guidelines	Setting the Stage
A3.2 VAT	Setting the Stage
E3.1 Angel of the North	Setting the Stage
E3.3 Maps	Setting the Stage
E3.5 Domino rectangles	Mystery Shopper

Challenge Plan: Year 6

A1: multiplying and dividing integers/decimals by 10, 100, or 1000; deriving facts; expressing a quotient as a fraction or decimal

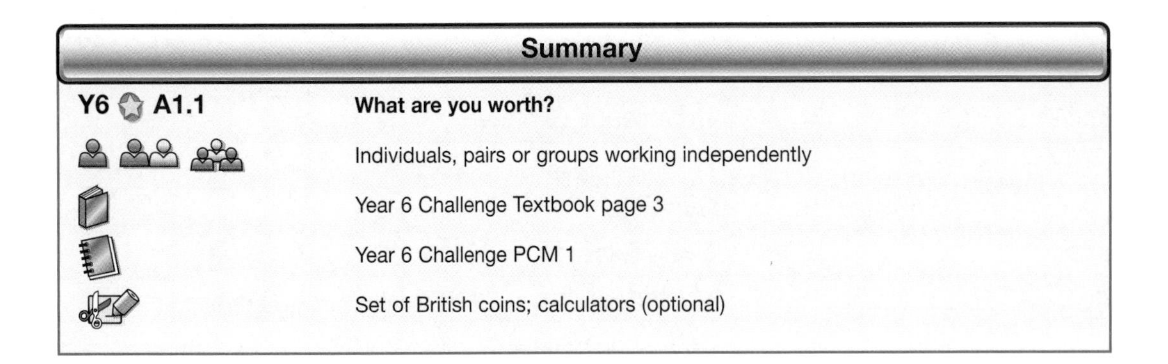

Summary

Y6 A1.1 **What are you worth?**

Individuals, pairs or groups working independently

Year 6 Challenge Textbook page 3

Year 6 Challenge PCM 1

Set of British coins; calculators (optional)

Abacus Evolve objectives

- Multiply any integer by 10, 100 or 1000 and understand the effect
- Recognise that multiplying by 100 is equivalent to multiplying by 10, then by 10 again
- Multiply decimal numbers by 10, 100 or 1000
- Divide decimal numbers by 10 or 100

Framework objectives

- *Use efficient written methods to add and subtract integers and decimals, to multiply and divide integers and decimals by a 1-digit integer, and to multiply 2- digit and 3-digit integers by a 2-digit integer*

Teacher notes

Preparation
Photocopy PCM 1, one copy per child, pair or group. Collect a full set of British coins for reference. Children will also need to know their own height and weight in metric units.

Getting started
Check that children are confident in understanding when they should divide or multiply to find an answer.

Activity
Children work from Textbook page 3. This activity looks at the measurements of British coins in circulation. Children are asked to consider what they would be 'worth' in certain coins, taking into account the thickness and weight of the coins. Questions require children to multiply and divide decimals. Children will be working to two decimal places for some of the coins; you may want to encourage the use of a calculator as an efficient approach to the calculations.

Further extension
You might like to look into Euro coinage; the website below will give you the technical details of each coin.

Be aware

- Check that children understand that the value of the coins is different from the number of coins.

Outcomes

- I can multiply and divide whole numbers by decimals to work out problems to do with coins.

Supporting resources

The Royal Mint website has information on British coinage:
- http://www.royalmint.com/Corporate/facts/circulation.aspx

Details of Euro coinage are available here:
- http://eur-lex.europa.eu/LexUriServ/LexUriServ.do?uri=OJ:L:1998:139:0006:0008:EN:PDF

Challenge Plan: Year 6

A1: multiplying and dividing integers/decimals by 10, 100, or 1000; deriving facts; expressing a quotient as a fraction or decimal

Summary

Y6 A1.2 **Let's cook**

A group working with an adult

Year 6 Challenge Textbook page 4

Year 6 Challenge PCM 2

Scales; ingredients to weigh (optional)

Abacus Evolve objectives

- **Y6-7** Rehearse the meaning of percentage
- **Y6-7** Know decimal and percentage equivalents of simple fractions
- **Y6-7** Use percentages to compare simple proportions, e.g. when interpreting pie charts
- **Y6-7** Rehearse converting a decimal to a fraction, and vice versa
- **Y6-7** Rehearse converting a percentage to a fraction, and vice versa

Framework objectives

- **Y6-7** Recognise approximate proportions of a whole and use fractions and percentages to describe and compare them, for example when interpreting pie charts
- **Y6-7** Consolidate and extend mental methods of calculation to include decimals, fractions and percentages

Teacher notes

Preparation
Photocopy PCM 2, one copy per child.

Getting started
Check that children are confident in finding equivalent fractions.

Activity
- Ask children what they know about percentages, fractions and decimals, to recall previous learning.
- Remind them of hundredths. Do they recall any fractions that make percentages easier to work out? Discuss how 50% is $\frac{1}{2}$, 25% is $\frac{1}{4}$ and 10% is $\frac{1}{10}$.
- *How would we work out 50%, 25%, 10% of anything?* Confirm that we find $\frac{1}{2}$, $\frac{1}{4}$, $\frac{1}{10}$. Remind children to divide by 10 using place value.
- *How do we work out $\frac{1}{2}$ of anything? $\frac{1}{4}$? $\frac{1}{3}$? $\frac{1}{6}$? What do $\frac{1}{2} + \frac{1}{4} + \frac{1}{3} + \frac{1}{6}$ total?* (Cut up the fraction wall on PCM 2 to confirm this if necessary.)
- Look at a percentage strip, fraction strip and decimal strip. Talk about equivalents.
- Children work from Textbook page 4. Look at each of the recipes and ask children to find equivalents for each type of proportion, e.g. $\frac{1}{10}$ is 10%.
- Work through one example of each recipe using the questions on the Textbook page.
- Allow children to finish the questions on their own.

If you have time
Children can make the recipes, deciding how many people they would like to serve and calculating the amount of ingredients accordingly.

Extra help
When using PCM 2, show children that all the ingredients total 1 or 100%.

Be aware

- Often children translate $\frac{1}{5}$ as 5% and $\frac{1}{20}$ as 20% because $\frac{1}{10}$ is 10%. Encourage them to see why this is incorrect.
- Children should be told that finding percentages such as 50%, 20%, 25% is more straightforward using the fraction equivalents.

Outcomes

- I can use decimals, percentages or fractions to find quantities in proportion with each other.

A1: multiplying and dividing integers/decimals by 10, 100, or 1000; deriving facts; expressing a quotient as a fraction or decimal

Summary

Y6 A1.3 — **Money for charity**

Individuals, pairs or groups working independently

Year 6 Challenge Textbook page 5

Year 6 Challenge PCM 1

Calculators (optional)

Abacus Evolve objectives

- Divide any integer by 10, 100 or 1000, and understand the effect
- Divide decimal numbers by 10 or 100
- Recognise that dividing by 100 is equivalent to dividing by 10, then by 10 again
- Use known number facts and place value to consolidate mental multiplication and division

Framework objectives

- *Use efficient written methods to add and subtract integers and decimals, to multiply and divide integers and decimals by a 1-digit integer, and to multiply 2-digit and 3-digit integers by a 2-digit integer*

Teacher notes

Preparation
Photocopy PCM 1, one copy per child.

Getting started
Check that children are confident in using place value to divide by 10, 100 and 1000.

Activity
Children work from Textbook page 5. This activity investigates the amounts of money raised by six classes in a school. Children must use information about the size and weight of the coins, as shown on PCM 1, to work out how much money was raised.

Further extension
Banks do not count bags of money, they weigh them. Children can explore how money is bagged and what each bag might weigh.

Extra help
You may want children to use a calculator for speed.

Be aware

- One of the measurements given could relate to two different coins; children will need to follow further clues in order to narrow this down to one coin.

Outcomes

- I can divide whole numbers and decimals by 10, 100 and 1000 and understand the answer if it is a decimal.
- I can multiply single digits by two or more digits to work out total values of coins.

Supporting resources

Details of British coins are available here:
- http://www.royalmint.com/Corporate/facts/circulation.aspx

A1: multiplying and dividing integers/decimals by 10, 100, or 1000; deriving facts; expressing a quotient as a fraction or decimal

Summary

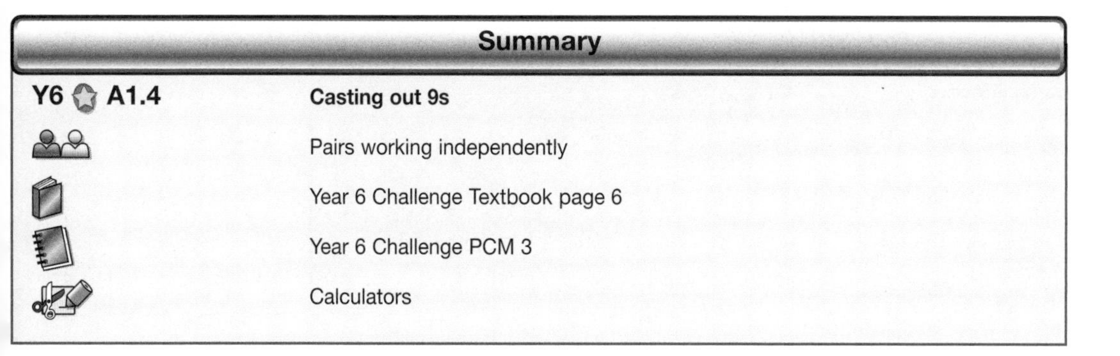

Y6 A1.4 **Casting out 9s**

Pairs working independently

Year 6 Challenge Textbook page 6

Year 6 Challenge PCM 3

Calculators

Abacus Evolve objectives

- Consolidate knowing by heart multiplication facts up to 10 × 10
- Continue to derive quickly division facts corresponding to multiplication facts up to 10 × 10
- Use the relationship between multiplication and division to multiply and divide mentally

Framework objectives

- *Use knowledge of place value and multiplication facts to 10 × 10 to derive related multiplication and division facts involving decimals (e.g. 0·8 × 7, 4·8 ÷ 6)*

Teacher notes

Getting started

Go through the 'casting out 9s' methods for addition, subtraction, multiplying and dividing shown on Textbook page 6. Check that children know how to find digit totals. Some children may need a little support when looking at the examples but encourage them to unpick the method themselves.

Activity

Children work from Textbook page 6. The activity looks at the 'casting out 9s' method, which can be used to check whether calculations could be correct. Examples are given for children to follow for each of the four operations. They then employ these methods to check the answers on PCM 3. They then use a calculator to check the answers.

Further extension

Children can explore that a change in place value generates a multiple of 9.

For example, if 150 is entered instead of 15, the difference is 135. 135 is a multiple of 9.

If 2100 is entered instead of 21 the difference is 2079. 2079 is a multiple of 9.

Be aware

- The 'casting out 9s' rule might suggest that a calculation is correct, but if digits have been inverted then it could be wrong. For example, the calculation 3**72**9 + 4861 = 8590 is correct. However if the digits are inverted to 3**27**9 + 4861 = 8590 the check will still work but the calculation is wrong.

Outcomes

- I can use the 'casting out 9s' method to check whether a calculation could be correct.
- I realise I cannot say whether or not the calculation is definitely correct.

Supporting resources

These websites describe the 'casting out nines' method:

- http://www.jimloy.com/number/nines.htm
- http://mathworld.wolfram.com/CastingOutNines.html

Summary

Y6 A1.5 — **Pay rise**

Individuals or pairs working independently

Year 6 Challenge PCMs 4 and 5

Calculators (optional)

Abacus Evolve objectives

- **Y6-7:** Rehearse finding fractions of quantities and measurements (whole number answer)
- **Y6-7:** Rehearse finding simple percentages of quantities and measurements (whole number answer)
- **Y6-7:** Find the outcome of a given percentage increase or decrease

Framework objectives

- **Y6-7:** Calculate percentage increases or decreases and fractions of quantities and measurements (integer answers)

Teacher notes

Preparation
Photocopy PCMs 4 and 5, one copy per child or pair.
PCM 4 could be enlarged as a learning poster.

Getting started
Show children PCM 4, and make sure they are all comfortable with methods for finding the fraction equivalents of simple percentages.

Activity
Children work from PCM 5. This activity looks at amounts of money children might earn as pocket money in exchange for doing jobs around the house. They have been given a pay rise, or in some case pay rates have been cut. Children have to calculate simple percentages and to find the increase or decrease in the pay rates given. Some amounts of money will need to be rounded.

Extra help
You may want to allow children to use calculators for speed, but the chart on PCM 4 should be used to encourage them to work out the amounts without a calculator.

Information
The method used here encourages children to calculate percentages first, then add to or subtract from original figures, rather than memorising a complicated algorithm they may not understand.

Be aware

- If children are aware of the fraction equivalents of simple percentages, they will find using these much easier than the common approach of dividing by 100 and multiplying by the number of per cent.

Outcomes

- I can find 5, 10 or 50 per cent of an amount and increase or decrease an amount of money by this percentage.

A1: multiplying and dividing integers/decimals by 10, 100, or 1000; deriving facts; expressing a quotient as a fraction or decimal

Summary

Y6 A1.6	**How many are needed?**
	A group working with an adult
	Year 6 Challenge Textbook page 7
	Tables chart (optional)

Abacus Evolve objectives

- Express a quotient as a fraction, or as a decimal rounded to one decimal place
- Consolidate rounding up or down after division, depending on the context
- Use known number facts and place value to consolidate mental multiplication and division

Framework objectives

- Relate fractions to multiplication and division (e.g. $6 \div 2 = \frac{1}{2}$ of $6 = 6 \times \frac{1}{2}$); express a quotient as a fraction or decimal (e.g. $67 \div 5 = 13{\cdot}4$ or $13\frac{2}{5}$); find fractions and percentages of whole-number quantities (e.g. $\frac{5}{8}$ of 96, 65% of £260)
- Solve multi-step problems, and problems involving fractions, decimals and percentages; choose and use appropriate calculation strategies at each stage, including calculator use
- Use a range of oral techniques to present persuasive argument

Teacher notes

Getting started

This activity rehearses mental division strategies, so a calculator should not be allowed. Children may use a tables chart as a reminder to speed up their calculations. All the calculations require knowledge of ×2, ×4, ×5, ×8 and ×10 tables only; all the multiplications can be worked out using these facts.

Activity

- Ask children to think of a quick way of dividing by 4 (*halve twice*) and by 8 (*halve three times*). Ask children in pairs to show each other.
- Ask children if they know a quick way of dividing by 5. If not, show the example *14 ÷ 5* and double each number: *28 ÷ 10,* then ask how to do this division. If they volunteer this method then agree and ask a child to give an example. Ask children in pairs to show each other if necessary.
- Confirm that there are mental ways to divide by 2, 4, 5, 8 and 10, and that if we divide by 2 we find $\frac{1}{2}$.
- Ask children what other fractions of amounts we can find using division by 4, 5, 8 and 10. Agree $\frac{1}{4}$, $\frac{1}{5}$, …
- *What do we do with remainders?* Ask children to discuss in pairs when remainders are important and when they are not, and when we need to round up to the next number or down to the number below.
- Confirm that this often depends on what the question says, e.g. *How many full boxes? How many are needed altogether?* … Can children suggest other phrases?
- Children work from Textbook page 7. They solve word problems by dividing and considering what to do with the remainder.

Be aware

- Using mental strategies to divide by small numbers is the most efficient approach to calculation. Children need to practise these skills alongside written methods.

Outcomes

- I can use mental methods including halving, doubling and place value to divide by 2, 4, 5, 8 and 10.
- I know when to round up or down in a division that has a remainder.

Summary

Y6 B1.1 — **Consecutive numbers**

Pairs or groups working independently

Year 6 Challenge Textbook page 8

Abacus Evolve objectives

- Recognise the properties of odd and even numbers, including their products

Framework objectives

- Represent and interpret sequences, patterns and relationships involving numbers and shapes; suggest and test hypotheses; construct and use simple expressions and formulae in words then symbols (e.g. the cost of c pens at 15 pence each is 15c pence)

Teacher notes

Getting started
Check that children have an understanding of consecutive numbers. This includes consecutive odd numbers (e.g. 1, 3, 5, 7...), consecutive even numbers (e.g. 2, 4, 6, 8…) and consecutive multiples (e.g. 5, 10, 15, 20…).

Activity
Children work from Textbook page 8. They explore adding consecutive numbers to make new numbers. Children then look into the properties of adding together particular amounts of consecutive numbers. They discuss patterns that they have observed.

Further extension
Explore the link to algebra. Adding three consecutive numbers can be written as $x + (x + 1) + (x + 2)$. This equals $3x + 3$. As each part of this expression has 3 as a factor, the total must be a multiple of 3. This can also be applied to four consecutive numbers, five consecutive numbers and so on.

Extra Help
Tell children that three consecutive numbers beginning with an odd number will always total an even number, and three consecutive numbers beginning with an even number will always total an odd number.

Information
All the odd numbers from 3 can be made by adding two consecutive counting numbers. The even numbers from 4 can be made by adding two consecutive odd numbers or two consecutive even numbers.

Be aware

- Children may only consider the consecutive counting numbers 1, 2, 3 and so on. Remind them of the consecutive odd and even numbers and multiples, if necessary.

Outcomes

- I can explore number patterns and properties.

Summary

Y6 B1.2 **Straw patterns**

Individual, pairs or groups working independently

Year 6 Challenge Textbook page 9

Drinking straws (33 straws per child)

Abacus Evolve objectives

- **Y6-7** Generate and describe simple integer sequences
- **Y6-7** Generate terms of a simple sequence, given a rule for finding each term from the previous term
- **Y6-7** Begin to find a rule for the nth term of simple sequences

Framework objectives

- **Y6-7** Generate sequences and describe the general term; use letters and symbols to represent unknown numbers or variables; represent simple relationships as graphs
- **Y6-7** Represent information or unknown numbers in a problem, for example in a table, formula or equation; explain solutions in the context of the problem

Teacher notes

Preparation
Cut each drinking straw into five segments. Children will need 165 straw segments each.

Getting started
Check that children are confident in working with growing patterns. Ask them to double the number 1 five times as a simple example of a growing pattern. (1, 2, 4, 8, 16, 32)
They should also understand the concept of triangular numbers (triangular numbers are made by adding the consecutive counting numbers from zero). Children should be able to list triangular numbers up to the tenth triangular number. (1, 3, 6, 10, 15, 21, 28, 36, 45, 55)

Activity
Children work from Textbook page 9. They are given an example of a pattern which grows, using drinking straws to make a series of triangles. They identify how many straws are needed to make the shapes and then find a pattern. Children use this pattern to predict further answers and identify a general pattern. They use drinking straws to construct the shapes up to shape 10, and then use patterns to predict answers with larger numbers.

Further extension
Children explore how many triangles there are in total in each shape. E.g. there are five in shape 2 – four small triangles and one large (made of the four small triangles). There are 13 in shape 3 – nine small triangles, three medium (each made of four small triangles) and one large (made of the nine small triangles).

Extra help
Once children have completed the table, encourage them to discuss the number patterns they can see developing. Make sure they have established these patterns before they move on to the rest of the activity.

Information
The number of triangles that can be made is the shape number squared (e.g. $1^2 = 1$, $2^2 = 4$). The number of straws is three times the triangular number (e.g. $3 \times 3 = 9$).
In the Extra activity, the number of rhombuses that can be made is the shape number squared (e.g. $1^2 = 1$, $2^2 = 4$). The number of straws is four times the triangular number (e.g. $4 \times 3 = 12$).

Be aware

- Children should be encouraged to talk about number patterns before trying to write them using algebra.
- Make sure children understand that the number of triangles is not the same as the triangular number.

Outcomes

- I can continue shape patterns and predict how the sequence grows.
- I can recognise some number patterns.

B1: odd and even numbers; common multiples; smallest common multiple; properties of 2D shapes; classifying quadrilaterals

Summary

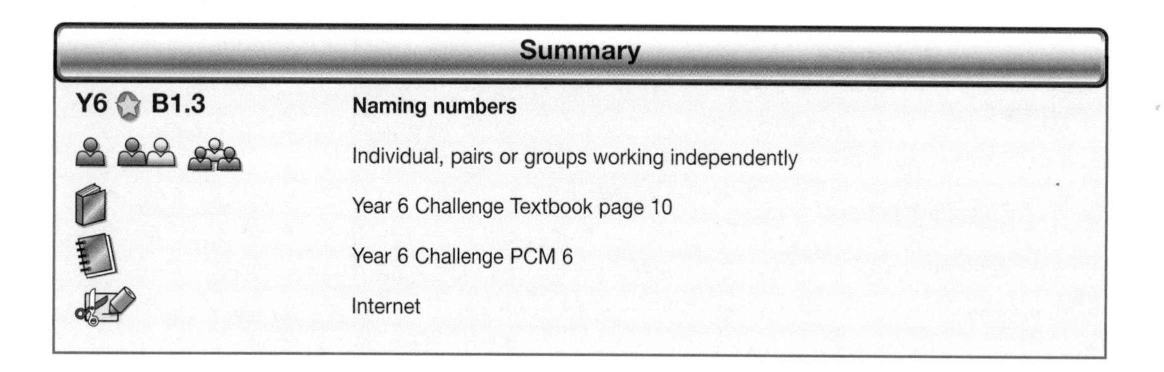

Y6 B1.3	**Naming numbers**
	Individual, pairs or groups working independently
	Year 6 Challenge Textbook page 10
	Year 6 Challenge PCM 6
	Internet

Abacus Evolve objectives

- Find common multiples of two or three numbers
- Find the smallest common multiple of two or three numbers
- Consolidate finding all the pairs of factors of any number up to 100
- Recognise that a number with an odd number of factors is a square number
- Recognise prime numbers up to at least 20
- Understand a prime number as one that has exactly two factors
- Factorise numbers up to 100 into prime factors

Framework objectives

- Recognise that prime numbers have only two factors and identify prime numbers less than 100; find the prime factors of 2-digit numbers

Teacher notes

Getting started
Check that children are confident in working with prime numbers, square numbers, digital roots, factors and multiples.

Activity
Children work from Textbook page 10. They are introduced to some types of numbers and their definitions:
- cardinal numbers
- ordinal numbers
- integers
- rational numbers
- irrational numbers.

Children then work from PCM 6, following clues involving prime numbers, square numbers, digital roots, factors and multiples to find out new numbers.

Further extension
Children explore all the number facts that they know for numbers up to 50 which have 2 as a factor.

Be aware

- Children may need to be reminded why 1 is not a prime number (it only has one factor; prime numbers have two factors). They may also forget that 2 is prime, as it is the only even prime number.

Outcomes

- I can recognise prime numbers.
- I can use products and factors of numbers.

Supporting resources

- Children can find more in-depth definitions for different types of numbers here:
- http://nrich.maths.org/public/viewer.php?obj_id=5805
- http://mathforum.org/library/drmath/sets/select/dm_classify_num.html
- http://www.mathsisfun.com/definitions/imaginary-numbers.html

Challenge Plan: Year 6

B1: odd and even numbers; common multiples; smallest common multiple; properties of 2D shapes; classifying quadrilaterals

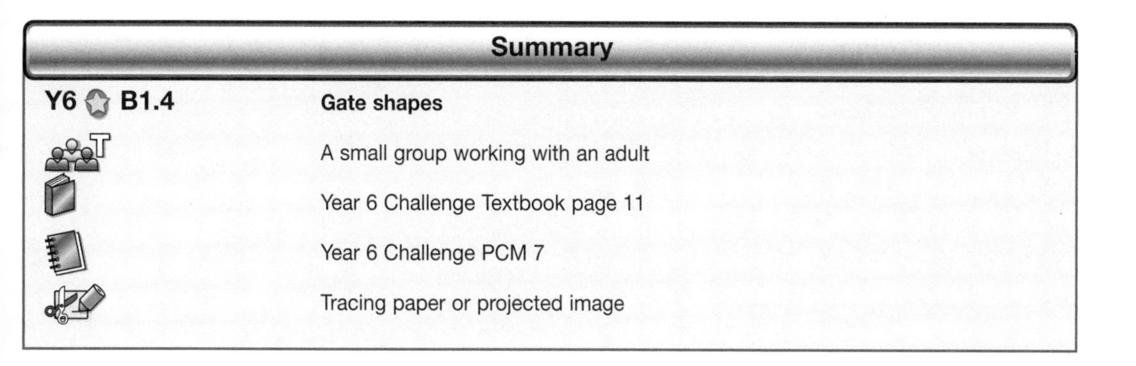

Summary

Y6 B1.4 — **Gate shapes**

A small group working with an adult

Year 6 Challenge Textbook page 11

Year 6 Challenge PCM 7

Tracing paper or projected image

Abacus Evolve objectives

- Use the terms 'parallelogram', 'rhombus' and 'trapezium'
- Begin to know the properties of parallelograms, rhombuses and trapezia

Framework objectives

- Describe, identify and visualise parallel and perpendicular edges or faces; use these properties to classify 2D shapes and 3D solids
- Use a range of oral techniques to present persuasive argument

Teacher notes

Preparation
Photocopy PCM 7 and cut out the pictures. Each child, pair or group should have a different picture.

Activity
- This activity explores the shapes which are created in the designs of gates.

- Give each child, pair or group one of the pictures from PCM 7.
- *Look at the gate in your picture. What shapes can you see?*
- Ask each child, pair or group to take turns to tell the rest of the group what shapes they can see.
- Encourage them to also discuss the properties of the shapes using vocabulary such as parallel, perpendicular, right angle and so on.
- *Can anyone see any other shapes in this gate?*
- Continue until each gate has been discussed.

- Children work from Textbook page 11. They identify what shapes can be found in the design of the gate in the photograph. They trace these shapes from the photo to show where they found the shape.
- *Can you find any shapes that aren't listed in the questions? Were there any shapes you couldn't find?*

If you have time
Children can look around the school for areas to photograph. They see what shapes they can find in their photographs.

Extra help
Provide children with the 2D shapes listed on the Textbook page if they need help finding the shapes in the photograph. Ask them to list the properties of each shape before they try to find it.

Be aware

- Due to the designs of the gates, some of the shapes may be slightly obscured, for example some corners may not be fully visible. Reassure children that these shapes do count and they are correct to have spotted them.

Outcomes

- I can recognise 2D shapes and their properties.
- I can use mathematical words to describe 2D shapes.

Summary

Y6 B1.5	**Constructing triangles**
	A group working with an adult
	Year 6 Challenge Textbook page 12
	Rulers; protractors; pairs of compasses; plain paper; geo-strips (optional)

Abacus Evolve objectives	Framework objectives
• **Y6-7** Construct a triangle given two sides and the included angle	• **Y6-7** Construct a triangle given two sides and the included angle

Teacher notes

Getting started
Check that children are confident in accurately using a ruler, a protractor and a pair of compasses.

Activity
- Children work from Textbook page 12. Ask them to look at the triangles.
- *What information are we given about these triangles?* (the right angles and the lengths of some of the sides)
- *Can we draw these triangles, using just this information?*

- Children draw a 12 cm horizontal line half way down a piece of paper, then measure an angle of 90° at one end using a protractor.
- They then draw an 8 cm line perpendicular to the original line, following the right angle.
- They join the ends of the two lines, measure the length of this line and measure each angle.
- Ask children to mark these measurements on the drawing. *We have drawn triangle 1!*

- Children then draw a 10 cm horizontal line, leaving about 12 cm of space above it.
- Children use a ruler to open a pair of compasses to 10 cm.
- They place the point of the compass at one end of line and draw a quarter circle from the other end of the line. They repeat this from the other end of line.

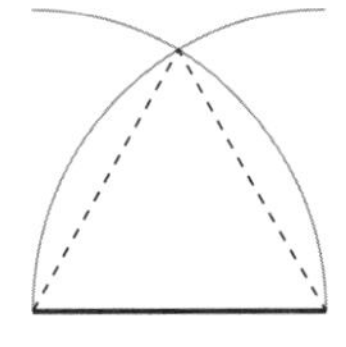

- *Where the circle marks cross is exactly 10 cm from each end of our line, so if we join them up we will get an equilateral triangle.*
- Children join up the three points to make a triangle. *We have drawn triangle 2!*
- Children use their protractors to confirm that it is an equilateral triangle. (Each angle is 60°)

- *Can you think how the third triangle could be constructed?* (It can be made using the compasses method, but changing the lengths.)
- Children draw triangle 3 and measure the angles to check that they have constructed it correctly. (The internal angles should add up to 180°.)

- Children then experiment with methods for drawing triangle 4. Remind them to check the angles when they have drawn their triangle.

Extra help
Children who are not confident with using compasses can practise with geo-strips first. They fasten one end to the base line and use the hole to draw the arc.

Be aware	Outcomes
• Children will need dexterity to use compasses accurately. Check that children are able to do this and support those that find it more difficult.	• I can construct triangles using a ruler, a protractor and a pair of compasses.

B1: odd and even numbers; common multiples; smallest common multiple; properties of 2D shapes; classifying quadrilaterals

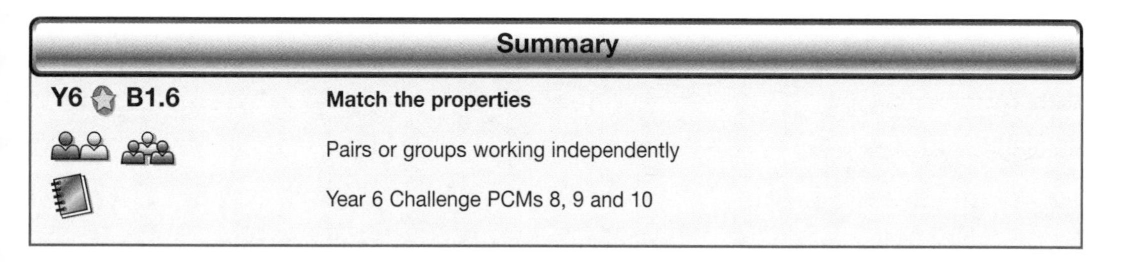

Summary

Y6 B1.6 — **Match the properties**

Pairs or groups working independently

Year 6 Challenge PCMs 8, 9 and 10

Abacus Evolve objectives

- Classify quadrilaterals, using criteria such as parallel sides, equal sides, equal angles

Framework objectives

- Describe, identify and visualise parallel and perpendicular edges or faces; use these properties to classify 2D shapes and 3D solids
- Understand and use a variety of ways to criticise constructively and respond to criticism

Teacher notes

Preparation
Photocopy PCMs 8, 9 and 10, one copy of each per pair or group. Cut up the sets of cards and the rules. Each pair or group should have 48 cards in total and one set of rules.

Getting started
Run through the properties of some 2D and 3D shapes. Check that children can use the shape words on .

Activity
In pairs or groups, children play a game similar to *Snap*.

- In each pair or group, children put all three sets of cards together. They shuffle the cards and share them out equally between the players. Each player places their pile of cards in front of them, face down.
- The cards either have a number, a picture of a 2D or a 3D shape, or a shape vocabulary word.
- Children all turn over their top card.
- A player shouts *Snap* if they can say see two or more cards that are linked, for example:
  - 3 and triangle are linked because a triangle has three sides.
  - 60 and equilateral triangle are linked because the angles are all 60°.
  - Tetrahedron or icosahedron and equilateral triangle are linked because each face is an equilateral triangle. They also link with 60 because the angles of the triangle are all 60°.
  - The parallelogram links with parallel, with adjacent because the adjacent sides are a different length, and with 2 because it has two pairs of equal sides.
- If the explanation for the link is correct then the child who called *Snap* keeps the cards that are linked.
- The first player to have all the cards wins.

If you have time
Children lay all the cards out face down and play ‘pelmanism’. Can they pair up all the cards?

Information
A Platonic solid is a regular polyhedron, with all its faces the same size and shape. The five Platonic solids are: cube, tetrahedron, octahedron, dodecahedron and icosahedron.
A dodecahedron has 12 faces, 20 vertices and 30 edges.
An icosahedron has 20 faces, 12 vertices and 30 edges.

Be aware

- In the case of a disputed *Snap* call, encourage each child in the pair or group to explain why they think the answer is correct or incorrect and reach a decision between them.

Outcomes

- I can recognise shapes and identify their properties.

Summary

Y6 C1.1 — **Science test**

Individuals, pairs or groups working independently

Year 6 Challenge Textbook page 13

Squared paper; rulers

Abacus Evolve objectives

- Group discrete data in equal intervals
- Construct a grouped frequency table
- Draw and interpret a bar graph based on grouped data
- Find the mode and range of a set of data

Framework objectives

- Construct and interpret frequency tables, bar charts with grouped discrete data, and line graphs; interpret pie charts
- Describe and interpret results and solutions to problems using the mode, range, median and mean

Teacher notes

Getting started

Look together at the frequency table on Textbook page 13. Read question 1, and discuss briefly what would be a suitable scale and a suitable symbol for children's pictograms.

Draw attention to questions 4–6 and ask children to think about how they will find the percentages, not just the number of children, in each case.

Activity

Children work from Textbook page 13. They draw a pictogram based on data from a grouped frequency table. The graph will show a reasonable approximation to a normal distribution curve.

Children then answer questions about the data, including finding the modal value, and working out what percentages of children scored within given ranges. Children can discuss the questions together, but they should each draw their own pictogram.

Children then try grouping the data in 20s rather than 10s, and draw a pictogram to represent this. The graph will be a similar shape to the first one, but the shape is compacted.

Information

For the initial pictogram, a symbol to represent four or five children will work well.

The Extra activity gives children opportunity to experiment with other scales. A good choice of symbol would be one that can be split easily into fractions. Different shapes work better for different scales; squares or circles work equally well when the scale is 1 shape to 4 children, but circles are better when the scale is 1 to 5.

Be aware

- Children may not notice the significance of the wording. Reinforce that 'More than 40' means all the children who scored 41 and above; '50 or less' means all the children who scored up to and including 50.
- Children may forget that there are 200 pupils sitting the test. In order to find the percentages they need to first find the number of children and then halve it.

Outcomes

- I can draw a pictogram from a grouped frequency table.
- I can find the mode of a set of data.
- I can find simple percentages.
- I can answer questions about a pictogram.
- I can group data in different ways.

Challenge Plan: Year 6

C1: grouped frequency tables; bar graphs using grouped data; metric and imperial units of length; metric and imperial units of weight

Summary

Y6 C1.2 — **Spelling scores**

A small group working with an adult

Year 6 Challenge PCMs 11 and 12

Squared paper; rulers

Abacus Evolve objectives

- **Y6–7** Draw and interpret graphs and diagrams to represent data
- **Y6–7** Draw simple conclusions based on the shape of graphs
- **Y6–7** Compare the data represented by two similar graphs

Framework objectives

- **Y6–7** Construct, interpret and compare graphs and diagrams that represent data, for example compare proportions in two pie charts that represent different totals

Teacher notes

Preparation
Photocopy PCMs 11 and 12, one copy per child, plus a few spares.

Activity
- Ask children to look at the table of scores from Monday's spelling test (PCM 11).
- *What was the lowest score? What was the highest score? Which score or scores appear to occur most frequently*? Ask children to quickly scan the data and give estimated answers.
- *What would be a good way to find out which scores occur most frequently?* Ask children to discuss this.
- *The range of scores is 1 to 20, so how might we present the data in a graph? What would be a good way to group the data, in intervals of two, three, four or five? Why is three not a good idea?* Discuss the advantages and disadvantages of grouping in 2s, 4s or 5s.
- Agree that it would be most helpful to group in 2s: 1–2, 3–4, 5–6, … making 10 groups.
- *How should we organise the data before drawing a graph?* See what children suggest, but the two best ways are to draw up a tally chart or to count up the occurrences of each score and record that in a frequency table. Either way a good strategy is for children to mark off the scores on the table of information as they collect the data. Model this for children.
- Children use the information on PCM 11 to draw up a bar graph.
- Ask questions about the graph: *What is the mode score? How many children scored 11 or more? 17 or more? 7 or fewer? 3 or fewer?*
- Give children PCM 12. Explain that this shows the scores the children got on Friday when they were tested on the same 20 words. *What do you think might have happened? What difference might you see in a graph of these results?*
- Ask children to draw graphs to represent the new set of data, and then ask questions as before.
- *What would happen if the children were tested again the following week?*

Further extension
Ask children to find out what percentage of children scored each group of scores. Looking from Monday to Friday, what were the percentage increases and decreases in each group of scores?

Be aware

- Children may use vocabulary inaccurately when they are discussing the work. Check their understanding of terms: raw scores, grouped data, tally chart, frequency table, bar graph, range, mode.

Outcomes

- I can decide how to group data.
- I can draw a bar graph based on grouped data.
- I can compare two graphs and discuss what they show.

C1: grouped frequency tables; bar graphs using grouped data; metric and imperial units of length; metric and imperial units of weight

Summary

Y6 C1.3 **Dice throws**

Pairs working independently

Year 6 Challenge Textbook page 14

Three 6-sided dice per pair; squared paper; rulers

Abacus Evolve objectives

- Group discrete data in equal intervals
- Construct a grouped frequency table
- Draw and interpret a bar graph based on grouped data

Framework objectives

- Construct and interpret frequency tables, bar charts with grouped discrete data, and line graphs
- *Solve problems by collecting, selecting, processing, presenting and interpreting data, using ICT where appropriate; draw conclusions and identify further questions to ask*
- Suggest, plan and develop lines of enquiry; collect, organise and represent information, interpret results and review methods; identify and answer related questions
- Understand and use a variety of ways to criticise constructively and respond to criticism

Teacher notes

Getting started
Check that children are clear about the process on Textbook page 14: demonstrate rolling three dice and finding the total, then explain that children are going to do this 100 times.

Activity
Children work from Textbook page 14. They start by predicting what they will find out if they roll three dice 100 times and record the totals. They design a tally chart, then carry out the experiment and record their results. They then decide how to group the data to create a frequency table. Children draw a graph of their choice to represent the data, then explain what their graph shows.
Children answer specific questions about their data, then suggest other questions that could be asked.
They consider what would happen if they threw the three dice another 100 times.

Information
Numbers in the centre of the range, 9–12, will come up most frequently since there are more combinations of three dice numbers that produce these totals. A bell-shaped pattern should emerge. The more times the dice are thrown the clearer this pattern will become.

Be aware

- Children may lose count of how many times they have thrown the dice. Encourage them to devise a system for ensuring exactly 100 throws.

Outcomes

- I can collect data and record it in a tally chart.
- I can draw a grouped frequency table from a tally chart.
- I can draw a bar graph from a grouped frequency table.
- I can answer questions about a bar graph.

Supporting resources

This website has a random dice thrower for up to five dice:
- http://www.neoprogrammics.com/randomisers/random_dice_thrower/index.php

Challenge Plan: Year 6

C1: grouped frequency tables; bar graphs using grouped data; metric and imperial units of length; metric and imperial units of weight

Summary

Y6 C1.4	**Metric lengths**
	Individuals, pairs or groups working independently
	Year 6 Challenge Textbook page 15
	Calculators (optional)

Abacus Evolve objectives

- Use, read and write standard metric units of length: mm, cm, m, km
- Convert from one smaller metric unit of length to another larger unit
- Multiply any integer by 10, 100 or 1000 and understand the effect
- Multiply decimal numbers by 10, 100 or 1000
- Divide any integer by 10, 100 or 1000, and understand the effect

Framework objectives

- *Select and use standard metric units of measure and convert between units using decimals to two places (e.g. change 2·75 litres to 2750 ml, or vice versa)*
- *Use efficient written methods to add and subtract integers and decimals, to multiply and divide integers and decimals by a 1-digit integer, and to multiply 2- and 3-digit integers by a 2-digit integer*

Teacher notes

Activity
Children work from Textbook page 15. They convert between mm, cm, m and km. Children should link place value to the relationships between units, increasing or decreasing the value of the digits by 10, 100 or 1000 as they move between different units.
They then place lengths using different units in order of size.

Extra help
If children struggle in the ordering activity, suggest that it would be helpful to change all the lengths to the same unit. Once a common unit has been established then ordering them is straightforward.

If you have time
Children can check answers in the table using a calculator.

Be aware

- Children may talk about moving decimal points when multiplying or dividing by 10, 100 or 1000. Instead, encourage them to think of the process as shifting the digits left or right.

Outcomes

- I know the relationship between millimetres, centimetres, metres and kilometres.
- I can convert between different metric units of length.

C1: grouped frequency tables; bar graphs using grouped data; metric and imperial units of length; metric and imperial units of weight

Summary

Y6 C1.5 **A pound of carrots**

A small group working with an adult

Year 6 Challenge Textbook page 16

Calculators; fruit or vegetables (optional); metric and imperial weights (optional); weighing scales (optional); old recipe books with only imperial measures (optional)

Abacus Evolve objectives

- Understand the relationship between imperial and metric units of weight

Framework objectives

- Select and use standard metric units of measure and convert between units using decimals to two places (e.g. change 2·75 litres to 2750 ml or vice versa)
- Solve multi-step problems, and problems involving fractions, decimals and percentages; choose and use appropriate calculation strategies at each stage, including calculator use
- Use a range of oral techniques to present persuasive argument

Teacher notes

Activity

- Discuss the issues raised in the article on Textbook page 16. *What other situations can you think of where imperial units are still used?* Examples include football and cricket pitch measurements (yards), road signs (miles), milk (pints) and recipe books (pounds, ounces, fluid ounces).
- Discuss question 1 on the Textbook page, identifying what information is given. *Why is it not easy to compare the two costs? What would be a good way to solve the problem?* Clarify that, in order to compare the costs, children will need to change one of the weights so that they both use the same units, or consider what weight can be bought for a given amount of money.
- Taking question 1 as an example, ask: *What would 1 kg of bananas weigh in imperial measures?* (2·2 lb) *So 2·2 lb would cost 50p. Is this better value than buying 1 lb for 25p?* Discuss this. *Yes, because at 25p per pound, you can only buy 2 lb for 50p, rather than 2·2 lb.*
- Emphasise how the calculations support the reasoning about which bananas are the better value; exact answers are not always necessary to do this.
- Children work from Textbook page 16. They answer questions comparing imperial and metric values. Ask them to work through the questions in pairs for 15 minutes, then pause to give them an opportunity to present their strategies and solutions to the group.

Be aware

- Children may have a poor sense of how much of the various fruit and vegetables constitute 1 kg or 1 lb. It would be helpful to have some real fruit and vegetables for children to compare or some real metric and imperial weights for them to handle.

Outcomes

- I understand the relationship between kilograms and pounds.
- I can work out which option is better value by estimating and calculating.

Supporting resources

The 'English Weights and Measures' website gives information about imperial measures:

- http://home.clara.net/brianp/index.html

The BBC news and *The Times* websites carry stories about the EU metric controversy:

- http://news.bbc.co.uk/1/hi/uk/6637587.stm
- http://www.timesonline.co.uk/tol/money/consumer_affairs/article1764093.ece

Challenge Plan: Year 6

C1: grouped frequency tables; bar graphs using grouped data; metric and imperial units of length; metric and imperial units of weight

Summary

Y6 C1.6 — **Imperial units**

Individuals working independently

Year 6 Challenge Textbook page 17

Calculators (optional)

Abacus Evolve objectives

- **Y6–7** Measure and calculate using imperial units

Framework objectives

- **Y6–7** Solve problems by measuring, estimating and calculating; measure and calculate using imperial units still in everyday use; know their approximate metric values
- **Y6–7** Solve problems by breaking down complex calculations into simpler steps; choose and use operations and calculation strategies appropriate to the numbers and context; try alternative approaches to overcome difficulties; present, interpret and compare solutions

Teacher notes

Activity

Children work from Textbook page 17. They start by converting lengths and weights between different imperial units (inches, feet, yards and miles; ounces, pounds and stones). If needed, children can use calculators to support their calculations.

Children then go on to perform simple addition and subtraction using imperial units. They will need to think carefully about relationships between units. The examples are mixed up, and it is better to prompt children to think this through on a case-by-case basis than to teach them a 'system' for solving these problems using column arithmetic.

Information

Calculating with imperial units can be likened to calculating with time, where children need to use a range of different relationships between units.

Be aware

- When calculating using imperial units many children will simply assume that everything works (as with metric units) in base 10. For example, for question 10 they may answer 14 feet 7 inches. Encourage them to convert all units accurately.

Outcomes

- I know the relationships between inches, feet, yards and miles.
- I know the relationships between ounces, pounds and stones.
- I can calculate using imperial measures.

Supporting resources

This website gives more information about British imperial measures:

- http://gwydir.demon.co.uk/jo/units/index.htm

D1: acute and obtuse angles; angles in a triangle; adding and subtracting near multiples of 10, 100 and 1000; mental subtraction strategies

Summary

Y6 D1.1	**Angles around a circle**
	Individuals working independently
	Year 6 Challenge Textbook page 18
	Protractors (ideally 360°); pairs of compasses (optional); rulers (optional)

Abacus Evolve objectives

- Use a protractor to measure and draw acute and obtuse angles to the nearest degree
- Measure and calculate angles at a point
- Continue to find differences by counting on
- Use known number facts and place value to consolidate mental subtraction

Framework objectives

- Estimate angles, and use a protractor to measure and draw them, on their own and in shapes; calculate angles in a triangle or around a point
- Calculate mentally with integers and decimals: U·t + U·t, U·t − U·t, TU × U, TU ÷ U, U·t × U, U·t ÷ U

Teacher notes

Getting started
Check that children are confident in using a protractor and a pair of compasses.
Ensure that children are clear that all measurements need to be made with the centre point of the protractor at the centre of the circle, and that all angles should be measured to the nearest degree.

Activity
Children work from Textbook page 18. They measure the angles between lines around a circle, starting from line A (0°) and working clockwise. If children are using a 180° protractor, when they get to lines F, G, H and J they will need to measure the corresponding anticlockwise angle and subtract this from 360°, or alternatively measure on from previous angles and add.
Children then calculate the angles between the lines, starting from line A and working anticlockwise. They should not need to measure to find these angles.
They then calculate (without measuring) the angles between pairs of lines that do not include line A. For example, since the angle from A to C is 70° and the angle from A to D is 105°, the angle from C to D must be 105° − 70° = 35°. Children can check their answers by measuring.

Further extension
Discuss the idea of bearings. Locate your home town on a map of the UK and demonstrate the bearings of some major towns. This is done by measuring the angle clockwise from north to the other towns, in the same way as children measured around from point A in the main activity.

If you have time
Children can discuss the relative advantages and disadvantages of using a 180° or 360° protractor for this activity.

Be aware

- Even able children who are good at number work can find using a protractor confusing. Demonstrate and discuss to help them master this skill.

Outcomes

- I can use a protractor to measure and draw angles at a point.
- I can calculate angles around a circle without measuring.

Supporting resources

This site gives guidance from the National Strategies on using a protractor:
- http://nationalstrategies.standards.dcsf.gov.uk/node/64537

Challenge Plan: Year 6

D1: acute and obtuse angles; angles in a triangle; adding and subtracting near multiples of 10, 100 and 1000; mental subtraction strategies

Summary

Y6 D1.2 — **Angles in quadrilaterals**

Pairs working independently

Year 6 Challenge Textbook page 19

Year 6 Challenge PCM 13

Protractors; rulers (optional)

Abacus Evolve objectives

- Use a protractor to measure and draw acute and obtuse angles to the nearest degree
- Recognise that the sum of the angles of a triangle is 180 degrees
- Use the terms 'parallelogram', 'rhombus' and 'trapezium'
- Begin to use the term 'kite'
- Begin to know the properties of parallelograms, rhombuses and trapezia
- Make and investigate a general statement about familiar numbers or shapes by finding examples that satisfy it

Framework objectives

- Estimate angles, and use a protractor to measure and draw them, on their own and in shapes; calculate angles in a triangle or around a point
- Describe, identify and visualise parallel and perpendicular edges or faces and use these properties to classify 2D shapes and 3D solids
- Represent and interpret sequences, patterns and relationships involving numbers and shapes; suggest and test hypotheses; construct and use simple expressions and formulae in words then symbols (e.g. the cost of c pens at 15 pence each is 15c pence)

Teacher notes

Preparation
Photocopy PCM 13, one copy per child or pair.

Getting started
Ensure children are familiar with the names of kites, parallelograms and isosceles trapeziums, and the names of angles (acute and obtuse). Also make sure that they understand the idea of consecutive and opposite angles. Consecutive angles are two angles in a polygon that share a common side.
Give each child or pair a protractor.

Activity
Children work from Textbook page 19. First they each measure the angles of the six shapes on PCM 13 and discuss what they notice about opposite and consecutive angles.
They then each draw one more shape of each type to confirm the general result they have found.
Children use this knowledge to find the missing angles in the shapes on Textbook page 19.

Extra help
If necessary provide the vocabulary as prompts for children to use in their discussions.

Information

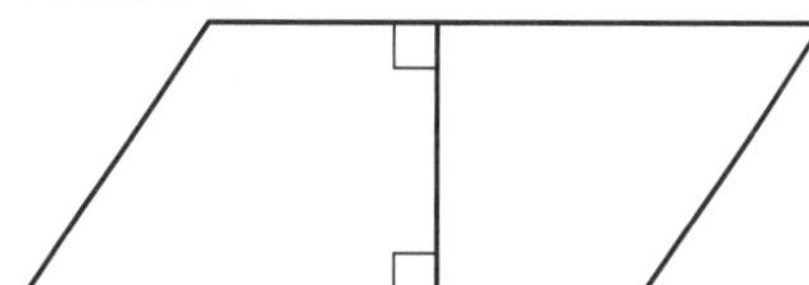

This diagram shows why consecutive angles in a parallelogram (or isosceles trapezium) total 180°. Divide the parallelogram using a line that is perpendicular to a pair of the parallel lines. Now consider either of the two quadrilaterals formed by this line. Since two of the angles are clearly right angles and since the total of all angles in a quadrilateral are 360°, the other two angles must total 180°. Understanding this will help with solving some of the missing angle problems in this and the following activity.

Be aware

- Some children may confuse consecutive and opposite angles. Use the discussion to make sure they understand the difference.

Outcomes

- I can measure angles in kites, parallelograms and trapeziums.
- I can calculate missing angles in kites, parallelograms and trapeziums.

D1: acute and obtuse angles; angles in a triangle; adding and subtracting near multiples of 10, 100 and 1000; mental subtraction strategies

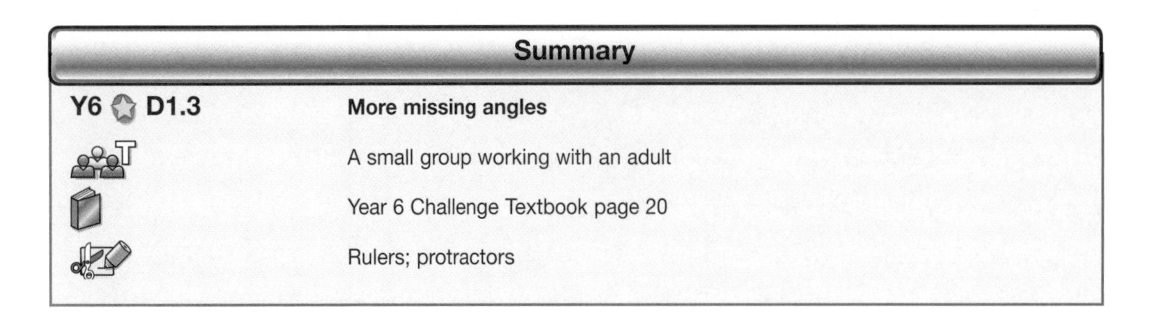

Summary

Y6 D1.3 — **More missing angles**

A small group working with an adult

Year 6 Challenge Textbook page 20

Rulers; protractors

Abacus Evolve objectives

- **Y6–7** Calculate angles given the size of other angles on a straight line
- **Y6–7** Rehearse the calculation of angles at a point, given the size of other angles
- **Y6–7** Know the sum of the angles of a triangle and use it to calculate missing angles
- **Y6–7** Recognise vertically opposite angles and use the properties to solve problems

Framework objectives

- **Y6–7** *Know the sum of angles on a straight line, in a triangle and at a point, and recognise vertically opposite angles*

Teacher notes

Activity

- Ask each child to draw a pair of parallel lines and then a slanted line across them. They measure with a protractor each of the eight angles formed where the slanted line crosses the parallel lines. *What do we find? Which angles are the same as each other? Which pairs total 180°? What if there was a third parallel line? What would the angles be around the point where that crossed the slanted line?*
- The key here is modelling for children how to solve angle problems using chains of logic. When children are giving explanations, encourage them to use phrases such as: *If I know that this angle is… then this angle must be… The angles of a quadrilateral are 360° and this angle is a right angle, so that must mean…*
- Children work from Textbook page 20. They find all the angles labelled *a* to *z*. In some cases that might mean finding other missing angles first. Stress that children should calculate using the properties of angles. (The diagrams are not to scale, so measuring will not help.) Children can work in pairs, rehearsing explanations with each other.
- Bring the group together and go through each question, ensuring children use correct vocabulary and give appropriate logical explanations. You may want to draw enlarged versions of the diagrams for this.

Be aware

- Some children may want to revert to measuring. Emphasise that the point of the activity is to use logical reasoning to solve the problems.

Outcomes

- I can find missing angles, using what I know about angles along a straight line, around a point, and in triangles and quadrilaterals.

Supporting resources

This site has a useful reference for finding angles around a point and in shapes:

- http://www.mathsrevision.net/gcse/pages.php?page=17

D1: acute and obtuse angles; angles in a triangle; adding and subtracting near multiples of 10, 100 and 1000; mental subtraction strategies

Summary

Y6 D1.4 **Finding differences**

Pairs working independently

Year 6 Challenge PCMs 14 and 15

Paper clips; sharp pencils; calculators

Abacus Evolve objectives

- Add or subtract the nearest multiple of 10, 100 or 1000, then adjust
- Continue to find differences by counting on
- Use known number facts and place value to consolidate mental subtraction
- Recognise that there are several different mental subtraction strategies

Framework objectives

- Calculate mentally with integers and decimals: U·t + U·t, U·t − U·t, TU × U, TU ÷ U, U·t × U, U·t ÷ U
- Solve multi-step problems, and problems involving fractions, decimals and percentages; choose and use appropriate calculation strategies at each stage, including calculator use
- Understand and use a variety of ways to criticise constructively and respond to criticism

Teacher notes

Preparation
Photocopy PCM 14, one copy per child. Photocopy PCM 15, one copy per pair.

Getting started
Read through the game rules on PCM 14, and check that children understand how to play the game.
Give each pair a paperclip and a sharp pencil, and make sure they all know how to make a spinner using PCM 15.

Activity
Children play the game in pairs. In each round each child spins the spinner four times, writing each number on their copy of PCM 14 beside A, B, C and D respectively. They find the difference between each pair of numbers and then the difference between those two answers ('the difference between the differences'). For example:

Round 1			
	A 912	B 59	Difference? 853
	C 111	D 3200	Difference? 3089
			Difference between the differences? 2236

The player whose final answer is the larger gets a point for the round. After five rounds players swap sheets and check each other's answers. If necessary, they could use a calculator, or written methods. Alternatively, children can play individually against the clock. Can they complete five rounds of the game in 10 minutes?

Extra help
Children should be solving these questions using mental arithmetic with supporting jottings, not by standard written methods. If children are reverting to purely written methods, model how they can use mental methods to solve the questions. For example, the difference between 912 and 59 can be found by adding on from 59: 41 to make 100, 800 to make 900 then 12 to get to 912, so the difference is 800 + 41 + 12 = 853.

Further extension
Children can make a harder version of the game by making their own spinner including 5-digit numbers.

Be aware

- The numbers on the spinner have been chosen to support mental subtraction strategies, so the 'difference between the differences' question is usually harder than the original two questions. If children are struggling with the final calculation they may solve it using standard written methods.

Outcomes

- I can use number facts and place value to solve subtraction questions mentally.

Summary

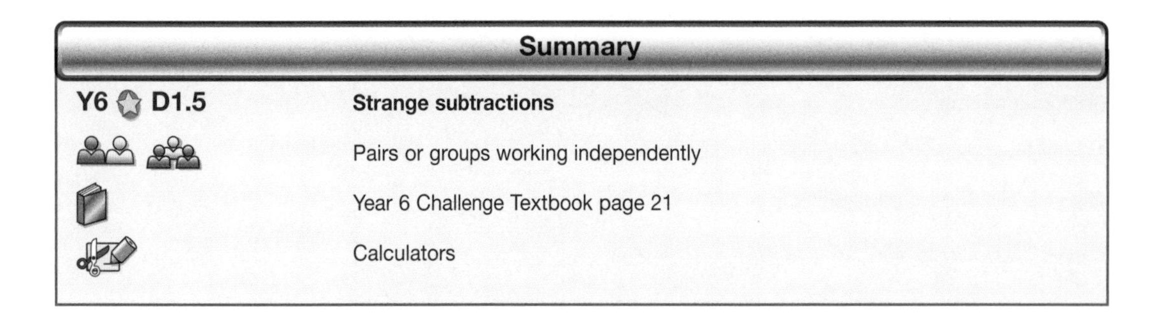

Y6 D1.5 — **Strange subtractions**

Pairs or groups working independently

Year 6 Challenge Textbook page 21

Calculators

Abacus Evolve objectives

- Add or subtract the nearest multiple of 10, 100 or 1000, then adjust
- Continue to find differences by counting on
- Use known number facts and place value to consolidate mental subtraction
- Recognise that there are several different mental subtraction strategies

Framework objectives

- Calculate mentally with integers and decimals: U·t + U·t, U·t − U·t, TU × U, TU ÷ U, U·t × U, U·t ÷ U
- Suggest, plan and develop lines of enquiry; collect, organise and represent information, interpret results and review methods; identify and answer related questions
- Represent and interpret sequences, patterns and relationships involving numbers and shapes; suggest and test hypotheses; construct and use simple expressions and formulae in words then symbols (e.g. the cost of c pens at 15 pence each is 15c pence)
- Use a range of oral techniques to present persuasive argument

Teacher notes

Activity

Children work from Textbook page 21. They start with a 2-digit number, then reverse the digits and find the difference between the two numbers. For example, 52 − 25 = 27. They try this for at least 10 numbers, and describe what they notice about the answers. They then try out a few more examples to test their hypotheses. For 2-digit numbers they should first find that only a limited set of answers occur, and then recognise that the answers are always in the 9 times-table. Children repeat the investigation for 3-digit numbers, and compare their findings to those for 2-digit numbers. They should find that the answers are still multiples of 9, although this may not be obvious at first because the numbers will be greater than 100. However, they should notice that all the answers have a 9 in the tens place. They can use a calculator to check for divisibility.
They predict what will happen with 4-digit numbers, then test it out. Again, they should find that the answers are all multiples of 9.

Information

This result can be explained algebraically as follows. If the digits in a 2-digit number are referred to as x and y respectively then we have set up the following subtraction: $(10x + y) - (10y + x)$. This can be simplified to $9x - 9y$ or $9(x - y)$ which is clearly a multiple of 9. This can be extended to explain the result for 3- and 4-digit numbers. Another explanation involves use of negative numbers.
For example, for 62 − 26; partitioning each number gives
(60 + 2) − (20 + 6) = 40 − 4 = 36. For any pair of numbers, since the number of units subtracted is always the same as the number of tens, the answer must be a multiple of 9.

Be aware

- Children may find and confirm the result but find it difficult to explain. You could introduce some simple algebra here as a quick way to explain a pattern.

Outcomes

- I can find differences between numbers.
- I can suggest and test a hypothesis.

Supporting resources

This site provides some curious number problems:
- http://www.easymaths.com/Curious_Maths_magic.htm

D1: acute and obtuse angles; angles in a triangle; adding and subtracting near multiples of 10, 100 and 1000; mental subtraction strategies

Summary

Y6 D1.6 — **Viewing figures**

A small group working with an adult

Year 6 Challenge Textbook page 22

Calculators (optional)

Abacus Evolve objectives

- **Y6–7** Add or subtract decimals by adding or subtracting too much, then compensating, e.g. for 13·6 + 19·7, start by adding 13·6 + 20
- **Y6–7** Add or subtract decimals by partitioning
- **Y6–7** Subtract decimal numbers with up to three decimal places, using standard written methods
- **Y6–7** Subtract decimal numbers with different numbers of digits

Framework objectives

- **Y6–7** Consolidate and extend mental methods of calculation to include decimals, fractions and percentages
- **Y6–7** Use standard column procedures to add and subtract integers and decimals, and to multiply two-digit and three-digit integers by a one-digit or two-digit integer; extend division to dividing three-digit integers by a two-digit integer

Teacher notes

Activity
- Read through the viewing figures on Textbook page 22 with the group.
- Write *4·69 million* and *4 690 000*. Discuss the fact that *4·69 million* is a way of writing 4 690 000.
- *Why do you think the figures are presented as 'decimal millions' rather than the real number of viewers? What does this tell us about how exact the viewing figures are?*
- Children work from Textbook page 22. In the first set of questions they find the difference between two numbers of viewers mentally and give the answer both as a decimal million and as a whole number. They can work on this part individually.
- In the second set of questions, children work out whether statements are true or false. They should be able to work these out without finding exact answers. You could ask children to work in pairs for this part.

If you have time
Use the viewing figures on the BARB website to develop an investigation of the popularity of the children's favourite programmes.

Be aware

- Children may at first be surprised that the viewing figures on the Textbook page are such round numbers. If necessary explain that all of these viewing figures are approximate.

Outcomes

- I can mentally subtract decimal numbers with two decimal places.
- I can solve true or false questions about decimals with two decimal places.

Supporting resources

The BARB website is here:
- hhttp://www.barb.co.uk/index/index

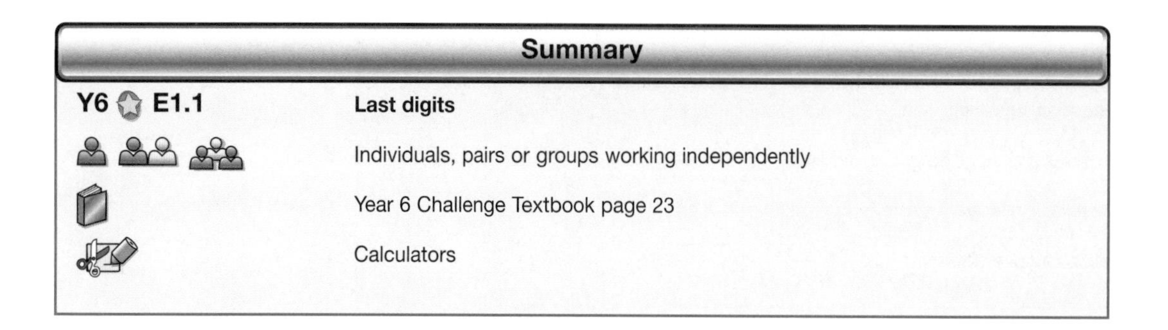

Summary

Y6 E1.1 **Last digits**

Individuals, pairs or groups working independently

Year 6 Challenge Textbook page 23

Calculators

Abacus Evolve objectives

- **Y6-7** Recall quickly doubles and halves of decimal numbers, e.g. double 7·6 and half of 13·2
- **Y6-7** Generate terms of a simple sequence, given a rule for finding each term from the previous term

Framework objectives

- **Y6-7** Compare and order integers and decimals in different contexts
- **Y6-7** Generate sequences and describe the general term; use letters and symbols to represent unknown numbers or variables; represent simple relationships as graphs

Teacher notes

Getting started
Children need to be confident in doubling digits until they reach at least four digits in their answer.

Activity
Children work from Textbook page 23. This activity explores number patterns formed when numbers are doubled. Doubling of most numbers results in the same cyclic pattern in the last digits: 2, 4, 8, 6, 2, 4, 8, 6, …
The only exception comes when children start with a multiple of 5, in which case the last digit is always 0 after the first double.

Extra help
Give children this information to help them with the 'Extra' activity: *When halving, the sequence in the last digits is always 8, 4, 2, 1, 8, 4, 2, 1, … or 6, 3, 6, 3, …*

Further extension
If the second rule for the halving pattern in the 'Extra' activity is changed to *If it is odd, add 1*, the last digits become 4, 2, 4, 2, …
You could encourage children to make up their own rule for odd numbers, e.g. *Subtract 1*.
What would happen with the halving pattern if you added 5 rather than 3 to an odd number? The result would be 8, 4, 2, 1, 8, 2, 4, 1, … or 10, 5, 10, 5, … depending on the starting number.

Be aware

- Simple slips in calculation could disrupt number patterns in the sequences. Encourage children to check their calculations if they cannot see a pattern.

Outcomes

- I can generate sequences and find number patterns.

Challenge Plan: Year 6

E1: multiplying using doubling and halving; improper fractions and mixed numbers; converting, reducing, comparing and ordering fractions

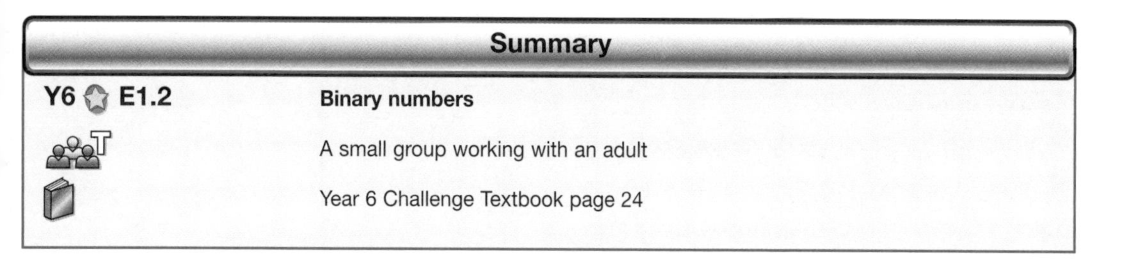

Summary

Y6 E1.2 — **Binary numbers**

A small group working with an adult

Year 6 Challenge Textbook page 24

Abacus Evolve objectives

- **Y6-7** Begin to recall rapidly division facts corresponding to the multiplication facts up to 10 × 10
- **Y6-7** Generate and describe simple integer sequences

Framework objectives

- **Y6-7** Consolidate rapid recall of number facts, including multiplication facts to 10 × 10 and the associated division facts
- **Y6-7** Generate sequences and describe the general term; use letters and symbols to represent unknown numbers or variables; represent simple relationships as graphsinates of points determined by geometric information

Teacher notes

Activity

The number system that we usually work with is called 'denary', or 'base 10'. This means that the numbers are grouped in 10s and multiples of 10. When we talk about 'place value', we are referring to the base 10 system.

Draw this table to show how the base 10 system works:

10 × 10 × 10 × 10	10 × 10 × 10	10 × 10	10	1
10 000	1000	100	10	1

This table is the same as a normal place-value table.
This is how we would represent 100 in the base 10 table:

10 000	1000	100	10	1
		1	0	0

However, not everything uses the base 10 system. For example, there are 60 minutes in an hour, not 100.
We could use a base 4 system if we wanted:

4 × 4 × 4 × 4	4 × 4 × 4	4 × 4	4	1
256	64	16	4	1

100 in base 4 would be 16 in denary:

256	64	16	4	1
		1	0	0

We could also use a base 2 system:

2 × 2 × 2 × 2	2 × 2 × 2	2 × 2	2	1
16	8	4	2	1

100 in base 2 would be 4 in denary:

16	8	4	2	1
		1	0	0

Explain that base 2 is a real number system, called 'binary'. Use the Textbook page to explain how the binary system works.
Children work from Textbook page 24. They write binary numbers in denary, and vice versa.

Be aware

- Children may think that 10 and 2 are the only number bases. Show them other examples, such as base 3.

Outcomes

- I understand how to make binary numbers.

Summary

Y6 E1.3 — **Russian multiplication**

Individuals, pairs or groups working independently

Year 6 Challenge Textbook page 25

Abacus Evolve objectives

- Consolidate the use of doubling and halving to help multiply

Framework objectives

- Calculate mentally with integers and decimals: U·t ± U·t, TU × U, TU ÷ U, U·t × U, U·t ÷ U

Teacher notes

Getting started
Check that children are confident in halving and doubling 2-digit numbers.

Activity
Children work from Textbook page 25. This activity explores a method of multiplication used by Russian peasants in the past. The method uses doubling and halving to find products. Children follow an example of the method and go on to use this to multiply 2-digit numbers. They are encouraged to make an estimate of each answer first.

Further extension
You could encourage children to try using the Russian method to multiply two decimal numbers together. They will need to think about what to do with odd numbers in the left column before halving (subtract 0·1 from tenths and 0·01 from hundredths). They will also need to adjust the total by ÷ 10 for numbers with one decimal place and ÷ 100 for numbers with two decimal places.
For example

1·3	×	6·2
~~0·6~~	~~×~~	~~12·4~~
0·3	×	24·8
0·1	×	48·6
Total		80·6

The correct answer however is not 80·6 as the number on the left has one decimal place. The answer needs to be ×0·1 or ÷10.

So the correct answer is 1·3 × 6·2 = 8·06

The number on the left has two decimal places. This answer needs to be × 0·01 or ÷ 100.

~~2·32~~	~~×~~	~~14~~
~~1·16~~	~~×~~	~~28~~
~~0·58~~	~~×~~	~~56~~
0·29	×	112
~~0·14~~		~~224~~
0·07		448
0·03		896
0·01		1792
Total		3248

Informataion
The Russian method can readily be used to multiply whole numbers by decimals.

Be aware

- This is a very straightforward approach to multiplication but children might have problems with the last stage of crossing off numbers. Demonstrate this to them if necessary.

Outcomes

- I can use a doubling and halving method to multiply numbers together.

Challenge Plan: Year 6

E1: multiplying using doubling and halving; improper fractions and mixed numbers; converting, reducing, comparing and ordering fractions

Summary

Y6 E1.4 — **Fair shares**

A small group working with an adult

Year 6 Challenge PCM 16

Paper to cut up, calculators

Abacus Evolve objectives

- Consolidate changing an improper fraction to a mixed number, and vice versa
- Develop calculator skills and use a calculator effectively

Framework objectives

- Express a larger whole number as a fraction of a smaller one (e.g. recognise that 8 slices of a 5-slice pizza represents $\frac{8}{5}$ or $1\frac{3}{5}$ pizzas); simplify fractions by cancelling common factors; order a set of fractions by converting them to fractions with a common denominator
- Understand and use a variety of ways to criticise constructively and respond to criticism

Teacher notes

Preparation

Photocopy PCM 16, one copy per child or pair. Cut up paper circles and strips to represent the items on the PCM.

Getting started

Check that children understand fractions as division. They will need good recall of tables facts to make this approach more efficient.

Activity

- Show children a paper circle. *Here is a pizza. How would you share it evenly between four? Between five? Between six?* Ask children to discuss this with a partner.
- *What if we had two pizzas shared between four? Between five? Between six?* Ask pairs to cut up paper circles to work this out.
- Write: *1 ÷ 4* and $\frac{1}{4}$, *1 ÷ 5* and $\frac{1}{5}$, and *1 ÷ 6* and $\frac{1}{6}$. Agree that these fractions show what we would get if we divided one pizza between four, five and six people.
- Write *2 ÷ 4* and $\frac{2}{4}$ and agree this is $\frac{1}{2}$. *Do we need to do this calculation?* Agree that sometimes we can see immediately how much each person gets.
- Write fractions for 2 ÷ 5 and 2 ÷ 6.
- *What would happen if we had more pizzas than people? We could give them one each and share the rest. So how do we share five pizzas between four people?* Agree that we could cut one up to give $1\frac{1}{4}$ pizzas each.
- *What if we had nine pizzas and four people?* Agree we would have two pizzas each and one left over.
- Children work from PCM 16. They complete the first part of each question and compare their answers to check.
- Discuss how to work out the cost of each share. *How do you work out the total cost of six pizzas?* Model this as a written multiplication or using a calculator, writing the answer as a decimal with two decimal places. *How do we find each share? We divide by 5.* Model using a calculator for efficiency.
- Ask children to complete the money calculations for the rest of the questions.

Extra help

This approach to dividing with fraction answers uses multiples of numbers rather than improper fractions. E.g. Share 26 chocolates between 3 people. *What is the nearest whole multiple of 3 below 26?* (24 giving 8 sweets each.) Confirm 3 × 8 = 24 and 24 ÷ 3 = 8. *This leaves 2 left over to be shared between 3. This can be written as* $\frac{2}{3}$. Writing the calculation as an improper fraction $\frac{26}{3}$ then cancelling also reaches the same answer but the first approach will help children link multiples with division.

Be aware

- Children may find the money calculations hard. Encourage them to use a calculator for efficiency.

Outcomes

- I can use fractions to do divisions and show mixed-number answers.

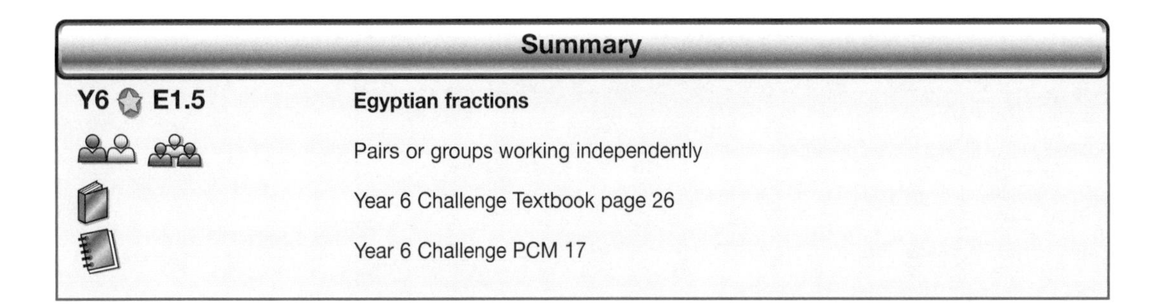

Summary

Y6 E1.5 — **Egyptian fractions**

Pairs or groups working independently

Year 6 Challenge Textbook page 26

Year 6 Challenge PCM 17

Abacus Evolve objectives

- Consolidate recognition of equivalent fractions
- Order fractions by converting them to fractions with a common denominator

Framework objectives

- Express a larger whole number as a fraction of a smaller one (e.g. recognise that 8 slices of a 5-slice pizza represents $\frac{8}{5}$ or $1\frac{3}{5}$ pizzas); simplify fractions by cancelling common factors; order a set of fractions by converting them to fractions with a common denominator

Teacher notes

Preparation
Photocopy PCM 17, one copy per child or pair.

Getting started
Check that children understand the concept of a unit fraction, and are confident in converting fractions to common denominators and cancelling down where necessary.

Activity
Children work from Textbook page 26. This activity explores how the Ancient Egyptians used fractions. The approach makes it easy to compare fractions with different numerators and denominators. Children have to convert a fraction, e.g $\frac{2}{3}$, into an Egyptian fraction: $\frac{1}{2} + \frac{1}{6}$. They convert another fraction, e.g. $\frac{3}{4}$: $\frac{1}{2} + \frac{1}{4}$. By comparing these two sets of Egyptian fractions they should be able to see that $\frac{1}{2}$ is the same in each fraction, but $\frac{1}{4}$ is bigger than $\frac{1}{6}$, so $\frac{3}{4}$ must be bigger than $\frac{2}{3}$.
PCM 17 shows the Egyptian fraction equivalents of some non-unit fractions. The table will allow children to answer the questions on the Textbook page without having to generate the Egyptian fractions themselves. Explain that the Egyptian fractions shown on the PCM are not necessarily the only ways of writing the fractions.

If you have time
Explore the conversion facility on the website (see below).

Be aware

- Children may find fractions that cannot be written as two unit fractions. Reassure them that not all fractions can be written in this way, e.g. $\frac{4}{5}$ cannot.

Outcomes

- I can work out which of two fractions is bigger.

Supporting resources

These websites give comprehensive information about Egyptian fractions. The first has a facility to convert fractions to Egyptian fractions.
- http://www.mcs.surrey.ac.uk/Personal/R.Knott/Fractions/egyptian.html
- http://nrich.maths.org/public/viewer.php?obj_id=1173

For information about the Rhind Papyrus:
- http://www.britishmuseum.org/explore/highlights/highlight_objects/aes/r/rhind_mathematical_papyrus.aspx
- http://openlearn.open.ac.uk/mod/resource/view.php?id=170885
- www.bristol-cyps.org.uk/teaching/primary/maths/pdf/littlebit.pdf
- http://www.ems.bbk.ac.uk/faculty/hart/ForFun/rhindpapyrus

E1: multiplying using doubling and halving; improper fractions and mixed numbers; converting, reducing, comparing and ordering fractions

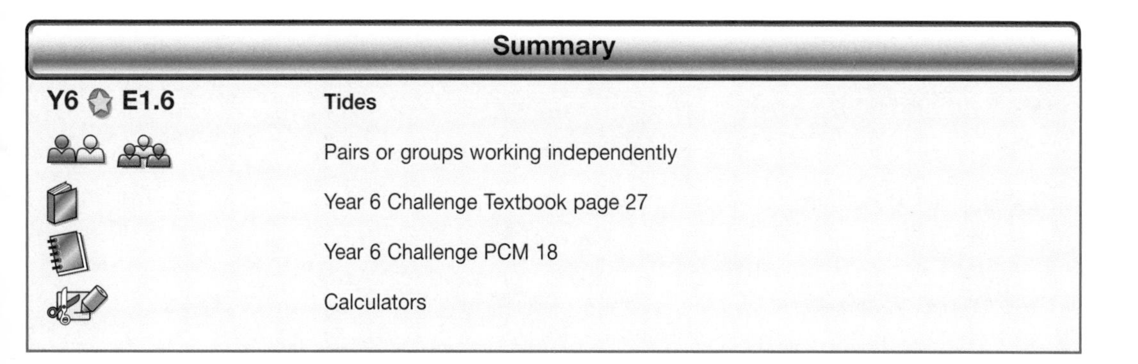

Summary

Y6 E1.6 **Tides**

Pairs or groups working independently

Year 6 Challenge Textbook page 27

Year 6 Challenge PCM 18

Calculators

Abacus Evolve objectives

- Recognise relationships between fractions, e.g. $\frac{1}{16}$ is half of $\frac{1}{8}$
- Use a fraction as an 'operator' to find fractions, including tenths and hundredths, of numbers and quantities

Framework objectives

- Solve multi-step problems, and problems involving fractions, decimals and percentages; choose and use appropriate calculation strategies at each stage, including calculator use
- Use a calculator to solve problems involving multi-step calculations

Teacher notes

Preparation
Photocopy PCM 18, one copy per child or pair.

Getting started
Check that children are familiar with equivalent fractions and understand that $\frac{1}{12} + \frac{2}{12} = \frac{3}{12} = \frac{1}{4}$ and $\frac{1}{12} + \frac{2}{12} + \frac{3}{12} = \frac{6}{12} = \frac{1}{2}$.
You might want to ask children to use a calculator for efficiency.

Activity
Children work from Textbook page 27 and PCM 18. This activity looks at the amount the water falls between high and low tide. There is an illustration of the 'rule of twelfths' which sailors use to calculate if there is enough water under their boat so they do not run aground. Children then complete a table of ports around Britain where they use the 'rule of twelfths' to calculate the height of the water at different times.

Further extension
This activity could be extended to working with other numbers of twelfths as each hour passes.

Be aware

- Children may think that the tide suddenly jumps at the end of each hour. Explain that the water rises gradually but always follows a pattern.

Outcomes

- I can calculate depths in metres.
- I can find $\frac{1}{4}$ and $\frac{1}{2}$ of heights in metres.

Supporting resources

Use the links below for background information about tides and for published tide data:

- http://www.nmm.ac.uk/explore/astronomy-and-time/astronomy-facts/solar-system/tides-and-tidal-forces
- http://www.bbc.co.uk/weather/coast/tides/

Challenge Plan: Year 6

A2: rounding to 10, 100 or 1000 and decimals to whole number or tenth; decimal notation and ordering; finding factors of any number up to 100

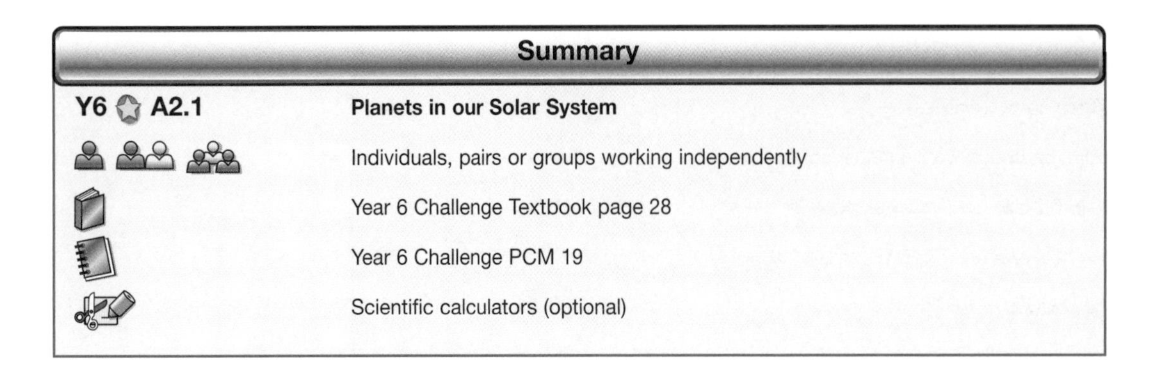

Summary

Y6 A2.1 — **Planets in our Solar System**

Individuals, pairs or groups working independently

Year 6 Challenge Textbook page 28

Year 6 Challenge PCM 19

Scientific calculators (optional)

Abacus Evolve objectives

- Round any integer to the nearest 10, 100 or 1000
- Round a number with two decimal places to the nearest tenth

Framework objectives

- Use decimal notation for tenths, hundredths and thousandths; partition, round and order decimals with up to three places, and position them on the number line

Teacher notes

Preparation
Photocopy PCM 19, one copy per child, pair or group.

Getting started
Check that children are confident in reading numbers to hundreds of thousands and understanding multiples of millions.

Activity
Children work from Textbook page 28. This activity explores the relative sizes of the eight planets in our Solar System. Children look at the data given for each planet on PCM 19 and follow instructions to round the numbers accordingly.

Further extension
Children can explore how scientific calculators can be used for working with very large numbers.
For example the number 420 can be written as $4{\cdot}2 \times 100$ or $4{\cdot}2 \times 10^2$.
12 000 000 can be written as $1{\cdot}2 \times 10^7$.

If you have time
Uranus is bigger in diameter than Neptune but the weight of Neptune is greater than that of Uranus. Children can explore why this is.

Information
- Pluto is no longer considered a planet so some reference information might be out of date.
- 4 function calculators have a limit to the size of the numbers that can be calculated with. Scientific calculators work with any size of number by converting to standard form which uses powers of 10. For example, $100 = 10^2$.

Be aware

- Children can become confused when dealing with very large numbers. Encourage awareness of place value to avoid errors.

Outcomes

- I can round numbers to the nearest 100, 1000 and 1 000 000.
- I can round decimal numbers to the nearest tenth.

Supporting resources

Find out more about planets and the Solar System here:
- http://www.enchantedlearning.com/subjects/astronomy/planets/
- http://www.bbc.co.uk/science/space/solarsystem/

Children can read about standard form here:
- http://www.mathsrevision.net/gcse/pages.php?page=43

Challenge Plan: Year 6

A2: rounding to 10, 100 or 1000 and decimals to whole number or tenth; decimal notation and ordering; finding factors of any number up to 100

Summary

Y6 A2.2 **Which calculation?**

A small group working with an adult

Year 6 Challenge Textbook page 29

Year 6 Challenge PCMs 20 and 21

Calculators; thin card; digit cards

Abacus Evolve objectives

- Use decimal notation for tenths, hundredths and thousandths
- Recognise that multiplying by 100 is equivalent to multiplying by 10, then by 10 again
- Recognise that dividing by 100 is equivalent to dividing by 10, then by 10 again
- Develop calculator skills and use a calculator effectively

Framework objectives

- Use decimal notation for tenths, hundredths and thousandths; partition, round and order decimals with up to three places, and position them on the number line
- *Use efficient written methods to add and subtract integers and decimals, to multiply and divide integers and decimals by a 1-digit integer, and to multiply 2- and 3-digit integers by a 2-digit integer*
- Use a calculator to solve problems involving multi-step calculations
- Understand and use a variety of ways to criticise constructively and respond to criticism

Teacher notes

Preparation

Photocopy PCM 20 onto thin card, one copy per pair. Photocopy PCM 21, one copy per pair.

Getting started

Check that children are familiar with decimals and are able to read them. For example, they should read 0·001 as a thousandth.

Activity

- Write: × *10. What will happen to a number if we do this multiplication?* Discuss the responses, which should include *It will get bigger.*
- Ask children to calculate *156 × 10.* Ask a child to demonstrate this with a place-value board (PCM 20) and digit cards, moving digits to the left. Write the answer to the calculation.
- Repeat for ÷ *10*, eliciting the response: *It will get smaller.* Give an example: *156 ÷ 10* and ask a child to demonstrate. Ask children to confirm with a calculator.
- *What happens if we multiply by 0·1? We are finding a tenth, which is the same as dividing, so the answer will be smaller.* Ask children to confirm with a calculator. *Can you see that × 0·1 is the same as ÷ 10?*
- Now consider ÷ *0·1. This is like saying 'how many tenths in...?' The answer will be bigger. Can you see that ÷ 0·1 is the same as × 10?*
- *Multiplying by 0·01 gives the same answer as dividing by what?*
- Repeat this for ÷ 0·01 and × 100.
- Children work from Textbook page 29. Look at the page and discuss the first two calculations for question 1.
- Ask children to discuss and complete the questions in pairs. They record some of their answers on PCM 21. Encourage them to consider × 0·1 as being the same as ÷ 10, and so on.

Be aware

- Children may think that multiplying always makes a bigger product. However multiplying by 1 keeps the product the same and multiplying by less than 1 makes a smaller product. Dividing by a whole number makes a smaller quotient, dividing by 1 keeps the quotient the same and dividing by a decimal makes a bigger quotient.

Outcomes

- I can recognise when a number will get bigger or smaller if I multiply or divide by whole numbers or decimals.
- I can recognise when calculations are equivalent, such as ÷ 10 and × 0·1.

Summary

Y6 A2.3	**Posting a parcel**
	Individuals, pairs or groups working independently
	Textbook page 30
	Parcels of different weights (optional); weighing scales (optional)

Abacus Evolve objectives

- **Y6-7:** Rehearse ordering a mixed set of decimal numbers with up to three decimal places
- **Y6-7:** Know that when comparing measurements they must be in the same units
- **Y6-7:** Convert between related metric units using decimals to three places (e.g. convert 1375 mm to 1·375 m, or vice versa)

Framework objectives

- **Y6-7:** Compare and order integers and decimals in different contexts
- **Y6-7:** Convert between related metric units using decimals to three places (e.g. convert 1375 mm to 1·375 m, or vice versa)

Teacher notes

Preparation
You could prepare parcels of different weights and sizes for children to weigh to give an idea of how heavy 1 kg is.

Getting started
Check that children are confident in converting grams to kilograms, or kilograms to grams, to compare weights.

Activity
Children work from Textbook page 30. This activity explores the cost of sending a parcel. Children convert weights from kg to g and then use a table to find the cost of postage. The table shows ranges of weights so children will have to decide which weight band each parcel falls into. Children then order the parcels, according to their weight.

If you have time
Prepare other parcels which weigh more or less than the ones on the Textbook page and ask children to find the cost of posting them.

Be aware

- Children may mistakenly think that 0·05 of a kilogram is 5 grams. Remind them that 1 kg is 1000 grams so 0·05 of a kilogram is 50 grams.

Outcomes

- I can convert grams to kilograms and kilograms to grams.
- I can read a table correctly to decide how much a parcel will cost to post.

Supporting resources

The Royal Mail website has more information about parcels here:
- http://www.royalmail.com/portal/rm/jump1?catId=400023&mediaId=400028

A2: rounding to 10, 100 or 1000 and decimals to whole number or tenth; decimal notation and ordering; finding factors of any number up to 100

Summary

Y6 A2.4	**Where does the number go?**
	Individuals, pairs or groups working independently
	Year 6 Challenge PCM 22
	Blank number lines (optional)

Abacus Evolve objectives

- Use decimal notation for tenths, hundredths and thousandths
- Know what each digit represents in a number with up to three decimal places
- Order a mixed set of decimal numbers with up to three decimal places
- Say a decimal number lying between two others

Framework objectives

- Use decimal notation for tenths, hundredths and thousandths; partition, round and order decimals with up to three places, and position them on the number line
- Use a range of oral techniques to present persuasive argument

Teacher notes

Preparation
Photocopy PCM 22, one copy per child, pair or group.

Getting started
Check that children are able to work out numbers on a number line without marked divisions.

Activity
Children work from PCM 22. They identify numbers on a number line, working with tenths and hundredths. They need to use their judgement to decide what the number is, as the divisions given are not detailed enough. Children then identify where numbers would be after a shift on the number line.

If you have time
Children could mark divisions on blank number lines and add markers of their own, and ask others to identify the numbers.

Further extension
Give children questions that require them to use the number line to subtract numbers with 2 decimal places.
For example, 10·00 − 0·26 or 7·61 − 1·02.

Be aware

- Children may have trouble adding 0·75 when crossing a whole number (e.g. 2·75 + 0·75 = 3·5). They should be encouraged to recognise what each division on the number line represents and count on accordingly.

Outcomes

- I can decide what a number could be on an unmarked scale.
- I can identify numbers on a number line to two decimal places.

Challenge Plan: Year 6

A2: rounding to 10, 100 or 1000 and decimals to whole number or tenth; decimal notation and ordering; finding factors of any number up to 100

Summary

Y6 A2.5	**Exploring powers of numbers**
	A group working with an adult
	Year 6 Challenge Textbook 31
	Year 6 Challenge PCMs 23, 24 and 25
	Calculators

Abacus Evolve objectives

- Recognise that a number with an odd number of factors is a square number
- Know squares of numbers to at least 12 × 12
- Calculate squares of larger numbers
- Make and investigate a general statement about familiar numbers or shapes by finding examples that satisfy it
- Recognise and explain patterns and relationships, generalise and predict

Framework objectives

- Use knowledge of multiplication facts to derive quickly squares of numbers to 12 × 12 and the corresponding squares of multiples of 10
- Represent and interpret sequences, patterns and relationships involving numbers and shapes; suggest and test hypotheses; construct and use simple expressions and formulae in words then symbols, e.g. the cost of c pens at 15 pence each is 15c pence

Teacher notes

Preparation
Photocopy PCMs 23 and 24, one copy of each per child. Each child will also need a copy of PCM 25 if there is time.

Getting started
Check that children are familiar with square numbers, and know that a number can be represented by *n*.

Activity
- Show children PCMs 23 and 24. *We call these powers of numbers. Do you recognise any?* (Square numbers.)
- *Do you know what names we give to other powers*? Establish that n^2 is said as *n squared* and is the calculation $n \times n$; and that n^3 is said as *n cubed* and is the calculation $n \times n \times n$. *Do you know why it is called n cubed?* (*It is like the height × width × depth of a cube.*)
- Children work from Textbook page 31. They complete questions 1–3, using a calculator to complete rows 4, 10 and 7 of the tables on PCMs 23 and 24, and filling in the squared and cubed numbers from 13 to 20. Give guidance if necessary, particularly with the concept of cubing.
- *Can you see any patterns? Try looking at the final digit in each box. What do you notice?* (Some repeat, some are palindromic, some count up.)
- Children work through the rest of Textbook page 31 together. Give support in finding patterns in:
  - Row 5 (numbers end in 25, 125, 625, 125, 625, ...)
  - Row 10 (a zero is added on each time)
  - Row 15 (numbers always end in 625, 375, 625, 375, ...)
  - Row 20 (A zero is added on and the initial digits are doubled each time).
  - Numbers with a difference of 10, e.g. 6 and 16. (The final digit is the same)
  - Numbers and their multiple of 10, e.g. 2 and 20 ($20^2 = 2^2 \times 10^2$)
- Children use what they have found to predict answers for powers of other numbers. Encourage them to discuss all patterns that they notice, even if they are not expressly mentioned on the Textbook page.

Further extension
Children can explore patterns with powers greater than n^{10} and numbers greater than 20.

Be aware

- Children may think that 1 × 1 = 2 or that n^2 is the same as n × 2. If necessary use square diagrams to support learning and demonstrate squaring.
- Children may want to use a calculator for × 4 but encourage them to use the double-double strategy.

Outcomes

- I can understand how numbers to powers get larger.
- I can look for patterns that repeat in numbers.

Challenge Plan: Year 6

A2: rounding to 10, 100 or 1000 and decimals to whole number or tenth; decimal notation and ordering; finding factors of any number up to 100

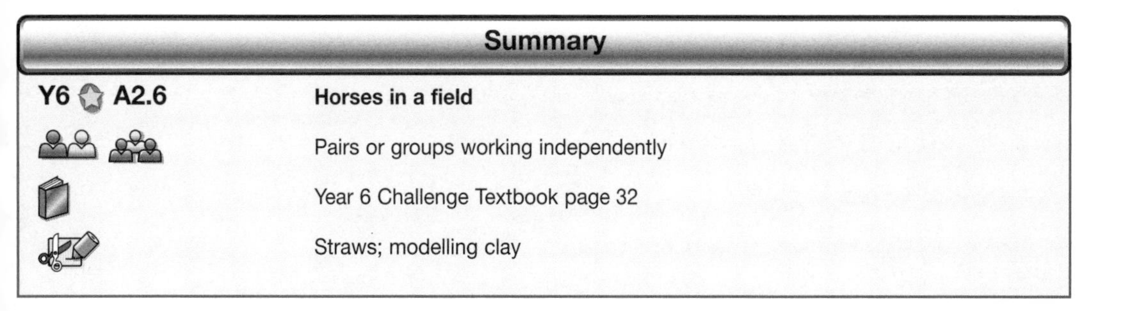

Summary

Y6 A2.6	**Horses in a field**
	Pairs or groups working independently
	Year 6 Challenge Textbook page 32
	Straws; modelling clay

Abacus Evolve objectives

- **Y6-7:** Generate and describe simple integer sequences
- **Y6-7:** Generate terms of a simple sequence, given a rule for finding each term from the previous term
- **Y6-7:** Begin to find a rule for the nth term of simple sequences

Framework objectives

- **Y6-7:** Generate sequences and describe the general term; use letters and symbols to represent unknown numbers or variables; represent simple relationships as graphs

Teacher notes

Getting started
Set out drinking straws and modelling clay on the table so that children can model the paddocks if they need to.

Activity
Children work from Textbook page 32. They are presented with a situation: a farmer builds triangular paddocks for his horses; only one horse can fit in each paddock. They investigate the number of fence strips and fasteners needed to build adjoining paddocks. They must look at how a pattern develops and identify rules to predict the number of fence strips and fasteners they would need for *n* paddocks. They also work out how many paddocks they can make from a given number of fence strips and fasteners. They go on to write an explanation of the rules they have discovered.

Extra help
You could give children these rules to help them with their investigation:
- The number of fence strips needed is the number of paddocks × 2 then add 1.
- The number of fasteners needed is the number of paddocks + 2.

Further extension
The farmer removes one fence panel between each paddock, so that there are now two horses in a larger paddock. How does this change the number of fence panels and fasteners needed for each number of horses?

Be aware

- Children should join each new paddock to the right of the paddock before. If they use a different arrangement, the pattern they will generate will be much more complex and they may not be able to find a formula for it.
- Children should not be expected to use algebra; they are starting to do this by describing the pattern in words.

Outcomes

- I can recognise how a pattern grows.
- I can write in words what the *n*th number in the pattern will be.

B2: multiplication: partitioning and using close facts; coordinates in all quadrants; 3D shapes; visualise 3D shapes from 2D drawings

Summary

Y6 B2.1	**Where do the brackets go?**
	Individual, pairs or groups working independently
	Year 6 Challenge Textbook page 33
	Calculators; scientific calculators (optional); digit cards (optional); bracket cards (optional)

Abacus Evolve objectives

- Use known number facts and place value to consolidate mental multiplication and division
- Use brackets

Framework objectives

- *Use knowledge of place value and multiplication facts to 10 × 10 to derive related multiplication and division facts involving decimals (e.g. 0·8 × 7, 4·8 ÷ 6)*

Teacher notes

Getting started
Introduce children to the BODMAS rule for the correct sequence in which to perform the functions in a calculation: Brackets first, then Order, Division, Multiplication, Addition, and finally Subtraction. In this context Order means a number to the power of another number.

If you have scientific calculators, show children how they work and how to use them for calculations where brackets are required. Enter $2 + 2 \times 3 =$ into a standard four function calculator. *It gives the answer 12.* Now enter $2 + 2 \times 3 =$ into a scientific calculator. *It gives the correct answer which is 8. Scientific calculators use the BODMAS rule so the scientific calculator knows that the sum should be $2 + (2 \times 3) = 12$.*

Activity
Children work from Textbook page 33. The activity explores how brackets make a difference to a calculation. Children work out where the brackets go to make sure each calculation gives the correct answer. Children may use calculators to check but should be encouraged to work the calculations out mentally first.

Extra help
Digit cards and brackets cards might be useful for children to manipulate the position of the brackets.
Children should be encouraged to write down intermediate steps when working through the calculations.

Be aware

- Calculators work in different ways. If the calculator is scientific it will follow the BODMAS rule.
- Sometimes a calculation does not require brackets despite having different operations.

Outcomes

- I can work out how the position of brackets in a calculation affects the answer.
- I understand why some calculators will not give the same answers.

Challenge Plan: Year 6

B2: multiplication: partitioning and using close facts; coordinates in all quadrants; 3D shapes; visualise 3D shapes from 2D drawings

Summary

Y6 B2.2	**Music maths**
	Individual or pairs
	Year 6 Challenge Textbook page 34
	Calculators; the internet

Abacus Evolve objectives

- **Y6-7** Rehearse multiplying and dividing an integer by 10, 100 or 1000
- **Y6-7** Rehearse multiplying U.th × U using standard and informal methods
- **Y6-7** Rehearse finding simple percentages of quantities and measurements (whole number answer)

Framework objectives

- **Y6-7** Use standard column procedures to add and subtract integers and decimals, and to multiply two-digit and three-digit integers by a one-digit or two-digit integer; extend division to dividing three-digit integers by a two-digit integer
- **Y6-7** Calculate percentage increases or decreases and fractions of quantities and measurements (integer answers)
- **Y6-7** Solve problems by breaking down complex calculations into simpler steps; choose and use operations and calculation strategies appropriate to the numbers and context; try alternative approaches to overcome difficulties; present, interpret and compare solutions

Teacher notes

Activity
Children work from Textbook page 34. They read about singles and album sales, charts and awards. Children use sales figures to decide which award singles and albums should receive. They then calculate what amount of album sales were made up of digital sales. Children should use calculators for this.

Further Extension
Children can explore the value for money of downloading singles compared with buying albums. How many singles from one album can they download before it would be better value to buy the whole album? Does this change if they download the album or buy it on CD?

If you have time
Children could collect their own data of music the whole class has downloaded compared to buying CDs. This could be compared with adults in their family.

Be aware

- Children may need to be reminded of a straightforward way to calculate percentages: (percentage ÷ 100) × number.

Outcomes

- I can interpret data shown in a table.
- I can work out percentages of a larger number using a calculator.

Supporting resources

Children can find information about music sales at:
- http://www.bpi.co.uk
- http://www.theofficialcharts.com/index.php

Challenge Plan: Year 6

B2: multiplication: partitioning and using close facts; coordinates in all quadrants; 3D shapes; visualise 3D shapes from 2D drawings

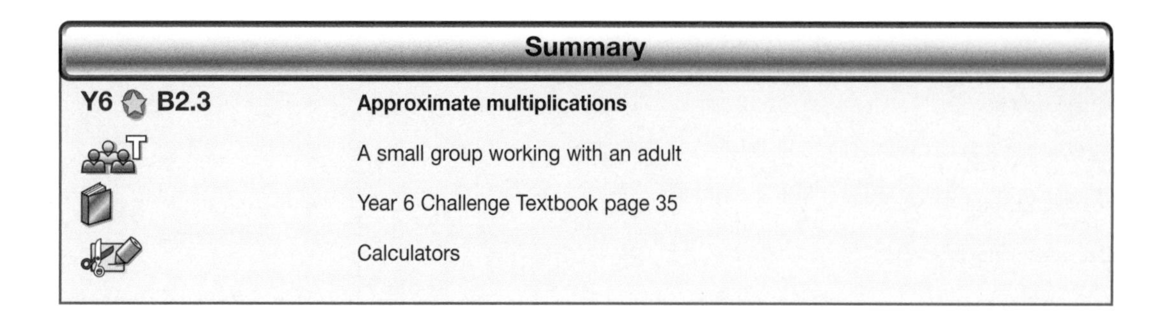

Summary

Y6 B2.3 — **Approximate multiplications**

A small group working with an adult

Year 6 Challenge Textbook page 35

Calculators

Abacus Evolve objectives

- Continue to multiply using closely related facts
- Develop higher multiplication tables, e.g. the ×17 table from the ×10 and ×7 tables
- Know squares of numbers to at least 12 × 12
- Begin to find a number that has a given square, i.e. its square root
- Develop calculator skills and use a calculator effectively

Framework objectives

- *Use knowledge of place value and multiplication facts to 10 × 10 to derive related multiplication and division facts involving decimal numbers (e.g. 0·8 × 7, 4·8 ÷ 6)*
- Use knowledge of multiplication facts to derive quickly squares of numbers to 12 × 12 and the corresponding squares of multiples of 10
- Use a calculator to solve problems involving multi-step calculations

Teacher notes

Activity

- Confirm that children know the square numbers up to 12 × 12.
- Look at the Textbook page together. *How could you find an approximate answer to the calculation? We can use trial and improvement. What is special about the number 36?* Elicit that it is a square number. *What is the square root of 36?* (6) *So if we know that one of the multipliers is 5·6, what can we say about the missing number?* (It must be greater than 6, but quite close to it.) *So what number might we try out first?* Either go through the example attempts shown on the Textbook page, or encourage children to make their own attempts. Give each child a calculator and encourage them to test out each attempt after it has been made. After each attempt, discuss how close children are getting to the answer, and what you have found out so far (for example, that the number must be between 6·4 and 6·5). Stop when children have found the answer to two decimal places. *We could go further than this, but two decimal places is close enough for now.* We can use a calculator to see how close our answer was. Ask children to enter *36 ÷ 5·6* on their calculators. *How close were we?*
- Children work from Textbook page 35. They solve three similar missing-number multiplications, to two decimal places, starting with what they know about square numbers. They should record all their attempts. When everyone has finished, ask children to discuss their answers with a partner.
- Children move on to solving six more multiplications to three decimal places. Again, they discuss their answers in pairs.

Be aware

- Children will need perseverance to refine their estimates with this method.

Outcomes

- I can use trial and improvement to find approximate answers to missing-number multiplications.

Challenge Plan: Year 6

B2: multiplication: partitioning and using close facts; coordinates in all quadrants; 3D shapes; visualise 3D shapes from 2D drawings

Summary

Y6 B2.4 — **Coordinates**

Individuals, pairs or groups working independently

Year 6 Challenge PCM 26

Squared paper; tracing paper; mirrors

Abacus Evolve objectives

- **Y6-7:** Rehearse the reading and plotting of coordinates in all four quadrants
- **Y6-7:** Find coordinates of points determined by geometrical information (e.g. the fourth point of a square, a reflection about the y-axis)

Framework objectives

- **Y6-7:** Use all four quadrants to find coordinates of points determined by geometric information

Teacher notes

Preparation
Photocopy PCM 26, one copy per child.

Getting started
Set out tracing paper and mirrors on the table for children to use if they like.
Check that children are familiar with plotting coordinates in four quadrants and recognising negative coordinates.

Activity
Children work from PCM 26. This activity explores plotting coordinates, finding missing points to complete shapes, naming shapes and identifying lines of symmetry. Children also find and join mid-points and reflect shapes across the vertical and the horizontal axes on a four-quadrant grid.

Further Extension
Children explore adding 1 to each of the coordinates, for example (1, 3) becomes (2, 4). They plot the new positions to see what effect this has.

Be aware

- Children may make the mistake of plotting (4, 1) as four up and one right rather than four right and one up. Make sure children are reading coordinates carefully. Remind children that coordinates are plotted as (x, y). *The x-axis is left or right, the y-axis is up or down. The x-axis comes first, just like x comes before y in the alphabet.*

Outcomes

- I can plot points in four quadrants.
- I can recognise 2D shapes on a grid.
- I can reflect a shape across the vertical and horizontal axes to make a symmetrical shape.

Challenge Plan: Year 6

B2: multiplication: partitioning and using close facts; coordinates in all quadrants; 3D shapes; visualise 3D shapes from 2D drawings

Summary

Y6 B2.5 — **Bird's eye view**

Individuals, pairs or groups working independently

Year 6 Challenge Textbook page 36

Interlocking cubes (blue, green, grey, pink, red, yellow); a digital camera (optional)

Abacus Evolve objectives

- Accurately make and draw shapes
- Visualise 3D shapes from 2D drawings and identify different nets for a closed cube

Framework objectives

- Make and draw shapes with increasing accuracy and apply knowledge of their properties
- Describe, identify and visualise parallel and perpendicular edges or faces; use these properties to classify 2D shapes and 3D solids

Teacher notes

Getting started
Provide six interlocking cubes (blue, green, grey, pink, red, yellow) per child / pair / group.
If you would like children to photograph their shapes, check that they are able to use a digital camera.

Activity
Children work from Textbook page 36. They join interlocking cubes to match the shapes shown and look at the shapes from the front, the top and the side. Children can also photograph the views of the shape. They answer questions about the possible views of each shape.

Children will find that there are six different viewpoints for each shape and that, depending on the shape, some cubes cannot be seen from certain viewpoints. If cubes are stacked only one cube can be seen from the end on view.

Further extension
How many different shapes can children make using four cubes of the same colour? Five cubes of the same colour?

Extra help
- It may be useful for children to use an isometric drawing tool (see below).
- Eight shapes can be made from four cubes. 29 shapes can be made from five cubes. Mathematicians are yet to find the formula for this sequence.

If you have time
Children can use their photos to make a poster about what they have found out.

Be aware

- Initially children may not always appreciate that some cubes will be unseen from certain views. Building their own shapes should help them to become aware of this.

Outcomes

- I can make 3D shapes and match them to 2D views.
- I can solve visual problems with shapes.

Supporting resources

Children can use this isometric drawing tool:
- http://illuminations.nctm.org/ActivityDetail.aspx?ID=125

Challenge Plan: Year 6

B2: multiplication: partitioning and using close facts; coordinates in all quadrants; 3D shapes; visualise 3D shapes from 2D drawings

Summary

Y6 B2.6	**Seeing shapes**
	A small group working with an adult
	Year 6 Challenge Textbook page 37
	Year 6 Challenge PCM 27
	Tracing paper; 3D shapes (cuboids)

Abacus Evolve objectives

- Recognise parallel and perpendicular faces and edges on 3D shapes
- Begin to know the properties of parallelograms, rhombuses and trapezia

Framework objectives

- Describe, identify and visualise parallel and perpendicular edges or faces; use these properties to classify 2-D shapes and 3-D solids
- Use a range of oral techniques to present persuasive argument

Teacher notes

Preparation
Photocopy PCM 27, one copy per child.

Activity
Look together at the photograph on Textbook page 37. Ask children to suggest some shape and space words and phrases to describe the photograph. Use the words on PCM 27 as a prompt. Each time children suggest a word, ask them to point to an example on the photograph.

Show children a cuboid. *What shapes can we see here? (a square face, a rectangular face)*
I can also see a rhombus. Where? Show that you are looking at the side.
Discuss that from straight on, the side is a square but from an angle it looks like a rhombus.
Use the cuboid to show children how perspective changes the shapes we can see.

Look at the carpet in the first picture. *It looks like a trapezium, but if we were standing on it, it would look like a rectangle.*

Children work from Textbook page 37. They find and trace or sketch the shapes in the list.

If you have time
Look at photographs of Portcullis House, an English Parliament building (see below). Children discuss what shapes can be seen.

Information
A concave polygon has two of the sides pointing towards the middle of the shape, for example an arrowhead.

A convex polygon is the opposite of concave shape, for example a trapezium.

Be aware

- Some children may not see that a shape appears differently depending on the angle from which it is viewed. Tracing the shapes in the pictures should help with this.

Outcomes

- I can recognise 2D shapes from pictures of real-life 3D objects.

Supporting resources

Children can see photos of Portcullis House here:
- http://www.buildingopinions.com/Archive/portcullishouse.html

C2: areas of rectangles and compound shapes; areas of right-angled triangles; mean, median and mode; conversion graphs

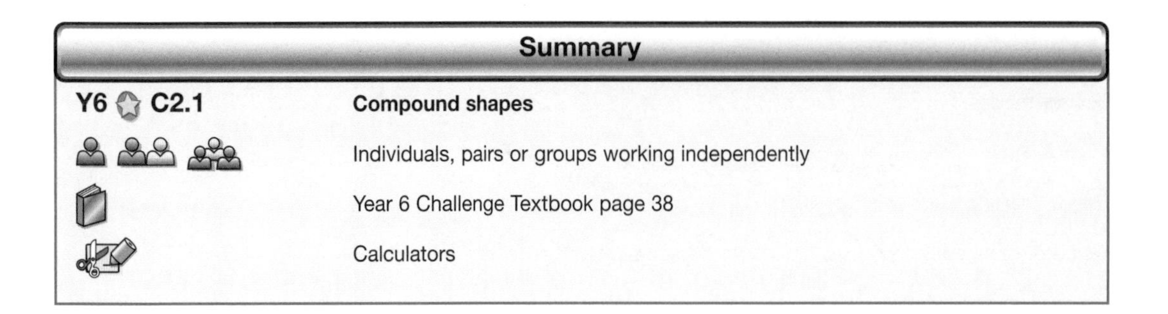

Summary

Y6 C2.1 — **Compound shapes**

Individuals, pairs or groups working independently

Year 6 Challenge Textbook page 38

Calculators

Abacus Evolve objectives

- Calculate the area of a rectangle
- Calculate the area of compound shapes that can be split into rectangles
- Develop from explaining a generalised relationship in words to express it in a formula using letters as symbols

Framework objectives

- Calculate the perimeter and area of rectilinear shapes; estimate the area of an irregular shape by counting squares
- Represent and interpret sequences, patterns and relationships involving numbers and shapes; suggest and test hypotheses; construct and use simple expressions and formulae in words then symbols, e.g. the cost of c pens at 15 pence each is 15c pence
- Explain reasoning and conclusions, using words, symbols or diagrams as appropriate

Teacher notes

Getting started
Explain that a compound shape is a shape that is made up of other shapes. Ask children to look at the dimensions of the shapes on Textbook page 38 and use estimating strategies to suggest which has the greatest area and which has the smallest area.
Explain that children should investigate different ways of splitting each shape up in order to calculate the area of the whole shape.

Activity
Children work from Textbook page 38. They make a rough copy of each shape and note down the calculations needed to find the total area. They may use a calculator to perform the calculations.

Extra help
Encourage children to divide their sketches into the smaller shapes they want to split it into. They can then note the dimensions of each smaller shape, calculate the areas, and label each smaller shape with its area, before adding them together.

Information
Each of the shapes can be split into smaller rectangles using either horizontal or vertical lines; a combination of vertical and horizontal lines is also possible, breaking the shape into more pieces.
Another solution involves finding the maximum area the shape is contained in (i.e. multiplying the longest vertical length by the longest horizontal length) and subtracting the bits 'cut out'. This works best for the 'C' and 'L' shapes where only one smaller rectangle needs to be removed, but the approach could also be used for the other two shapes. If children are unfamiliar with this method it is worth demonstrating it as it should help with the Extra activity, where children could begin with a larger rectangle of say 300–400 cm^2 and then remove parts.

Be aware

- Children may forget to state the units when working with area. Remind them that all their answers should be given in cm^2.

Outcomes

- I can calculate the area of a compound shape that can be split into rectangles.

Challenge Plan: Year 6

C2: areas of rectangles and compound shapes; areas of right-angled triangles; mean, median and mode; conversion graphs

Summary

Y6 C2.2 — **Cuboid boxes**

A small group working with an adult

Year 6 Challenge Textbook page 39

Cuboid-shaped boxes, e.g. cereal boxes; rulers; calculators; 1 cm cubes

Abacus Evolve objectives

- **Y6–7** Rehearse using the formula for calculating the area of a rectangle
- **Y6–7** Consolidate calculating the surface area of cubes and cuboids
- **Y6–7** Begin to understand the concept of volume, and the units for its measurement
- **Y6–7** Calculate the volume of cubes and cuboids, with integer side lengths

Framework objectives

- **Y6–7** Calculate the area of right-angled triangles given the lengths of the two perpendicular sides, and the volume and surface area of cubes and cuboids

Teacher notes

Preparation
Collect some cuboid-shaped boxes, or ask children to bring them in.

Activity
- Give each child a box. *It's a cuboid, so how many faces? Six.*
- *How would you find the total area of the six faces? This is called the surface area.* Let children discuss this.
- *What information would you need to know? What can you say about the six rectangles that make up the surface area?* Children should realise that opposite faces are equal in area, so they only need to find the area of three rectangles and then double this to find the whole surface area. *You need three measurements, the length, height and depth of the cuboid, and you can combine these values to find the area of each rectangle.*
- Remind children of the formula to calculate the area of a rectangle: $area = l \times w$. The length, depth and height measures of the cuboid will be the length or width of two or more of its rectangle faces.
- Ask children to use a ruler to find the dimensions (to the nearest cm) of the box they are holding, and then work out the total surface area.
- Now introduce the idea of volume. Give each child a cm cube and ask them to discuss how many of these could fit inside their box. They will have to consider how they would pack them in systematically, leaving no spaces between them, taking account of the length, height and depth of the box.
- Show how the volume of a box can be found by multiplying the three dimensions. Introduce the formula $volume = l \times h \times d$.
- Children work from Textbook page 39. They calculate the surface area and volume of each cuboid, using a calculator.

Extra help
If children find working from the textbook drawings difficult, repeat modelling an example with a real box.

Information
Although volume is generally introduced after surface area, it is actually easier to calculate. As with perimeter and area, working on both volume and surface area simultaneously for cuboids should help children be clear about which is which.

Be aware

- Children may confuse the units for area and volume. Remind them that surface area is measured in cm^2 and volume in cm^3.

Outcomes

- I can find the surface area of a cuboid when I know the length, height and depth.
- I can find the volume of a cuboid when I know the length, height and depth.
- I know the formula $volume = l \times h \times d$.

Challenge Plan: Year 6

C2: areas of rectangles and compound shapes; areas of right-angled triangles; mean, median and mode; conversion graphs

Summary

Y6 C2.3 — **More compound shapes**

Individuals, pairs or groups working independently

Year 6 Challenge Textbook page 40

Calculators; internet (optional); square dot paper (optional)

Abacus Evolve objectives

- Calculate the area of a rectangle
- Calculate the area of a right-angled triangle by considering it as half a rectangle
- Calculate the area of compound shapes that can be split into rectangles
- Develop from explaining a generalised relationship in words to express it in a formula using letters as symbols

Framework objectives

- Calculate the perimeter and area of rectilinear shapes; estimate the area of an irregular shape by counting squares
- Represent and interpret sequences, patterns and relationships involving numbers and shapes; suggest and test hypotheses; construct and use simple expressions and formulae in words then symbols, e.g. the cost of c pens at 15 pence each is 15c pence
- Explain reasoning and conclusions, using words, symbols or diagrams as appropriate

Teacher notes

Getting started
Check that children know the formula for finding the area of a rectangle (*area* = *l* × *w*), and the formula for finding the area of a right-angled triangle (*area* = *l* × *w* ÷ 2).

Activity
Children work from Textbook page 40. They make a rough copy of each shape and split it into rectangles and right-angled triangles. They find the area of each shape by calculating and adding the areas of the smaller shapes. Children may use a calculator.

Extra help
Some children may need help seeing how to split up the more complicated shapes (C–E), or with finding some of the lengths needed for the calculations. They may find it helpful to label each separate rectangle and triangle with their individual dimensions.

Further extension
Children use the internet to find out more about finding the areas of triangles.

If you have time
Children can draw their own shapes on square dot paper, made of rectangles and right-angled triangles. They exchange them with a partner who works out the area.

Be aware

- Children may try to split shapes using diagonal lines. Encourage them to use horizontal and vertical lines only.

Outcomes

- I can find the area of a right-angled triangle using the formula *area* = *l* × *w* ÷ 2.
- I can find the area of a compound shape that can be split into rectangles and right-angled triangles.

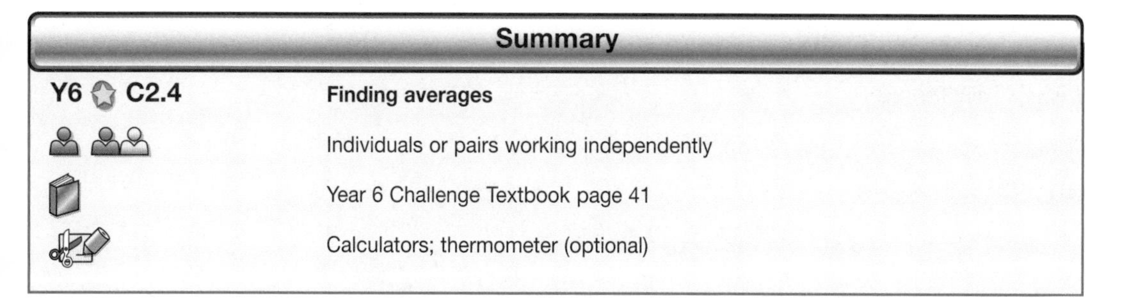

Summary

Y6 C2.4 — **Finding averages**

Individuals or pairs working independently

Year 6 Challenge Textbook page 41

Calculators; thermometer (optional)

Abacus Evolve objectives

- Find the mode and range of a set of data
- Begin to find the median and mean of a set of data
- Calculate different types of average for a set of data

Framework objectives

- Describe and interpret results and solutions to problems using the mode, range, median and mean

Teacher notes

Activity
Children work from Textbook page 41. They find the mean, mode, median and range of the temperatures on each day. They then work out which day had the highest mean temperature, which day had the highest mode, and which day had the highest median. They repeat for the lowest average temperatures. Children then investigate the effect of adding two more temperatures to one of the days.
A calculator will be useful for checking the mean.

Extra help
If children are unclear about the different averages, you could work through Monday's data, modelling how to find each value.

Further extension
Children devise their own survey and organise the data to find the mean, mode, median and range.

If you have time
Children can set up a thermometer in the classroom to monitor the temperature over a period of time and organise and interpret their data.

Information
To find the mean, children should add all the temperatures together and divide by 8. To find the mode, they should look for the most commonly occurring temperature. To find the median, children should arrange the temperatures in order from coolest to warmest and find the temperature in the middle. As there are an even number of cities, the median is between the fourth and the fifth temperature. To find the range, children should find the difference between the highest and the lowest temperature.

Be aware

- Children may think that 'average' refers only to the mean. Reinforce the idea that mean, mode and median are all types of average.

Outcomes

- I can find the mean, mode, median and range of a set of data.

Supporting resources

The Met Office website provides lots of weather data, plus activities and learning materials for children:
- http://www.metoffice.gov.uk/education/index.html

Challenge Plan: Year 6

C2: areas of rectangles and compound shapes; areas of right-angled triangles; mean, median and mode; conversion graphs

Summary

Y6 C2.5	**Average word lengths**
	Individuals or pairs working independently
	Year 6 Challenge PCM 28
	Calculators; tabloid and broadsheet newspapers (optional)

Abacus Evolve objectives

- Find the mode and range of a set of data
- Begin to find the median and mean of a set of data
- Calculate different types of average for a set of data
- Group discrete data in equal intervals
- Construct a grouped frequency table
- Draw and interpret a bar graph based on grouped data

Framework objectives

- Describe and interpret results and solutions to problems using the mode, range, median and mean
- Construct and interpret frequency tables, bar charts with grouped discrete data, and line graphs; interpret pie charts
- *Solve problems by collecting, selecting, processing, presenting and interpreting data, using ICT where appropriate; draw conclusions and identify further questions to ask*
- Suggest, plan and develop lines of enquiry; collect, organise and represent information, interpret results and review methods; identify and answer related questions

Teacher notes

Preparation
Photocopy PCM 28, one copy per child or pair.

Activity
Children work from PCM 28. They find the mean, median and mode word length for the two articles. Children will have to devise a system for counting and recording the word lengths, and then use their raw data to calculate the averages.
Once children have done this, they draw a graph to represent each set of data. They must decide which type of graph will be most useful, and consider whether grouping the data will help. They then say which type of average their graph will show.

Extra help
Support children through the stages of collating the data. If there are 23 words of five letters then that gives $23 \times 5 = 115$ letters. To calculate the total number of letters a similar calculation is needed for each of the word lengths.

Further extension
Choose two real newspaper stories and compare them. It is generally believed that broadsheet newspapers are wordier than tabloids – children might like to test this out.

Be aware

- Children may think they can only compare the average word length in articles that have the same number of words. Explain that it is not necessary to have exactly the same number of words to find an average.

Outcomes

- I can use a tally chart to collect data.
- I can calculate the mean, median and mode averages of a set of data.
- I can draw a graph to represent a set of data.

Supporting resources

Find more articles here to generate more similar exercises:
- http://news.bbc.co.uk/cbbcnews/default.stm

Challenge Plan: Year 6

C2: areas of rectangles and compound shapes; areas of right-angled triangles; mean, median and mode; conversion graphs

Summary

Y6 C2.6	**Conversion graphs**
	A small group working with an adult
	Year 6 Challenge Textbook page 42
	Calculators; graph paper; rulers; graph computer software, e.g. Excel (optional)

Abacus Evolve objectives

- Construct and interpret line graphs in which intermediate values have meaning
- Construct and interpret a conversion graph
- Understand the relationship between imperial and metric units of length

Framework objectives

- Construct and interpret frequency tables, bar charts with grouped discrete data, and line graphs; interpret pie charts
- Select and use standard metric units of measure and convert between units using decimals to two places (e.g. change 2·75 litres to 2750 ml, or vice versa)
- Participate in a whole-class debate using the conventions and language of debate

Teacher notes

Activity

- Ask children to look at the graph on Textbook page 42 and discuss what it shows.
- *How many centimetres is 10 inches?* Model how to look up the 10 inch line, see where it meets the diagonal line, then place a ruler across from the diagonal to the y axis to find the equivalent number of centimetres.
- *10 inches is around 25 cm. So what does 1 inch equal?* (about 2·5 cm) Ask more questions, converting from inches to centimetres or vice versa.
- Children work from Textbook page 42. They answer questions 1 to 8 using the conversion graph.
- Bring the group together to answer questions 9 to 11. Explain that they can multiply inches by 2·54 to convert to centimetres, and divide centimetres by 2·54 to convert to inches. *Why does the calculator give a more accurate answer*? (A reading to 2 d.p., or even 1 d.p., is not possible from the graph.)
- Explain that children will now draw their own graph for converting miles to km up to 50 miles. *What do you need to know?* They can draw the graph by hand or use computer software such as a spreadsheet. As this will be a straight line graph, no more than three points are needed. Including zero ensures the graph goes through the origin.
- To create a graph in Excel, first set up a table of data. Highlight the table and use the chart wizard. Experiment with the different XY scatter graphs.

Miles	Kilometres
0	0
10	16
50	80

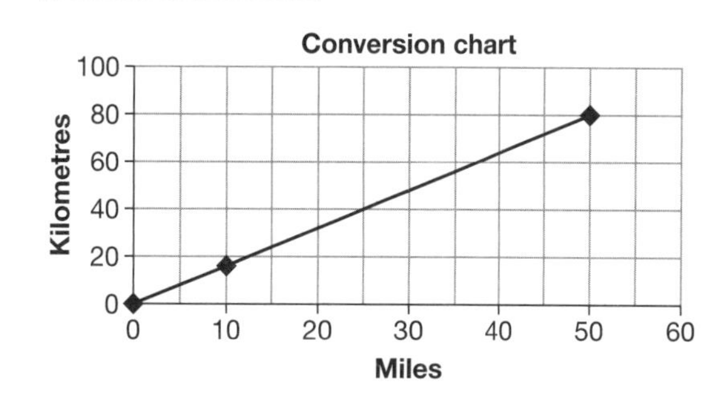

Be aware

- Children may think the point of origin is always where both axes are zero. This is not always the case, e.g. in a temperature conversion graph.

Outcomes

- I can answer questions using a conversion line graph.
- I can construct a conversion line graph.

Supporting resources

Children can use this website to find out the relationship between other measures:
- http://www.onlineconversion.com

Challenge Plan: Year 6

D2: adding and subtracting decimals; adding numbers using standard written methods; square numbers; number sequences

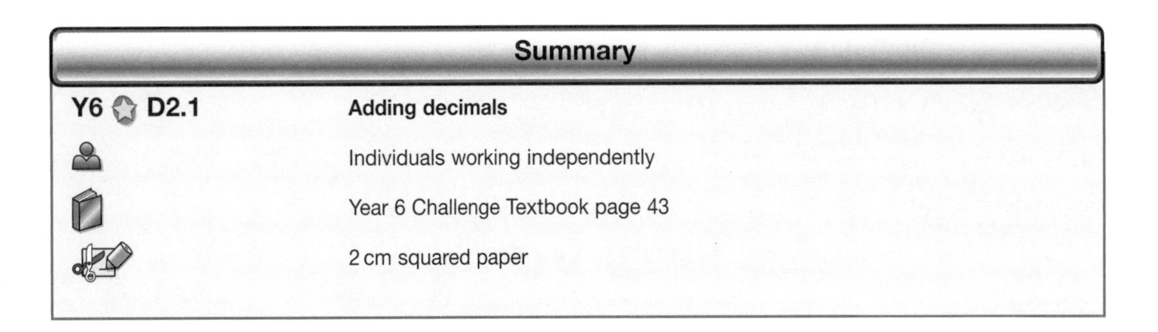

Summary

Y6 D2.1	**Adding decimals**
	Individuals working independently
	Year 6 Challenge Textbook page 43
	2 cm squared paper

Abacus Evolve objectives

- Mentally add or subtract a pair of decimal numbers, each less than 1 and with up to two decimal places
- Find what to add to a decimal with units, tenths and hundredths to make the next higher whole number or tenth
- Continue to find differences by counting on
- Use known number facts and place value to consolidate mental subtraction
- Check with the inverse operation

Framework objectives

- Calculate mentally with integers and decimals: U·t + U·t, U·t − U·t, TU × U, TU ÷ U, U·t × U, U·t ÷ U
- Use approximations, inverse operations and tests of divisibility to estimate and check results

Teacher notes

Getting started
Look at Textbook page 43 together. Check children understand the task. Choose a couple of example questions, such as 2·09 + 10·37 or 12·62 − 3·7 and discuss how these can be solved mentally. Stress that there is no need to set out these questions formally in columns, although jottings are a good idea for some.
Give each child a sheet of squared paper for copying the grid.

Activity
Children work from Textbook page 43. They work systematically through the grid, filling in the missing numbers. Children check six answers at random using the inverse operation. They then find the column and row with the largest total.

Further extension
Children could be set the challenge of completing the grid within a certain time, for example15 minutes.

Be aware

- Questions with different numbers of decimal places are usually the trickiest. Explain that a good strategy is to mentally put zeros at the end of the number with the fewest decimals. For example, think of 12·62 − 3·7 as 12·62 − 3·70.

Outcomes

- I can add and subtract decimals mentally.

Challenge Plan: Year 6

D2: adding and subtracting decimals; adding numbers using standard written methods; square numbers; number sequences

Summary

Y6 D2.2	**Dinner out**
	Individuals or pairs working independently
	Year 6 Challenge Textbook page 44
	Year 6 Challenge PCM 29
	Calculators

Abacus Evolve objectives

- Mentally add or subtract a pair of decimal numbers, each less than 1 and with up to two decimal places
- Find what to add to a decimal with units, tenths and hundredths to make the next higher whole number or tenth
- Add several numbers
- Develop calculator skills and use a calculator effectively
- Check with the inverse operation when using a calculator

Framework objectives

- Calculate mentally with integers and decimals: U·t + U·t, U·t − U·t, TU × U, TU ÷ U, U·t × U, U·t ÷ U
- Use a calculator to solve problems involving multi-step calculations
- Use approximations, inverse operations and tests of divisibility to estimate and check results

Teacher notes

Preparation
Photocopy PCM 29, one copy per child or pair.

Getting started
Check that children understand how to use the price list on PCM 29 to price up the bills on Textbook page 44. Discuss good ways to estimate, for example by rounding each item up or down to the nearest £1.

Activity
Children work from Textbook page 44. They start by estimating which of four food bills is the largest. They then work out the prices exactly and see how close their estimates were. They check their answers using a calculator.
Children then choose a meal for themselves and a friend and work out the bill.

If you have time
You might want to set children a similar task using a real menu from a local restaurant.

Be aware

- When adding several items quickly, children can often make a mistake keying in numbers, or put the decimal point in the wrong place. Encourage children to estimate and check their calculations to make sure they are accurate.

Outcomes

- I can estimate the total of several decimal amounts of money.
- I can add several decimal amounts of money.
- I can use a calculator to check my answers.

Challenge Plan: Year 6

D2: adding and subtracting decimals; adding numbers using standard written methods; square numbers; number sequences

Summary

Y6 D2.3 — **Addition walls**

Individuals or pairs working independently

Year 6 Challenge PCM 30

A4 paper

Abacus Evolve objectives

- Consolidate adding two or more integers less than 10 000 using standard written methods
- Consolidate estimating by approximating an addition of two or more integers, less than 10 000, then checking result

Framework objectives

- *Use efficient written methods to add and subtract integers and decimals, to multiply and divide integers and decimals by a 1-digit integer, and to multiply 2- and 3-digit integers by a 2-digit integer*
- Suggest, plan and develop lines of enquiry; collect, organise and represent information, interpret results and review methods; identify and answer related questions

Teacher notes

Preparation
Photocopy PCM 30, one copy per child. Children may also use extra paper for drawing further addition walls.

Activity
Children work from PCM 30. They add each pair of numbers in the bottom row of the addition wall and fill in the totals in the row above. They estimate each total first, then use column addition to find the exact total. Children continue until they have filled in the top number.
Children then experiment with writing the same four starting numbers in a different order, in order to get a larger top number. Generally the solution is to place the larger numbers in the centre of the bottom row, so that they get used more times.
They move on to investigating where to position four starting numbers to achieve the largest and smallest possible top numbers.
Finally, they try to position five starting numbers in the bottom row of a larger wall to achieve the largest top number.

Further extension
Make up similar problems with 6- or 7-row walls. Be careful as the totals can get very large.

Be aware

- Children may think that the number at the top of the wall is simply the sum of the four numbers at the bottom. Work through the first example to show that this is not the case.

Outcomes

- I can add large numbers using standard written methods.

Challenge Plan: Year 6

D2: adding and subtracting decimals; adding numbers using standard written methods; square numbers; number sequences

Summary

Y6 D2.4	**Square roots**
	A small group working with an adult
	Year 6 Challenge Textbook page 45
	Calculators

Abacus Evolve objectives

- **Y6–7** Rehearse recognition of square numbers up to 12 × 12
- **Y6–7** Understand the concept of square roots
- **Y6–7** Estimate a square root
- **Y6–7** Use the square root key of a calculator to find square roots

Framework objectives

- **Y6–7** Recognise the square roots of perfect squares to 12 × 12
- **Y6–7** Solve problems by breaking down complex calculations into simpler steps; choose and use operations and calculation strategies appropriate to the numbers and context; try alternative approaches to overcome difficulties; present, interpret and compare solutions

Teacher notes

Activity

- Discuss what a square number is. Children should identify that it is the result of multiplying a number by itself.
- Ask children to tell you the squares of some familiar numbers. For example: *What is 4 squared?* (16)
- Explain that a square root is the inverse of a square number. *It is the number that, when multiplied by itself, gives the target number. What is the square root of 100?* (10) *64?* (8) *36?* (6) *144?* (12)
- Children work from Textbook page 45. They complete a table showing the square roots of the first 15 square numbers.
- Read through the cartoon on the Textbook page with the children. It may be useful to ask two children to read Samira and Sean's discussion while the others reproduce the calculations on their calculators.
- Children use the method of trial and improvement to find approximate square roots of numbers that are not square. If the calculators have a square root key, children can use this to check their answers.

Extra help

If children are stuck, another useful way to tackle square roots is to think of a square of a certain area and to think what length its side must be. *A square with an area of 100 cm^2 would have sides 10 cm long; a square with an area of 81 cm^2 would have sides 9 cm long.* You could draw squares on squared paper to support this visually. *So what would be the length of sides of a square with area 88 cm^2?* Establish that they would be somewhere between 9 cm and 10 cm long.

Information

For most integers the square root will be a long decimal number, so the method here will only give an approximate answer (to 2 or 3 places is sufficient).

Be aware

- Some children may get disconcerted when multiplying the square root by itself doesn't give exactly the starting number. Explain that the square roots are only approximate.

Outcomes

- I understand the relationship between square numbers and square roots.
- I can use trial and improvement to find approximate square roots of numbers that are not square.

D2: adding and subtracting decimals; adding numbers using standard written methods; square numbers; number sequences

Summary

Y6 D2.5 — **Brackets**

A small group working with an adult

Year 6 Challenge Textbook page 46

Abacus Evolve objectives

- **Y6–7** Rehearse the use of brackets
- **Y6–7** Know and use the order of operations: add, subtract, multiply and divide
- **Y6–7** Develop the order of operations to include brackets

Framework objectives

- **Y6–7** Understand how the commutative, associative and distributive laws, and the relationships between operations, including inverse operations, can be used to calculate more efficiently; use the order of operations, including brackets
- **Y6–7** Solve problems by breaking down complex calculations into simpler steps; choose and use operations and calculation strategies appropriate to the numbers and context; try alternative approaches to overcome difficulties; present, interpret and compare solutions

Teacher notes

Activity

- Go through the first example on Textbook page 46, discussing which gives the larger result, $3 \times (6 + 7)$ or $(3 \times 6) + 7$. *Why does the first one give a larger answer?*
- Look at questions 1–5. Ask children to discuss in pairs which calculation gives the larger result, before working them out.
- Discuss the results that they have found. Ask each child to make up one more number puzzle like this and to then ask the group which will produce the greater result.
- Now look at the second example on the Textbook page. Ask children to discuss which will produce the larger answer before trying out and finding answers.
- Children then work through questions 6–10 in pairs. They investigate the effect of putting a pair of brackets in different places in these calculations, and note down the different answers that can be generated by using brackets.
- Bring the group together and discuss what they have found out about the number of different options for the placement of brackets in these examples.

Information

Children should find that the larger answers are likely to come from calculations in which brackets are used to maximise the effect of multiplying. So they should add before multiplying, and in question 5 multiply before subtracting. Encourage children to use examples from these questions or others they have made up to make these sorts of generalisations.

Be aware

- When children are making up their own puzzles, they should remember that in examples involving division, calculations will be difficult if the resulting answer isn't a whole number.

Outcomes

- I understand how to use brackets in a calculation.
- I can find different possible answers by putting brackets in different places.
- I can explain patterns and relationships by making predictions and trying out ideas.

Supporting resources

This site explains the effect of different orders of operations:
- http://www.easymaths.com/What_on_earth_is_Bodmas.htm

D2: adding and subtracting decimals; adding numbers using standard written methods; square numbers; number sequences

Summary

Y6 D2.6	**Matchstick patterns**
	Pairs working independently
	Year 6 Challenge Textbook page 47
	Spent matchsticks or small sticks; squared paper

Abacus Evolve objectives

- Recognise and extend number sequences
- Explore patterns created by number sequences
- Recognise and explain patterns and relationships, generalise and predict
- Develop from explaining a generalised relationship in words to express it in a formula using letters as symbols

Framework objectives

- Represent and interpret sequences, patterns and relationships involving numbers and shapes; suggest and test hypotheses; construct and use simple expressions and formulae in words then symbols, e.g. the cost of c pens at 15 pence each is 15c pence
- Tabulate systematically the information in a problem or puzzle; identify and record the steps or calculations needed to solve it, using symbols where appropriate; interpret solutions in the original context and check their accuracy
- Use a range of oral techniques to present persuasive argument

Teacher notes

Getting started
Provide matchsticks and squared paper. Check that children understand how the sequences on Textbook page 47 are extended, modelling if necessary with matchsticks.

Activity
Children work from Textbook page 47. They explore the increasing number of matchsticks used to create square patterns. Children should discuss their findings as they go along and aim to find a general rule to describe them.

Extra help
Most children will benefit from modelling the first few patterns with matchsticks. If they are stuck then encourage them to continue modelling the patterns.
When reproducing patterns or extending them on squared paper it is useful to use different colours for the matchsticks added each time, or to strike them out as they are counted.

Further extension
Children could find the number of matchsticks needed for further patterns in each sequence (such as the 20th, the 50th, the 100th or the *n*th).

Information
The succinct algebraic expressions for the three sequences are $(3n + 1)$, $(5n + 2)$ and $(7n + 3)$ respectively, where n is the number in the sequence.
Some children will find the number of matchsticks needed for the 10th pattern in the sequences by finding $(9 \times 3) + 4$, $(9 \times 5) + 7$, and $(9 \times 7) + 10$, respectively. Here they have seen the 10th as the 9th one on from the original number and multiplied by the number the sequence increases by each time.

Be aware

- Children may find the 10th number in the sequences by counting on. Encourage them to think about a more general way to work them out.

Outcomes

- I can extend a number sequence.
- I can explore patterns and find general rules for number sequences.

E2: multiplying using standard methods; using a fraction as an operator; ordering and converting fractions and decimals; tests of divisibility

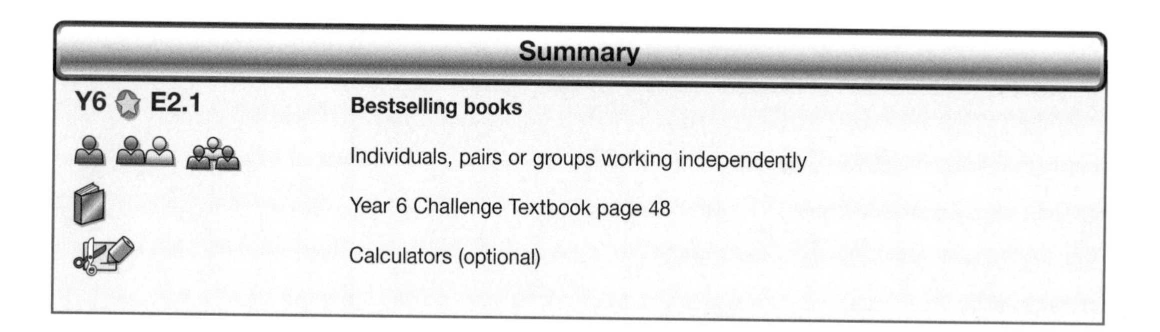

Summary

Y6 E2.1 — **Bestselling books**

Individuals, pairs or groups working independently

Year 6 Challenge Textbook page 48

Calculators (optional)

Abacus Evolve objectives

- Multiply ThHTU × U using standard written methods
- Consolidate adding two decimal numbers, with one or two decimal places, using standard column addition
- Consolidate adding two or more integers less than 10 000 using standard written methods

Framework objectives

- *Use efficient written methods to add and subtract integers and decimals, to multiply and divide integers and decimals by a 1-digit integer, and to multiply 2- and 3-digit integers by a 2-digit integer*
- Solve multi-step problems, and problems involving fractions, decimals and percentages; choose and use appropriate calculation strategies at each stage, including calculator use
- Understand and use a variety of ways to criticise constructively and respond to criticism

Teacher notes

Activity
Children work from Textbook page 48. This exercise about bestselling book sales gives them practice in multiplication and division, addition and subtraction. There is also an element of problem solving as children have to decide whether an answer could be true. Although the numbers involved are large, they are whole numbers or end in 99 so there is no need for children to use a calculator, but you may choose to allow their use for efficiency.

Further Extension
Children could survey their class or the school to compile a favourite book list and explore the sales figures using the internet.

If you have time
Children could look at real bestseller lists in some Sunday newspapers or on the internet, and compare sales figures. They could also look up the selling prices and compare the value of the sales.

Be aware

- Children may not realise how to multiply numbers that end in 99. Encourage them to use the adjusting method for working out the total cost by rounding up to nearest pound and then subtracting the penny.

Outcomes

- I can add and subtract large numbers.
- I can multiply large numbers by a single digit and adjust where necessary.

Supporting resources

The Guardian website shows the bestseller lists each week:
- http://www.guardian.co.uk/books/series/bestsellers

Challenge Plan: Year 6

E2: multiplying using standard methods; using a fraction as an operator; ordering and converting fractions and decimals; tests of divisibility

Summary

Y6 E2.2 **Food guidelines**

A small group working with an adult

Year 6 Challenge Textbook page 49

Calculators

Abacus Evolve objectives

- **Y6-7** Rehearse finding simple percentages of quantities and measurements (whole number answer)

Framework objectives

- **Y6-7** Calculate percentage increases or decreases and fractions of quantities and measurements (integer answers)
- **Y6-7** Solve problems by breaking down complex calculations into simpler steps; choose and use operations and calculation strategies appropriate to the numbers and context; try alternative approaches to overcome difficulties; present, interpret and compare solutions

Teacher notes

Activity

This activity extends children's use of fractions into converting to percentages and asks them to find percentages of given amounts by using the decimal equivalent. They also use a calculator to divide decimals to calculate percentages.

- Rehearse with children their understanding of a fraction such as $\frac{2}{5}$ and confirm that it could be interpreted as a division, or as 2 out of 5. If necessary repeat with some other fractions such as $\frac{1}{2}$ and $\frac{5}{100}$.
- Link fractions with percentages by writing $\frac{1}{2}$. *What would this be as a decimal and a percentage?* Children should be able to identify 0·5 and 50%. Confirm with a calculator that $\frac{1}{2}$ is 50% and 5/100 is 0·05 which is 5%. Show on a calculator that 2/5 is 0·4 and that this is 40%.
- *How can we find the decimal equivalent of a fraction like $\frac{2}{7}$?* Agree that we could use a calculator.
- Take the first table (pizza) on Textbook page 49 and show children how to find the fraction of a woman's recommended daily allowance of calories that is provided by the pizza: $\frac{460}{2000}$. Confirm that we can do this division on a calculator: $460 \div 2000 = 0{\cdot}23$, and that this is equal to 23%. *This means the calories in this pizza will give 23% of the recommended daily amount.*
- Take the second figure, for sugars, and confirm that this is $4 \div 90$ which is 0·044, which rounds to 4%. Ask children to put this into words: *This is 4% of the recommended daily amount of sugars.*
- Repeat the process for the next fraction, $\frac{19}{70}$, and agree that this is 0·271 which rounds to 27%.
- *How can we work out the amount of saturated fat in grams when we only have the percentage?* Agree that $40\% = \frac{40}{100} = 0{\cdot}4$ as a decimal. So we want 0·4 of 20, or $0{\cdot}4 \times 20$, which gives us 8 g.
- Children work from Textbook page 49. They find the missing numbers in the other tables.

If you have time

Ask children to make up their own nutrition tables for foods of their choice, with some information missing. Children then swap with a partner and find the missing information in each other's tables.

Be aware

- Children need to be confident in reading a calculator readout of 0·5 as 50% ($\frac{50}{100}$) and 0·05 as 5% ($\frac{5}{100}$). If they need extra support, explain that they can multiply the decimal by 100 to see the percentage more clearly.

Outcomes

- I can turn a fraction into a decimal and a percentage using a calculator.
- I can find a percentage of an amount using a calculator.

Supporting resources

These websites may be useful for finding out more about nutritional requirements:

- http://www.nutrition.org.uk/home.asp?siteId=43§ionId=s
- http://www.eatwell.gov.uk/foodlabels/labellingterms/nutritionalinfo/

Challenge Plan: Year 6

E2: multiplying using standard methods; using a fraction as an operator; ordering and converting fractions and decimals; tests of divisibility

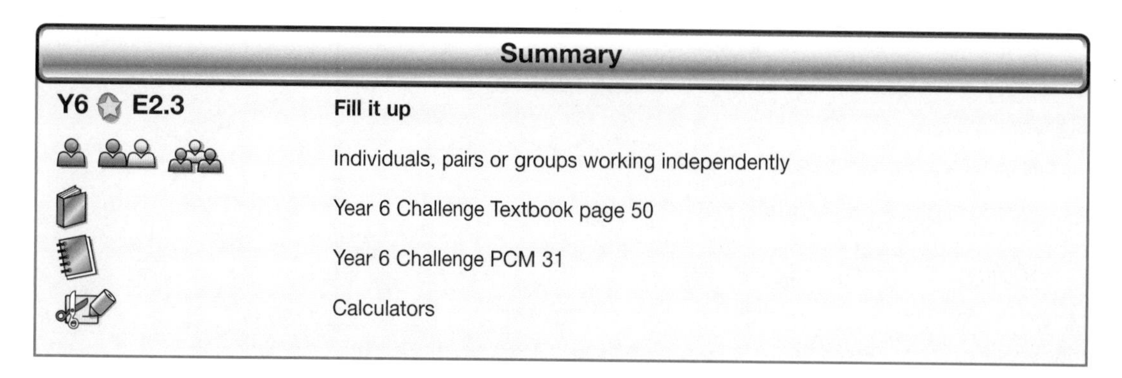

Summary

Y6 E2.3 — **Fill it up**

Individuals, pairs or groups working independently

Year 6 Challenge Textbook page 50

Year 6 Challenge PCM 31

Calculators

Abacus Evolve objectives

- Use a fraction as an 'operator' to find fractions, including tenths and hundredths, of numbers and quantities

Framework objectives

- Relate fractions to multiplication and division (e.g. $6 \div 2 = \frac{1}{2}$ of 6 $= 6 \times \frac{1}{2}$); express a quotient as a fraction or decimal (e.g. $67 \div 5 = 13{\cdot}4$ or $13\frac{2}{5}$); find fractions and percentages of whole-number quantities (e.g. $\frac{5}{8}$ of 96, 65% of £260)
- Solve multi-step problems, and problems involving fractions, decimals and percentages; choose and use appropriate calculation strategies at each stage, including calculator use

Teacher notes

Preparation
Photocopy PCM 31, one copy per child.

Activity
Children work from Textbook page 50. They answer questions about a car's petrol tank capacity and the petrol consumption of the car. They look at petrol gauges on PCM 31 to work out how much fuel is in each car. All the gauges on the PCM are divided into a different number of sections and all show different readings. Children have to convert the readings to a standard measurement so they can compare what proportion of each tank is full.
As an added challenge both metric and imperial measurements are used for distance and capacity, and children have to convert between the two. Petrol consumption is also stated in a mixture of metric and imperial units.

Extra Help
Approximate conversions:
- 4·5 litres is approximately 1 gallon
- 0·22 gallons is approximately 1 litre
- 1 mile is approximately 1·6 kilometres
- 1 kilometre is approximately 0·62 miles
- 1 kilometre per litre is approximately 3 miles per gallon
- 1 kilometre per gallon is approximately 0·62 miles per gallon
- 1 mile per gallon is approximately 0·35 kilometres per litre
- 1 mile per gallon is approximately 1·6 kilometres per gallon

If you have time
Children can use the internet to find out about the cost per mile of using 'green cars', such as electric cars, hybrid petrol and LPG-powered cars, and compare this with the cost per mile of diesel and petrol-powered cars.

Be aware

- Children may be unsure how to compare the proportions. They will probably find it most straightforward to convert them all to percentages.

Outcomes

- I can read scales with different numbers of divisions.
- I can convert proportions to compare them.

Supporting resources

These websites give information about 'green cars':
- http://www.whatgreencar.com/
- http://www.cleangreencars.co.uk/
- http://www.green-car-guide.com/

Challenge Plan: Year 6

E2: multiplying using standard methods; using a fraction as an operator; ordering and converting fractions and decimals; tests of divisibility

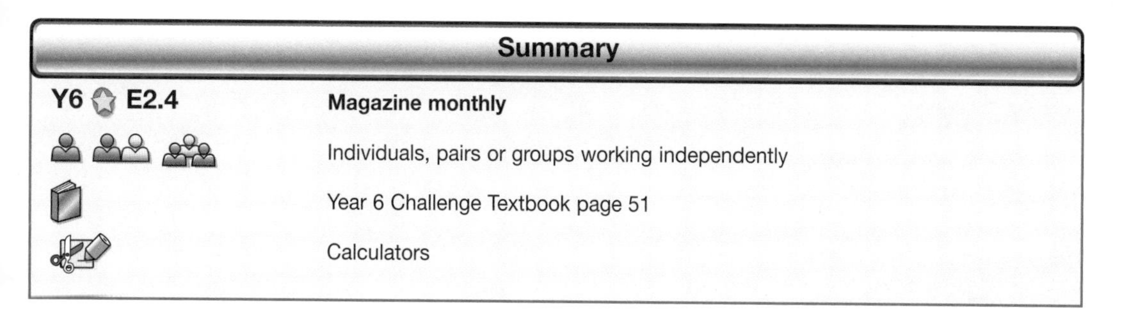

Summary

Y6 E2.4	**Magazine monthly**
	Individuals, pairs or groups working independently
	Year 6 Challenge Textbook page 51
	Calculators

Abacus Evolve objectives

- Consolidate recognition of equivalence between fractions and decimals
- Convert a fraction to a decimal using division
- Key in fractions on a calculator, recognising the equivalent decimal form

Framework objectives

- *Express one quantity as a percentage of another, e.g. express £400 as a percentage of £1000; find equivalent percentages, decimals and fractions*
- Solve multi-step problems, and problems involving fractions, decimals and percentages; choose and use appropriate calculation strategies at each stage, including calculator use

Teacher notes

Getting started
Check that children are confident in finding decimal equivalents using a calculator. Make sure children know that quarterly means four times a year, and biannually means twice a year.

Activity
Children work from Textbook page 51. This activity looks as words which are commonly used for recurrences over a year such as quarterly, biannually, monthly and weekly. Children use the information given to work out how many magazines are bought over a year, the total cost of the publications, and the relative cost per week. Children are required to convert fractions to decimals using a calculator, and then use these to calculate total costs.

Extra help
Increasing prices by 10% can be done simply by multiplying by 1·1. Increasing by 15% can be done simply by multiplying by 1·15, and so on.

Further Extension
All prices are increased by 10% for next year. What will the new costs be for the whole year?

If you have time
Children could complete their own class surveys to see what magazines are bought, and their relative costs.

Be aware

- Children might think that every four weeks means every month. Reinforce that there are 52 weeks in a year, which makes 13 lots of four weeks.

Outcomes

- I can convert decimals to fractions and vice versa.
- I can use decimals and fractions to calculate money totals.
- I can work out individual prices from total amounts.

E2: multiplying using standard methods; using a fraction as an operator; ordering and converting fractions and decimals; tests of divisibility

Summary

Y6 E2.5	**Decimal dominoes**
	A small group working with an adult
	Year 6 Challenge PCMs 32, 33, 34 and 35
	Thin coloured card; calculators

Abacus Evolve objectives

- **Y6-7** Divide, giving the quotient as a decimal to one or two places
- **Y6-7** Rehearse ordering a mixed set of decimal numbers with up to three decimal places
- **Y6-7** Know decimal and percentage equivalents of simple fractions

Framework objectives

- **Y6-7** Compare and order integers and decimals in different contexts
- **Y6-7** Recognise approximate proportions of a whole and use fractions and percentages to describe and compare them, for example when interpreting pie charts

Teacher notes

Preparation
Photocopy PCMs 32–35, one copy of each. If possible use different coloured card for each PCM. Cut out the 40 dominoes.

Getting started
Check that children are able to convert between fractions, decimals and percentages. They need to understand that they can convert a fraction to a decimal by dividing the numerator by the denominator, and convert a decimal answer to a percentage by keying × 100 on a calculator.

Activity
Lay out all the dominoes face up on the table. Hold up the two dominoes 0·3 / 75% and $\frac{3}{4}$ / $\frac{95}{100}$. Ask children to tell their partner what each side of the dominoes has written on it. *Which side is the bigger proportion?* Children estimate which side is bigger.

Confirm that we have $\frac{3}{10}$ on the first domino. *Can we say this a different way? What would it be if we had 100 as the denominator? It would be* $\frac{30}{100}$.

We have $\frac{3}{4}$ *on the second domino. How do we find the decimal equivalent of* $\frac{3}{4}$*?* Encourage children to say *0·75*, which leads to 75 hundredths or $\frac{75}{100}$.

Then take all four domino amounts and write them in order: $\frac{30}{100}$, $\frac{75}{100}$, $\frac{75}{100}$, $\frac{95}{100}$. *Which is biggest? Which is smallest? What can we say about 75% and ¾?*

Ask children to take two dominoes and convert all the amounts to fractions with a denominator of 100, and then to write them all in order. *Can you find two dominoes with an amount on each that matches, such as 10% and* $\frac{1}{10}$ *or 0·1 and* $\frac{10}{100}$*?* Each child reads out their equivalences.

Children play a game of dominoes, matching equivalent amounts until they cannot play any more.

Further extension
Children can take ten dominoes and see how long a snake they can make by matching equivalents.

Be aware

- Children may wonder why some unit fractions do not appear on this set of dominoes. You may need to remind them that for some unit fractions there is no exact decimal/percentage equivalent. They can check this for themselves using a calculator.

Outcomes

- I can match equivalent decimals, percentages and fractions.

Challenge Plan: Year 6

E2: multiplying using standard methods; using a fraction as an operator; ordering and converting fractions and decimals; tests of divisibility

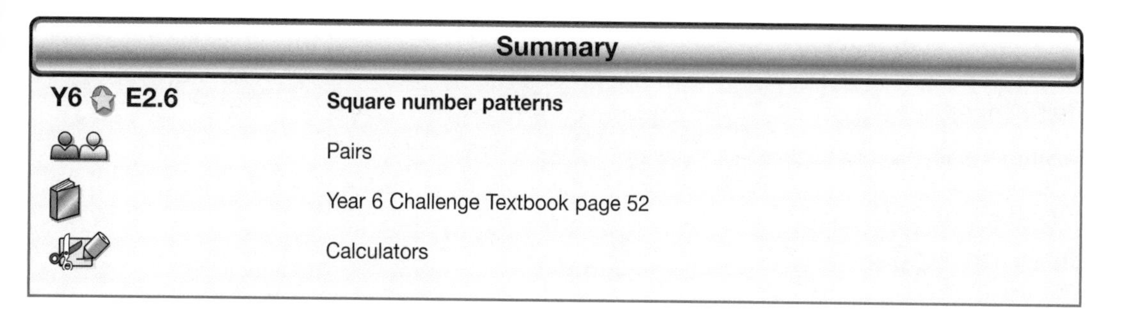

Summary

Y6 E2.6 — **Square number patterns**

Pairs

Year 6 Challenge Textbook page 52

Calculators

Abacus Evolve objectives

- Consolidate knowledge of tests of divisibility by 2, 4, 5, 10 and 100
- Use tests of divisibility to estimate and check results of calculations
- Know squares of numbers to at least 12 × 12
- Calculate squares of larger numbers

Framework objectives

- Use knowledge of multiplication facts to derive quickly squares of numbers to 12 × 12 and the corresponding squares of multiples of 10
- Use approximations, inverse operations and tests of divisibility to estimate and check results
- Explain reasoning and conclusions, using words, symbols or diagrams as appropriate
- Use a range of oral techniques to present persuasive argument

Teacher notes

Getting started
Check that children are confident in using and exploring different square numbers.

Activity
Children work from Textbook page 52. This activity explores some of the properties of square numbers.
Children read hypotheses about the results of dividing square numbers by a single digit, then explore the hypotheses to prove whether or not they are correct.

Extra help
The remainders do fall into patterns but not as regularly as the square numbers.

Further extension
Children could explore dividing square numbers by 2-digit numbers and looking for patterns in the remainders.

Be aware

- Children may not see the link between ÷ 5 and ÷ 10 and therefore not see why part of the hypothesis is the same for both, i.e. you never get a remainder of 2 or 3 with both 5 and 10. Encourage them to see that this is because 5 is a factor of 10.

Outcomes

- I can look for patterns when I divide square numbers.

A3: positive and negative numbers; simple percentages; fractions as decimals; multiplying HTU × TU, U·t × U, U·th × U

Summary

Y6 A3.1 — **Flying high**

Individuals, pairs or groups working independently

Year 6 Challenge Textbook page 53

Year 6 Challenge PCM 36

Abacus Evolve objectives

- Find the difference between a positive and a negative number
- Find the difference between two negative numbers
- Consolidate ordering a given set of positive and negative numbers

Framework objectives

- Find the difference between a positive and a negative integer, or two negative integers, in context

Teacher notes

Preparation
Photocopy PCM 36, one copy per child or pair.

Getting started
Check that children are confident with the concept of very cold temperatures, and in using negative numbers.

Activity
Children work from Textbook page 53 and PCM 36. This activity looks at negative numbers in the context of low temperatures at altitude – when flying and at the tops of mountains. Children read about why temperatures are colder at the tops of mountains. They then look at cruising heights for different aircraft. They convert the heights in feet to metres, and calculate the temperature at different heights above sea level.

Further extension
Children could explore how temperature changes with the depth of the sea. Although temperatures get colder the deeper you go, they do not reflect the extremes of the changes at height. The second link below will give some help with this.

Be aware

- The temperature does not depend only on height; it also depends on the ground temperature below the aircraft, so in desert conditions the air is warmer at a given height.

Outcomes

- I can relate a fall in temperature to negative numbers.
- I can convert feet to an approximate equivalent in metres.

Supporting resources

Find out more about temperature changes at altitude here:
- http://daphne.palomar.edu/jthorngren/adiabatic_processes.htm Lapse%20Rates

There is information about temperature and the depths of the oceans here:
- http://www.windows.ucar.edu/tour/link=/earth/Water/temp.html

Challenge Plan: Year 6

A3: positive and negative numbers; simple percentages; fractions as decimals; multiplying HTU × TU, U·t × U, U·th × U

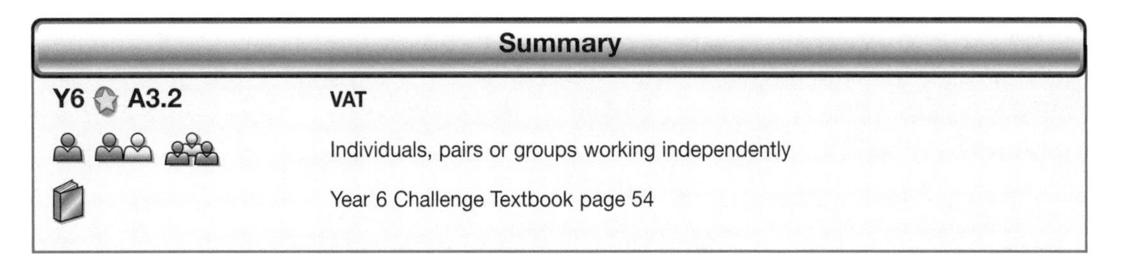

Summary

Y6 A3.2 — **VAT**

Individuals, pairs or groups working independently

Year 6 Challenge Textbook page 54

Abacus Evolve objectives

- Find simple percentages of small whole-number quantities
- Consolidate rounding up or down after division, depending on the context

Framework objectives

- Relate fractions to multiplication and division (e.g. $6 \div 2 = \frac{1}{2}$ of $6 = 6 \times \frac{1}{2}$); express a quotient as a fraction or decimal (e.g. $67 \div 5 = 13{\cdot}4$ or $13\frac{2}{5}$); find fractions and percentages of whole-number quantities (e.g. $\frac{5}{8}$ of 96, 65% of £260)

Teacher notes

Getting started
Check that children are confident in finding simple percentages, such as finding 10% by dividing by 10, 5% by halving this, and 2·5% by halving again.

Activity
This activity explores the calculation of VAT at 17·5% by finding 10%, 5% and 2·5%, then adding to find the total price. Children work out the VAT on items ranging in price from £15 to £6550. They then work out the total price of each item with VAT at 15%. Children will need to consider rounding some answers to the nearest penny.

Further Extension
Children can look at how they can use halving or doubling and known facts such as $10\% = \frac{1}{10}$ to find 25%, 30%, 40% and 45% of amounts.

If you have time
Children find out the rates of VAT (or its equivalent) in other countries and use them to find the VAT for the prices on the Textbook page.

Extra help
Encourage children to use the calculations they first made to find the new lower rates.

Be aware

- If children understand that they can work out percentages using fractions and simple division they will make fewer errors than learning the algorithm 'divide by 100 and multiply by percentage'.

Outcomes

- I can work out simple percentages by using the fact that 10% is $\frac{1}{10}$, halving this to find 5%, and halving again to find 2·5%.

Summary

Y6 A3.3 **Stretching and shrinking**

 A group working with an adult

Year 6 Challenge Textbook page 55

Abacus Evolve objectives

- **Y6-7** Rehearse finding simple percentages of quantities and measurements (whole number answer)
- **Y6-7** Find the outcome of a given percentage increase or decrease

Framework objectives

- **Y6-7** Calculate percentage increases or decreases and fractions of quantities and measurements (integer answers)

Teacher notes

Getting started
Check that children are confident in finding 1% of amounts.

Activity
- *How would you calculate 10% of something?*
- Write *10%*, along with children's suggestions. Encourage the answers *Divide by 10* and *10% is the same as one tenth.*
- Ask children to calculate 10% of 120 and 10% of 34.
- Write *1%*. Ask children how they would calculate 1% of something. Encourage them to think about using 10% and then dividing by 10.
- Ask children to find 1% of 120 and 1% of 34.
- Write *0·5%*. Ask what children understand this to be. Agree that it is half of 1%.
- Together find 0·5% of 120 and 0·5% of 34 by finding 1% then halving the answer.
- Children work from Textbook page 55. Ask them to complete the first question and compare answers.
- *How would we find 1·5%? Add together 1% and 0·5%.*
- Look at question 2 which uses 0·15%. Discuss what this means. *How can we work out such a small percentage without a calculator?*
- Ask children to compare 1·5% and 0·15%. *What is the same? What is different?*
- Answer the first part of question 2 together by finding 1%, 0·5% and then 0·15%.
- Ask children to complete question 2 and then question 3 which uses percentages bigger than 1%.

If you have time
Ask children to collect newspaper articles which mention percentage increases or decreases in a real-life context, such as house prices.

Be aware

- If children understand that they can work out percentages using fractions and simple division they will make fewer errors than learning the algorithm 'divide by 100 and multiply by percentage'.
- It is easy for children to confuse 1·5% and 0·15%.

Outcomes

- I can find percentages less than 1%.
- I can calculate how much something has decreased or increased.

Summary

Y6 A3.4 — **Messy maths book**

A group working with an adult

Year 6 Challenge Textbook page 56

Calculators

Abacus Evolve objectives

- Multiply HTU × TU using standard written methods
- Multiply U·th × U using standard written methods

Framework objectives

- *Use efficient written methods to add and subtract integers and decimals, to multiply and divide integers and decimals by a 1-digit integer, and to multiply 2-digit and 3-digit integers by a 2-digit integer*
- Use a range of oral techniques to present persuasive argument

Teacher notes

Getting started

Check that children are familiar with the grid method of multiplication.

Activity

- This activity provides practice of the grid method of multiplication to multiply 2-digit by 2-digit numbers, 3-digit by 2-digit numbers, and decimals.
- Children work from Textbook page 56. For each calculation they must correct any errors, insert any omissions, and check whether the answer is correct.
- Look together at the first calculation. *What do you think the approximate answer will be?* Ask children to discuss in pairs.
- Copy the first grid and ask children to tell their partner what number is missing. (2) *What is the wrong number in the grid?* (120 should be 12.) Ask children to work out the correct answer and agree it in pairs.
- Children work through the other questions on the page.
- You could allow children to use calculators to check their answers.

Further extension

The standard written method follows on from this grid method. You can show children how the first few questions are written using the standard written method, and ask them to complete the rest this way.

For example:

```
   65
  ×87
  455
    3
 5200
   4
 5655
```

Be aware

- The multiplication algorithm may lead to errors if children do not consider place values, e.g. 34 is 30 and 4 not 3 and 4.

Outcomes

- I can use the grid method to multiply 2-digit and 3-digit numbers.
- I can use the grid method to multiply decimals in the context of money.

Challenge Plan: Year 6

A3: positive and negative numbers; simple percentages; fractions as decimals; multiplying HTU × TU, U·t × U, U·th × U

Summary

Y6 A3.5 — **Summer holiday**

Individuals, pairs or groups working independently

Year 6 Challenge Textbook page 57

Year 6 Challenge PCM 37

Calculators (optional)

Abacus Evolve objectives

- Rehearse multiplying U·t × U using standard written methods
- Multiply U·th × U using standard written methods

Framework objectives

- *Use efficient written methods to add and subtract integers and decimals, to multiply and divide integers and decimals by a 1-digit integer, and to multiply 2-digit and 3-digit integers by a 2-digit integer*
- Use a range of oral techniques to present persuasive argument

Teacher notes

Preparation
Photocopy PCM 37, one copy per child, pair or group.

Getting started
Check that children are confident multiplying 3-digit numbers and decimals by 2, 3 and 4, in the context of money.

Activity
Children work from Textbook page 57. They look at accommodation options for a holiday and calculate prices involving hundreds of pounds to find the cheapest venue for a family's summer holiday. Question 3 asks children to calculate in pounds and pence the cost of items the family take on holiday. They use PCM 37 to record their calculations.

If you have time
Children describe their dream holiday, then use holiday brochures or the internet to work how much it would cost.

Be aware

- A calculator could be used for question 3 in the Textbook, but encourage children to complete questions 1 and 2 without a calculator.

Outcomes

- I can solve problems involving money.
- I can multiply by single numbers without a calculator.

Challenge Plan: Year 6

A3: positive and negative numbers; simple percentages; fractions as decimals; multiplying HTU × TU, U·t × U, U·th × U

Summary

Y6 A3.6 — **Well I never!**

Individuals or pairs working independently

Year 6 Challenge PCM 38

Calculators

Abacus Evolve objectives

- **Y6-7** Rehearse multiplying and dividing an integer by 10, 100 or 1000
- **Y6-7** Generate and describe simple integer sequences

Framework objectives

- **Y6-7** Use standard column procedures to add and subtract integers and decimals, and to multiply two-digit and three-digit integers by a one-digit or two-digit integer; extend division to dividing three-digit integers by a two-digit integer
- **Y6-7** Generate sequences and describe the general term; use letters and symbols to represent unknown numbers or variables; represent simple relationships as graphs

Teacher notes

Preparation
Photocopy PCM 38, one copy per child or pair.

Activity
Children work from PCM 38. This activity explores patterns when numbers are multiplied by 101, 1001, 10 001 and 100 001. Children multiply two different 2-digit numbers by each of these amounts, each time predicting the answer before calculating. They look for patterns and consider why the numbers appear the way they do.

If you have time
- *Take a 2-digit number and repeat it, such as 15 makes 1515. Subtract 101 and write down the answer. Then subtract 101 from this new number and write down the answer. Carry on until you get to a negative number. How many times could you subtract 101 and get a positive answer?*
- *Take the number 234 234 and divide it by 11. Divide the answer by 13 and then by 7. What do you notice?*

Further extension
Children can explore other numbers. What happens if you multiply a decimal number like 2·3 or 0·23 by 1001, 10 001 and 100 001? Will this always happen?

Be aware

- The answers are a result of place value; multiplying a 2-digit number by 100 effectively moves that number two places to the left.

Outcomes

- I can predict an answer to a calculation based on a multiplication pattern.
- I understand how the answers relate to place value.

Summary

Y6 B3.1 **More money**

Individuals, pairs or groups working independently

Year 6 Challenge Textbook page 58

Internet

Abacus Evolve objectives	Framework objectives
• **Y6-7** Add decimal numbers with up to three decimal places using standard written methods • **Y6-7** Add decimal numbers with different numbers of digits	• **Y6-7** Use standard column procedures to add and subtract integers and decimals, and to multiply two-digit and three-digit integers by a one-digit or two-digit integer; extend division to dividing three-digit integers by a two-digit integer • **Y6-7** *Solve problems by measuring, estimating and calculating; measure and calculate using imperial units still in everyday use; know their approximate metric values* • **Y6-7** Solve problems by breaking down complex calculations into simpler steps; choose and use operations and calculation strategies appropriate to the numbers and context; try alternative approaches to overcome difficulties; present, interpret and compare solutions

Teacher notes

Getting started
Briefly discuss with children that the British currency changed significantly when decimal currency was introduced in 1971.

Activity
Children work from Textbook page 58. They read about some names for coins and amounts of money that are either slang or have become obsolete. Children learn how much each amount is worth now, and use the information to work out the cost of ten items.

If you have time
Children can make a collection of coins from Britain and around the world and compare their value.

Be aware	Outcomes
• Children may only be familiar with the decimal currency and may be confused by the concept of the pre-decimal currency. However, for this activity they will just need an awareness of the pre-decimal currency, and not an in-depth knowledge of how it was used.	• I can solve problems involving money.

Supporting resources

To find out more about pre-decimal currency:

- http://www.predecimal.com/predecimaldenominations.htm

Challenge Plan: Year 6

B3: adding, decimals; subtracting numbers less than 10 000; subtracting decimals; metric and imperial units of capacity

Summary

Y6 B3.2 — **Pop tour**

A small group working with an adult

Year 6 Challenge Textbook page 59

Year 6 Challenge PCMs 39, 40 and 41

Calculators

Abacus Evolve objectives

- Consolidate adding two decimal numbers, with one or two decimal places, using standard column addition
- Consolidate adding two or more integers less than 10 000 using standard written methods
- Develop calculator skills and use a calculator effectively
- Use the relationship between addition and subtraction

Framework objectives

- *Use efficient written methods to add and subtract integers and decimals, to multiply and divide integers and decimals by a 1-digit integer, and to multiply 2-digit and 3-digit integers by a two-digit integer*
- Use a calculator to solve problems involving multi-step calculations
- Solve multi-step problems, and problems involving fractions, decimals and percentages; choose and use appropriate calculation strategies at each stage, including calculator use

Teacher notes

Preparation
Photocopy PCMs 39 and 40, one copy of each per child.
For children who are likely to reach the Extra activity, photocopy PCM 41.

Getting started
Look at Textbook page 59 together. Encourage children to work together to familiarise themselves with the tour itinerary of the pop band and discuss approximately how far apart they think the cities are.

Activity

- Make a statement about the distance chart on PCM 39, e.g. *It is 414 km from Glasgow to Sheffield.*
- Ask children to demonstrate that they understand the distance chart and know where to find this information. *How far is it from London to Plymouth?* Ask children to show you where this information is on the chart.
- Repeat, this time with the time chart. Establish that times given are hours and minutes not hours and decimal hours. Discuss with children why these times must have been estimated. (The speed will vary.)
- Children work from Textbook page 59. They use the distance and time charts on PCM 40 to answer the questions.

Further Extension
Children can convert the distances travelled into miles.
1 mile = 1·609 km.

If you have time
Children can make up their own band name, and plan their British tour. Once they have decided what cities they would like to visit, they can use the internet to find the distances and travelling times between each place, and work out the total distance and time they would spend travelling.

Be aware

- When adding time it is important that children remember that there are 60 minutes in an hour, not 100 so they should not read times as decimals.

Outcomes

- I can add numbers and time intervals correctly.
- I can use a calculator to multiply efficiently
- I can consider what route might be more efficient

Supporting resources

Google maps will allow children to quickly find travelling times and distances between cities:

- http://maps.google.co.uk/maps?hl=en&tab=wl

Summary

Y6 B3.3 — **Subtracting with a difference**

Individuals, pairs or groups working independently

Year 6 Challenge Textbook page 60

Abacus Evolve objectives

- Continue to subtract one integer from another, each less than 10 000, using standard written methods

Framework objectives

- *Use efficient written methods to add and subtract integers and decimals, to multiply and divide integers and decimals by a 1-digit integer, and to multiply 2-digit and 3-digit integers by a two-digit integer*
- Represent and interpret sequences, patterns and relationships involving numbers and shapes; suggest and test hypotheses; construct and use simple expressions and formulae in words then symbols (e.g. the cost of c pens at 15 pence each is 15c pence)

Teacher notes

Getting started
Check that children are familiar with using negative numbers.

Activity
Children work from Textbook page 60. They learn the negative number method for subtracting. Children carry out some subtractions with 3-digit reversed numbers (e.g. 721 − 127) using this method. They continue the reversals and subtractions and note the number sequence that develops.
Children then use this method with 4-digit reversed numbers (e.g. 5431 − 1345) and explore the sequence of subtractions and reversals.

Further extension
Children can investigate the difference between reversed 2-digit numbers. (It is always a multiple of 9).

Information
With 3-digit numbers, children will reach 594 − 495. The sequence ends at 99.
With 4-digit numbers several numbers recur.

Be aware

- Children may not want to use the negative number subtraction method regularly but encourage them to use it for this activity.

Outcomes

- I can use negative numbers to help me subtract.
- I can explore number patterns that come from subtracting reversed numbers.

Challenge Plan: Year 6

B3: adding, decimals; subtracting numbers less than 10 000; subtracting decimals; metric and imperial units of capacity

Summary

Y6 B3.4 **Making a bird table**

A small group working with an adult

Year 6 Challenge Textbook page 61

Year 6 Challenge PCM 42

Abacus Evolve objectives

Y6-7 Subtract decimal numbers with up to three decimal places, using standard written methods
Y6-7 Add decimal numbers with up to three decimal places using standard written methods
Y6-7 Solve problems by measuring, estimating and calculating

Framework objectives

Y6-7 Use standard column procedures to add and subtract integers and decimals, and to multiply two-digit and three-digit integers by a one-digit or two-digit integer; extend division to dividing three-digit integers by a two-digit integer
Y6-7 *Solve problems by measuring, estimating and calculating; measure and calculate using imperial units still in everyday use; know their approximate metric values*

Teacher notes

Getting started
Together familiarise yourselves with the instructions for building a bird table on PCM 42. Note that the dimensions are given in a combination of cm and mm.

Activity
Look together at the instructions on PCM 42 to see the dimensions of the wooden pieces that Matthew, Asha, Leigh, Emma and Tariq will need to build a bird table.
Compare these to the wooden pieces that can be bought in the shop. *Is it easy to see how much wood the children should buy?* Encourage the group to convert all the dimensions to mm.

Children work from Textbook page 61. They complete question 1 by using the measurements to work out how many pieces of wood the children must buy from the shop, and therefore the total cost of building one bird table.
Encourage the group to draw scale images of each full-sized piece of wood so that they can visualise how much is needed for each section of the bird table. *Don't forget the cost of the other materials!*

How much wood is left over when the children have built one bird table? Do they have enough to build one more table? Two more? If they want to build five bird tables, will they have to buy more wood? Children use their scale drawings to plan how many full-sized pieces of wood the children need to build five bird tables. They answer question 2 on Textbook page 61, calculating the total cost of building five bird tables.

The children share equally the cost of building the five bird tables. How much does each child spend? The group uses this information to answer question 3 on Textbook page 61 and calculate how much one bird table costs when five bird tables are built at once.
Relatively, how much cheaper is it for the children to build five bird tables together, than to each buy the wood to build their own bird table separately? This demonstrates the benefits of buying in bulk.

If you have time
Children can use these instructions to build a real bird table. They can research the cost of the wood they will need.

Be aware

Children may assume that it costs exactly five times as much to build five bird tables. Make sure they can see how money can be saved by cutting more that one piece from each full-sized piece.

Outcomes

I can use measurements to work out how much each piece of wood will cost.
I can calculate how much the wood will cost for one bird table and for five bird tables.

Challenge Plan: Year 6

B3: adding, decimals; subtracting numbers less than 10 000; subtracting decimals; metric and imperial units of capacity

Summary

Y6 B3.5 **How much juice?**

Pairs or groups working independently

Year 6 Challenge Textbook page 62

Balance scales; weights (100 g and 250 g); a sticky label

Abacus Evolve objectives

- Use, read and write standard metric units of capacity: l, ml
- Record estimates and readings from capacity scales
- Suggest suitable units and measuring equipment to estimate or measure capacity

Framework objectives

- Read and interpret scales on a range of measuring instruments, recognising that the measurement made is approximate and recording results to a required degree of accuracy; compare readings on different scales, e.g. when using different instruments
- Use a range of oral techniques to present persuasive argument

Teacher notes

Preparation
Use a sticky label to hide the weight on the 100 g weight.

Getting started
Place the two weights in the balance scale. Check that it clearly reads 350 g.
The balance reads 350 g. We know that one weight is 250 g. How much is the other? Children should recognise that they can subtract the known weight from the total weight to find the hidden weight.
350 g − 250 g = 100 g. *This shows how we can use known information to find missing information.*

Activity
Children work from Textbook page 62. The activity uses known information about total amounts to find missing information. Children look at the amount of juice made by each combination of fruits. They look at each picture in turn and use this information to work out how much juice is made by each fruit. They should discuss the possibilities in pairs or groups, working together to solve the problem.
Children need to be aware that some of the scales use intervals of 50 ml and others use intervals of 25 ml.

Extra help
Children will need to start by working out that two melons give 1 l of juice, so one melon gives 500 ml. From there they can work out each fruit.

If you have time
Children can make their own fruit juice drink and see how much juice is made from the real fruits they have chosen.

Be aware

- Children may try to work out the fruits in the order that they appear on the page. If necessary, demonstrate to them why this is not possible.

Outcomes

- I can solve problems using capacity.
- I can read a capacity scale.

B3: adding, decimals; subtracting numbers less than 10 000; subtracting decimals; metric and imperial units of capacity

Summary

Y6 B3.6	**How much petrol?**
	Individual, pairs or groups working independently
	Year 6 Challenge PCMs 39 and 43
	Calculators

Abacus Evolve objectives

- Understand the relationship between imperial and metric units of capacity
- Use, read and write standard metric units of length: mm, cm, m, km
- Develop calculator skills and use a calculator effectively

Framework objectives

- *Select and use standard metric units of measure and convert between units using decimals to two places (e.g. change 2·75 litres to 2750 ml, or vice versa)*
- Solve multi-step problems, and problems involving fractions, decimals and percentages; choose and use appropriate calculation strategies at each stage, including calculator use

Teacher notes

Preparation
Photocopy PCMs 39 and 43, one copy of each per child, pair or group.

Getting started
Check that children are able to read and understand the information on the distance chart on PCM 39.

Activity
Children use PCM 39 to find the distance between the cities that a band visit on their British tour.
Children complete the table on PCM 43. They calculate how much petrol is used in gallons in the drive between each city. They then convert these amounts to litres. They work out how much the petrol costs and if the band has enough money to pay for it.

Further extension
The petrol tank of the tour bus holds 50 litres of petrol. The band refill the tank each time it is down to exactly 5 litres. How many times will they need to refill the tank? How much will the refills cost in total? How much petrol will they have left in the tank when they reach Birmingham?
(The band will need to refill the tank with 45 litres of petrol five times. This will cost £191·25 in total. When they reach Birmingham they will have 40·82 litres of petrol left in the tank.)

Be aware

- Children should convert the amounts at each stage of the journey and add them up, rather than just converting the total. Otherwise their answer will be affected.

Outcomes

- I can solve problems involving capacity.
- I can convert from gallons to litres.

C3: likelihood and the probability scale; pie charts; perimeters of rectangles and compound shapes; units of time and time-zones

Summary

Y6 C3.1 **Dice probabilities**

Pairs working independently

Year 6 Challenge Textbook page 63

Two 6-sided dice per pair (two different colours, if possible); squared paper; rulers

Abacus Evolve objectives

- Recognise events that are equally likely
- Predict the outcome of equally likely events
- Draw and interpret a bar graph based on grouped data

Framework objectives

- Describe and predict outcomes from data using the language of chance or likelihood
- *Solve problems by collecting, selecting, processing, presenting and interpreting data, using ICT where appropriate; draw conclusions and identify further questions to ask*
- Construct and interpret frequency tables, bar charts with grouped discrete data, and line graphs; interpret pie charts
- Suggest, plan and develop lines of enquiry; collect, organise and represent information, interpret results and review methods; identify and answer related questions

Teacher notes

Preparation
Provide two dice for each pair of children. It is useful if they are different colours, so that children can see that there are two ways to make each addition. For example, 8 can be made up of 6 + 2 or 2 + 6.

Activity
Children work from Textbook page 63. They throw two dice and record the total each time in a tally chart. They describe what they find out, and try to explain it.

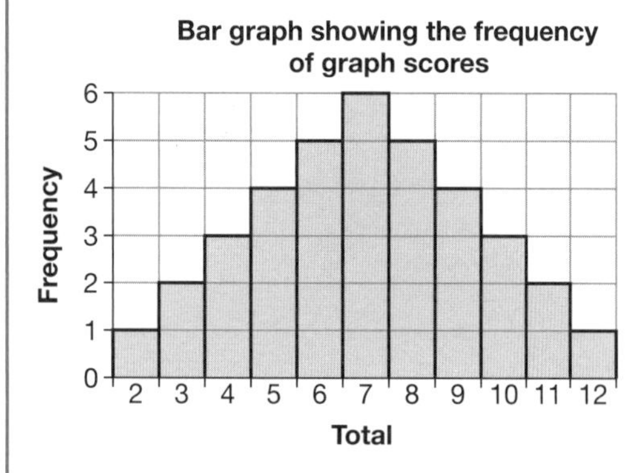

They copy and complete a table showing all the possible combinations of numbers and their totals. This table should help children to see that some totals come up more frequently than others, and they should be able to see patterns in the table. They then use the information in the table to answer questions about the probabilities of throwing particular dice numbers or totals. Children produce a graph to represent the possible scores.

Information
As there are 36 possible combinations, the odds of any particular total can be expressed as a fraction out of 36, e.g. *The chance of getting a total of 2 is 1 in 36*. Some of these expressions may be simplified, e.g. *The chance of getting a double is 6 in 36 or 1 in 6.*

Be aware

- Children may find it hard to see the difference between theoretical and actual probability. Explain that the more throws that are made, the more likely they are to see the theoretical probability occurring.

Outcomes

- I can predict, describe and discuss outcomes of a probability experiment.
- I can draw a bar graph to show probabilities.

Supporting resources

The following website gives results of multiple random dice throws:
- http://gwydir.demon.co.uk/jo/probability/dice.htm

Several interactive probability experiments are available here (click on the ‘Probability’ tab):
- http://www.shodor.org/interactivate/activities

C3: likelihood and the probability scale; pie charts; perimeters of rectangles and compound shapes; units of time and time-zones

Summary

Y6 C3.2 — **Probability game**

Pairs working independently

Year 6 Challenge PCMs 44 and 45

6-sided dice; counters

Abacus Evolve objectives

- Recognise events that are equally likely
- Predict the outcome of equally likely events
- Introduce the probability scale of 0 to 1 on the number line

Framework objectives

- Describe and predict outcomes from data using the language of chance or likelihood
- Suggest, plan and develop lines of enquiry; collect, organise and represent information, interpret results and review methods; identify and answer related questions
- Understand and use a variety of ways to criticise constructively and respond to criticism

Teacher notes

Preparation
Photocopy PCMs 44 and 45, one copy of each per pair.

Getting started
Give each pair the two PCMs, a 6-sided dice, and two different coloured counters. Check that children understand the rules of the game. Explain that the reason for playing the game 10 times is to see if the game is fair, i.e. whether each player has an equal chance of winning.

Activity
Children work in pairs, playing the game described on PCM 44, using the game board on PCM 45. Player A moves their counter four spaces on each turn. Player B rolls a dice each turn and moves the corresponding number of spaces. The two players see how many turns it takes each of them to reach the Finish and keep a record of this. Children should devise their own way to keep track of their results. They then answer questions about their findings and explore further variations.

Further extension
Children can use two dice and play using a 100-square. Player A rolls two dice and moves the total score; player B moves forward six spaces each turn. *Is this fair?* Investigate for different numbers of constant moves versus dice throws.

Information
On average player A who moves forward four each time should win more games (though obviously not every game) since player B will have a $\frac{3}{6}$ chance of throwing a lower score (a 1, 2 or 3), a $\frac{2}{6}$ chance of throwing a higher score (a 5 or a 6) and a $\frac{1}{6}$ chance of throwing the same score (a 4). If player A moves forward three each time then the odds swing the other way. To make this a fair game a constant move of $3\frac{1}{2}$ would be needed.

Be aware

- Children may find that it is possible for player B to win more often, even over 10 games. Use the odds of the dice throws to explain why this is possible, if unlikely.

Outcomes

- I can use the language of probability.
- I can describe and predict outcomes.

Supporting resources

Child-friendly explanations of key probability concepts are available at this site:
- http://www.bbc.co.uk/skillswise/numbers/handlingdata/probability

Summary

Y6 C3.3 — **Fruity pie charts**

A small group working with an adult

Year 6 Challenge Textbook page 64

Protractors; pairs of compasses

Abacus Evolve objectives

- **Y6–7** Construct and interpret pie charts to represent data
- **Y6–7** Compare the proportions in two pie charts that represent different totals
- **Y6–7** Draw simple conclusions based on the shape of graphs
- **Y6–7** Compare the data represented by two similar graphs

Framework objectives

- **Y6–7** Construct, interpret and compare graphs and diagrams that represent data, for example compare proportions in two pie charts that represent different totals
- **Y6–7** Develop and evaluate lines of enquiry; identify, collect, organise and analyse relevant information; decide how best to represent conclusions and what further questions to ask

Teacher notes

Activity

- Ask children to look at the pie chart on Textbook page 64. Discuss what it shows.
- *How many children preferred each fruit? How can you estimate this from the pie chart?* Children should notice that the section for oranges is $\frac{1}{4}$ of the whole circle, and from that they should deduce that this represents nine children (since $\frac{1}{4}$ of 36 is 9).
- *You may make a good guess about the others, but for an accurate answer you need to find out exactly what fraction of the circle each section is.* Introduce the idea of using a protractor, and show children how to place the protractor to measure sections. They then need to calculate what fraction of 360° this is, and then find that fractional amount of 36. Alternatively they may realise that each child takes up 10° of the circle.
- Children work from Textbook page 64. They draw a pie chart from the information given and answer the questions. As there are 180 children in the survey, they can use the idea that 2° represents each child to find the size of each slice.

Extra help

Some children may need help with the mechanics of drawing a pie chart. If they have trouble using a pair of compasses, they could draw around something circular instead. Emphasise the importance of marking the exact centre of the circle, and measuring and marking the angles accurately using a protractor.

If you have time

Children can use an IT-based application or a spreadsheet to create the second pie chart. They can then compare this with their hand-drawn version.

Be aware

- Some children find it difficult to draw angles at the centre of a circle. A circular (360°) protractor is helpful for this activity.

Outcomes

- I can draw a pie chart.
- I can compare two pie charts that represent different totals.

Supporting resources

This site gives a good visual presentation about drawing pie charts:

- http://www.subtangent.com/maths/piecharts.php

Summary

Y6 C3.4 **Fences**

A small group working with an adult

Year 6 Challenge Textbook page 65

Squared paper; rulers

Abacus Evolve objectives

- Consolidate the calculation of perimeters of rectangles
- Calculate the perimeters of compound shapes
- Calculate the area of a rectangle
- Calculate the area of compound shapes that can be split into rectangles

Framework objectives

- Calculate the perimeter and area of rectilinear shapes; estimate the area of an irregular shape by counting squares
- Solve problems by measuring, estimating and calculating; measure and calculate using imperial units still in everyday use; know their approximate metric values
- Represent and interpret sequences, patterns and relationships involving numbers and shapes; suggest and test hypotheses; construct and use simple expressions and formulae in words then symbols, e.g. the cost of c pens at 15 pence each is 15c pence

Teacher notes

Activity

- Discuss the problem on Textbook page 65. *What sort of L shape might have the largest area? A wide one or a narrow one? One with a large or a small foot?*
- Establish that the panels cannot be sub-divided, so the sides of the shape will always be a whole number of metres.
- If necessary, remind children how to find the area of a rectangle (*area* = *l* × *w*) and how to find the area of a compound shape.
- Children work from Textbook page 65. Ask pairs to draw some L shapes with perimeters of 40 squares on squared paper, and find their areas.
- Bring the group together and ask children to discuss their findings. Children should come to realise that the largest area will be produced by a short, wide L made by starting from a square and cutting out a 1 m by 1 m square in the top right-hand corner. Beware: some children may argue that this does not look like an L!

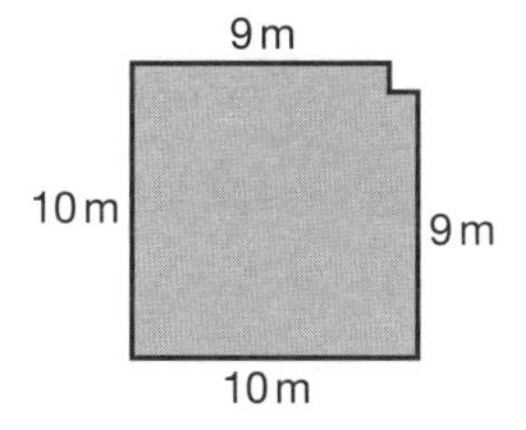

- When children have agreed that these dimensions produce the maximum area, they then work together to find the largest L-shaped area that can be made with 100 m of fencing.
- Lastly, children consider the maximum area of a T shape made using 40 m of fencing.

Be aware

- Children may forget to use all the fence panels. Remind them that whilst finding different areas they must constantly be checking whether they have used every panel.

Outcomes

- I can calculate the perimeter of a compound shape.
- I can use the formula for the area of a rectangle.
- I can calculate the area of a compound shape.
- I can identify information needed to solve a problem.

Challenge Plan: Year 6

C3: likelihood and the probability scale; pie charts; perimeters of rectangles and compound shapes; units of time and time-zones

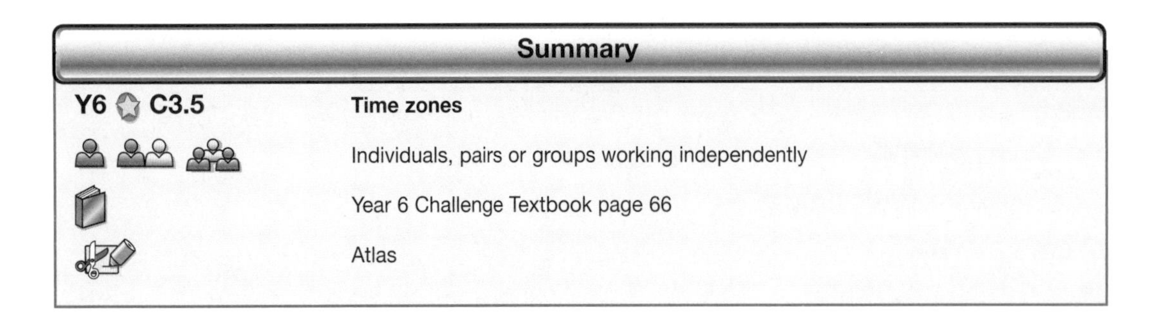

Summary

Y6 C3.5 — **Time zones**

Individuals, pairs or groups working independently

Year 6 Challenge Textbook page 66

Atlas

Abacus Evolve objectives

- Appreciate different times around the world

Framework objectives

- Select and use standard metric units of measure and convert between units using decimals to two places (e.g. change 2·75 litres to 2750 ml, or vice versa)
- Tabulate systematically the information in a problem or puzzle; identify and record the steps or calculations needed to solve it, using symbols where appropriate; interpret solutions in the original context and check their accuracy

Teacher notes

Getting started
Check that children are aware that there are different time zones around the world.
Give the group an atlas to share.

Activity
Children work from Textbook page 66. They draw up a table listing the eight times given for Jevan's activities in chronological order, and then work out the corresponding times in six other cities in different time zones.
Children then solve word problems in which they are given a flight duration between London and another city, and a departure time, and they must work out what time the plane will arrive, taking into account the time difference. Children then make up some similar word problems and swap with a partner.

Extra help
Some children may find it easier to start by finding the times in the cities closest to Manchester and then using those times to work out the next furthest; so for example, find out times in Baghdad which are 3 hours ahead of GMT and then find times from there in Hong Kong which is a further 5 hours ahead.

Further extension
Children can add more cities to their table, perhaps ones that they or their classmates have personal ties to.
Alternatively children can discuss what people in the other cities may be doing at the times when Jevan is doing his various activities.

Be aware

- Some children may find it confusing that two cities in one country can be in different time zones, and also that some cities that are far away, e.g. Lagos, are actually in the same time zone as the UK. Use the map to discuss this with them.

Outcomes

- I understand about time zones.
- I can work out times in other cities around the world.

Supporting resources

This site has information on time zones in all major cities:
- http://www.timeanddate.com/

Summary

Y6 C3.6 **Metric time**

Pairs working independently

Year 6 Challenge Textbook page 67

Abacus Evolve objectives

- Consolidate the relationship between units of time (including decade, millennium, leap year)

Framework objectives

- Select and use standard metric units of measure and convert between units using decimals to two places (e.g. change 2·75 litres to 2750 ml, or vice versa)
- Solve multi-step problems, and problems involving fractions, decimals and percentages; choose and use appropriate calculation strategies at each stage, including calculator use
- Use a range of oral techniques to present persuasive argument

Teacher notes

Getting started
Read the article on Textbook page 67 with children. Check that they understand the nature of the task. Draw attention to the significance of powers of 10 in metric units. Compare this idea with the different relationships that exist between minutes and hours, hours and days, days and weeks, etc.

Activity
Children work from Textbook page 67. The task is very open-ended; children are challenged to devise a system of units to divide up a day using the metric idea of relationships between units being based on powers of 10. Relating their units to a typical school day gives a focus for their new time units.

Extra help
Children can research the topic on the internet to get further ideas to incorporate into their own units.

Further extension
Children can use their time units to think about the times they will be doing things on a typical weekend day.

Be aware

- Children may be unsure how to start. It is best to start with a day and then think about sub-dividing it, rather than starting with a small unit and multiplying it up.

Outcomes

- I understand the relationships between units of time.
- I can invent a metric system of measuring time.

Supporting resources

These sites give background information on metric time:
- http://en.wikipedia.org/wiki/Metric_time
- http://zapatopi.net/metrictime

Summary

Y6 D3.1 — **Reflecting 3D shapes**

Individuals or pairs working independently

Year 6 Challenge Textbook page 68

Linking cubes; mirrors

Abacus Evolve objectives	Framework objectives
• Rehearse the concept of reflection • Recognise where a shape will be after reflection in a mirror line touching the shape at a point	• *Visualise and draw on grids of different types where a shape will be after reflection, after translations or after rotation through 90 degrees or 180 degrees about its centre or one of its vertices* • Understand and use a variety of ways to criticise constructively and respond to criticism

Teacher notes

Getting started

Choose one of the shapes on Textbook page 68 and ask children to discuss what its reflection would look like. *Where will the parts that are 'sticking out' be after the reflection? Would the reflection of each side be the same*?

Provide mirrors that are big enough to show each whole reflected cube shape.

Activity

Children work from Textbook page 68. They predict what the reflection of each 3D shape is likely to look like. Children then try out their ideas using linking cubes and a mirror and sketch the resulting reflections. It might be helpful for children to work in pairs with one person holding the mirror and describing the reflection whilst the other sketches, and then swap roles.

Extra help

It might help some children to make up the shapes using different coloured cubes. The reflection can then be described in terms of the relative positions of the different coloured cubes.

Further extension

Try placing the mirror at an oblique angle to the shapes.

Be aware	Outcomes
• Some children may find sketching the reflected shapes very tricky. Isometric paper may help.	• I can draw the 3D shapes reflected in a mirror line.

D3: reflection; rotation and translation; dividing HTU ÷ U using standard written methods; dividing TU·t ÷ U using standard written methods

Summary

Y6 D3.2 **Rotating shapes**

A small group working individually with an adult

Year 6 Challenge PCMs 46 and 47

Tracing paper; sharp pencils; rulers

Abacus Evolve objectives

- **Y6–7** Given a shape on a coordinate grid, rotate it about the origin
- **Y6–7** Rehearse the reading and plotting of coordinates in all four quadrants
- **Y6–7** Find coordinates of points determined by geometrical information (e.g. the fourth point of a square, a reflection about the y-axis)

Framework objectives

- **Y6–7** Identify all the symmetries of 2D shapes; transform images using ICT
- **Y6–7** Use all four quadrants to find coordinates of points determined by geometric information

Teacher notes

Preparation
Photocopy PCMs 46 and 47, one for each child. If possible, make an enlarged copy of PCM 46.

Activity
- Look together at the first diagram on PCM 46. *What are the coordinates of the corners of the shape?* Ask children to agree an answer between them and then tell you.
- *The point of origin of a coordinate grid is point (0, 0), the point where the horizontal and vertical axes cross each other.*
- Ask children to imagine that the shape has been rotated 90° clockwise around the point of origin. *Where is it now? What will be the coordinates of the corners of the rotated shape?* Ask children to discuss this in pairs before comparing ideas as a group.
- Model how to use tracing paper to find where the shape will be after the rotation. Do this by placing the tracing paper over the grid and tracing the shape. Mark an 'x' at the point of origin. Firmly hold a sharp pencil at this point and then carefully rotate the tracing paper 90° clockwise. This clearly shows where the shape should be. Use the pencil to mark the corners of the new position, remove the tracing paper and join the corner points up with a ruler.
- Children rotate the rest of the shapes on PCM 46, and record the coordinates of the shape's new position.
- Children then use the blank grid on PCM 47. They can either create and rotate their own shapes or return to the original shapes and see what happens when they are rotated 180° or 270° clockwise.

If you have time
Use IT to experiment with rotating shapes. This doesn't have to be a specialist piece of software; all computer drawing or painting software will have a facility for transforming shapes.

Be aware

- When using the coordinate grid some children may confuse rotational symmetry with reflective symmetry. Model this to clarify the difference.
- Some children may confuse rotating around the point of origin with rotating around one corner of the shape. Discuss in what cases these two rotations are the same.

Outcomes

- I can rotate a shape around the point of origin of a coordinate grid.

Challenge Plan: Year 6

D3: reflection; rotation and translation; dividing HTU ÷ U using standard written methods; dividing TU·t ÷ U using standard written methods

Summary

Y6 D3.3	**Transformations in patterns**
	Pairs working independently
	Year 6 Challenge Textbook page 69
	Mirrors; tracing paper

Abacus Evolve objectives

- Rehearse the concept of reflection
- Recognise where a shape will be after reflection in a mirror line touching the shape at a point
- Recognise where a shape will be after reflection in two mirror lines at right angles
- Begin to understand the concept of rotation
- Recognise where a shape will be after a rotation through 90 degrees about one of its vertices
- Recognise where a shape will be after two translations

Framework objectives

- *Visualise and draw on grids of different types where a shape will be after reflection, after translations or after rotation through 90 degrees or 180 degrees about its centre or one of its vertices*
- Explain reasoning and conclusions, using words, symbols or diagrams as appropriate
- Use a range of oral techniques to present persuasive argument

Teacher notes

Getting started
Remind children of the different transformations that they have studied: reflection, rotation and translation. *How could you use mirrors or tracing paper to check for reflection? Rotation? Translation?*

Activity
Children work from Textbook page 69. In pairs they examine the three patterns and use mirrors and tracing paper to look for different types of transformation within each one. They write a short summary of their findings to present to the group.

Extra help
If necessary prompt children by suggesting ways in which the mirror or tracing paper could be used to confirm transformations.

If you have time
Children can research other patterns using the internet; some suggested starting points for this are given below.

Be aware

- Some children may confuse the words *translation* and *transformation*. Explain that, in mathematics, translation refers to sliding a shape vertically or horizontally (or a combination of the two); transformation refers to a range of different ways of moving a shape which includes rotations and reflections as well as translations.

Outcomes

- I can recognise different transformations of shapes in patterns.

Supporting resources

This site gives Celtic patterns:
- http://karenswhimsy.com/celtic-patterns.shtm

Islamic patterns are available here:
- http://www.islamicart.com/members/geometric.html

This is a source of Roman-style mosaic patterns:
- http://www.gwydir.demon.co.uk/jo/mosaic/examples.htm

D3: reflection; rotation and translation; dividing HTU ÷ U using standard written methods; dividing TU·t ÷ U using standard written methods

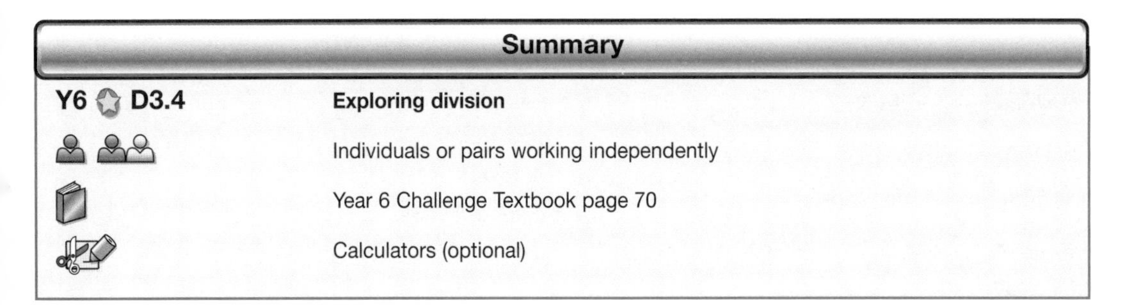

Summary

Y6 D3.4 **Exploring division**

Individuals or pairs working independently

Year 6 Challenge Textbook page 70

Calculators (optional)

Abacus Evolve objectives

- Rehearse dividing HTU ÷ U using standard written methods (mixed number answer)
- Divide HTU ÷ TU using standard written methods (whole number answer)

Framework objectives

- *Use efficient written methods to add and subtract integers and decimals, to multiply and divide integers and decimals by a 1-digit integer, and to multiply 2- and 3-digit integers by a 2-digit integer*
- Solve multi-step problems, and problems involving fractions, decimals and percentages; choose and use appropriate calculation strategies at each stage, including calculator use

Teacher notes

Getting started
Explain the meanings of the words *dividend*, *divisor* and *quotient* (dividend ÷ divisor = quotient)
Work through the two example boxes on Textbook page 70 with the group. Stress that children will be investigating an informal division method that only works for certain examples, and that they will then use standard written methods to check their answers. You may ask children to also use a calculator to check.

Activity
Children work from Textbook page 70. They use the methods they have learned to complete division calculations. They may work in pairs, or work individually and then compare findings with a partner.

Extra help
If children are stuck, suggest numbers for them to try dividing by (as in the first set of questions) or multiplying by (as in the second set).

Information
The methods modelled here work because if the dividend and the divisor are multiplied or divided by the same number, the ratio between them remains the same.

Be aware

- Children may not notice that they are making use of the ideas of common factors and common multiples in these activities. You may want to consider bringing this to their attention, as it may help them with answering the questions.

Outcomes

- I can simplify divisions by dividing both numbers by the same amount.
- I can use standard written methods of division.

D3: reflection; rotation and translation; dividing HTU ÷ U using standard written methods; dividing TU·t ÷ U using standard written methods

Summary

Y6 D3.5 **Missing-number divisions**

Pairs working independently

Year 6 Challenge Textbook page 71

Calculators (optional); 1–9 spinner (optional)

Abacus Evolve objectives

- Rehearse dividing HTU ÷ U using standard written methods (mixed number answer)
- Divide HTU ÷ TU using standard written methods (whole number answer)
- Check with the inverse operation
- Use tests of divisibility to estimate and check results of calculations

Framework objectives

- *Use efficient written methods to add and subtract integers and decimals, to multiply and divide integers and decimals by a 1-digit integer, and to multiply 2- and 3-digit integers by a 2-digit integer*
- Use approximations, inverse operations and tests of divisibility to estimate and check results
- Solve multi-step problems, and problems involving fractions, decimals and percentages; choose and use appropriate calculation strategies at each stage, including calculator use

Teacher notes

Getting started
Go through the first question on Textbook page 71 as a group. Children need to focus on what the divisor may have been to produce the answer 26. They should use their knowledge of inverse operations, rather try to guess what the 3-digit starting number is. *Supposing the divisor had been 3, what would the starting number have been? 3 × 26 = 78. We are looking for a 3-digit number, so this cannot be correct. What about 6? Since 6 × 26 = 156 that is a possible answer.* Children should then use a standard division method to check that answer. Explain that other answers are possible.

Activity
Children work from Textbook page 71. They find the possible division calculations that have given quotients. They can work in pairs, individually recording answers but comparing and trying out ideas together.

Extra help
Model further questions if necessary. Children could also use calculators to try out ideas for what the numbers could be before using standard division to check.

Further extension
Ask children to find several different answers for each question.

Be aware

- The examples with remainders can be confusing – some children may multiply the answer and the remainder to find the starting number. Encourage them to see that they have to multiply the answer and add the remainder.

Outcomes

- I can fill in digits in a missing-number division.
- I can use standard written methods of division to check my answers.

Challenge Plan: Year 6

D3: reflection; rotation and translation; dividing HTU ÷ U using standard written methods; dividing TU·t ÷ U using standard written methods

Summary

Y6 D3.6	**Long division**
	A small group working with an adult
	Year 6 Challenge Textbook page 72
	Calculators (optional)

Abacus Evolve objectives

- **Y6–7** Divide TU·th ÷ TU using standard written methods

Framework objectives

- **Y6–7** Use standard column procedures to add and subtract integers and decimals, and to multiply two-digit and three-digit integers by a one-digit or two-digit integer; extend division to dividing three-digit integers by a two-digit integer

Teacher notes

Activity

- *What might be the answer to 97·98 ÷ 23?* Stress the need to estimate the answer first. This will help to avoid problems with place value. Children may make a very rough estimate, such as 100 ÷ 25 = 4. If needed, lead them to the idea that the answer is somewhere between 4 and 5, since 4 × 23 = 92 and 5 × 23 = 115. *It looks like the answer is closer to 4 than 5, so an estimate of 4·2 or 4·3 is reasonable.*
- Find the exact answer using long division as modelled on Textbook page 72. Check that children have followed each step.
- *If I had come up with an answer of 42·6 or 426, what mistake would I have made?* (incorrect place values)
- Children work though questions 1–4 on Textbook page 72. They should estimate, then find the answer using long division. After a few minutes, stop and check that everyone is keeping up.
- Children then work through questions 5–7, estimating first. Note that these answers do not terminate after two decimal places. Work through one example showing this, and introduce the idea of stopping after three decimal places and rounding the answer to two decimal places. Ask children to check their answers using multiplication. They could also use calculators to check answers if appropriate.

Be aware

- Children may struggle with rounding. Explain that in order to give an answer to two decimal places it is only necessary to find the third decimal place. If the third place digit is 5, the second place will be rounded up regardless of the digit in the fourth place.

Outcomes

- I can estimate answers to divisions involving decimals.
- I can solve decimal division problems using standard methods.

Challenge Plan: Year 6

E3: understanding proportion; solving problems involving ratio and proportion; recognising prime numbers; factorising into prime factors

Summary

Y6 E3.1 — **Angel of the North**

Individuals, pairs or groups working independently

Year 6 Challenge Textbook page 73

Calculators

Abacus Evolve objectives

- Understand the concept of proportion
- Develop calculator skills and use a calculator effectively

Framework objectives

- Solve simple problems involving direct proportion by scaling quantities up or down
- Solve multi-step problems, and problems involving fractions, decimals and percentages; choose and use appropriate calculation strategies at each stage, including calculator use

Teacher notes

Getting started
Check that children are confident working with large numbers, and interpreting results on a calculator.

Activity
Children work from Textbook page 73. They learn about well-known landmarks such as the Angel of the North, Nelson's Column and the London Eye. Information is given about the measurements of the landmarks, and of scale models of them.
Children answer questions based on proportions and calculate various measurements. They also have to compare the measurements of the real and model objects and work out proportions. The monetary value of scale models and full-size objects is also considered.

Further extension
Model railways are made to different scales usually called gauges. Children could use the internet to find out what they can about the different scales used. The most common scales are 00 Gauge (1:76), 0 Gauge (1:43) and N Gauge (1:160).

If you have time
Nelson's Column was put up in about 1840 and cost approximately £30 000. Ask children to use the internet to find out about inflation and calculate the modern-day costs of making and putting up Nelson's Column now.
Children could explore other buildings or landmarks they know of and find out whether there are any scale models of them.

Be aware

- Children may not be familiar with tonnes and may assume that they are an imperial unit of measurement. Explain that children will not often need to measure in tonnes because a tonne is very heavy: 1000 kg.

Outcomes

- I can use proportion to solve problems involving measurements.
- I can use a calculator efficiently.

E3: understanding proportion; solving problems involving ratio and proportion; recognising prime numbers; factorising into prime factors

Summary

Y6 E3.2	**Walking speeds**
	A small group working with an adult
	Year 6 Challenge PCM 48
	Stopwatch; measuring tape for 20 m

Abacus Evolve objectives

- Understand the concept of proportion
- Develop calculator skills and use a calculator effectively
- Consolidate the relationship between units of time (including decade, millennium, leap year)

Framework objectives

- Solve simple problems involving direct proportion by scaling quantities up or down
- Use a calculator to solve problems involving multi-step calculations
- Solve multi-step problems, and problems involving fractions, decimals and percentages; choose and use appropriate calculation strategies at each stage, including calculator use
- Use a range of oral techniques to present persuasive argument

Teacher notes

Preparation
Photocopy PCM 48, one copy per child. You will need to organise access to the playground for children to measure out 20 m distances and time each other as they walk this distance.

Getting started
You might carry out the measuring and timing task in advance of the lesson, to save teaching time.

Activity
This activity uses the idea of scaling up to compare times taken to walk 20 m. Children learn how to convert time from seconds to minutes and distance from metres to kilometres, in order to compare speeds in both m/s and km/h.

- Ask a child how long it took them to walk 20 m. Model the division of 20 ÷ time taken in seconds on a calculator to find the speed in m/s.
- Ask children to complete the first two columns of the table on PCM 48. *Who walked the quickest?*
- *If we want to compare our speeds with the athletes we need them in kilometres per hour. We have to convert the time taken to hours. How can we do that?* Establish that × 60 would give us metres per minute and × 60 again would give us metres per hour. Agree that this is large number.
- Demonstrate multiplying children's speeds × 60 and × 60 on the board, giving metres per hour.
- *How is speed normally shown?* Discuss the units km/hour. *We can convert our metres per hour to kilometres per hour by dividing by 1000, the number of metres in one kilometre.*
- Ask children to divide each of their m/h speeds by 1000, using calculators if necessary. Agree that this is now km/h, and ask children to complete the first table.
- Discuss with children that × 60 × 60 ÷ 1000 could be shortened to × 3·6 (let them prove this on a calculator).
- Now look at the second table. *In which city do people walk the quickest?*
- Children complete PCM 48.

Further extension
Children could time themselves walking over a number of weeks, calculate any increase in speed and show the data on graphs.

Be aware

- Some children will say that the units of speed are mph. Explain that these are imperial units, and we need to compare with speeds that are in metric units.

Outcomes

- I can scale up distances to convert speeds from m/s to km/h.
- I can recognise which speed is the slowest and fastest.

Challenge Plan: Year 6

E3: understanding proportion; solving problems involving ratio and proportion; recognising prime numbers; factorising into prime factors

Summary

Y6 E3.3 — **Maps**

Individuals, pairs or groups working independently

Year 6 Challenge Textbook page 74

Year 6 Challenge PCM 49

Maps of the local area; string or map wheels; calculators

Abacus Evolve objectives

- Understand the meaning of ratio and relate this to proportion
- Solve simple problems involving ratio and proportion

Framework objectives

- Solve simple problems involving direct proportion by scaling quantities up or down

Teacher notes

Preparation
Children might like to look at maps of the local area or a road atlas. You could provide these, or ask children in advance to bring some in. Photocopy PCM 49, one copy per child or pair.

Getting started
Check that children are able to measure lengths accurately to within 1 mm. Remind them that they can use string to measure lines that are not straight.

Activity
Children work from Textbook page 74. This activity looks at a practical use of ratio. Children are given two different style maps on PCM 49 and have to measure distances between towns on these maps. Map 1 shows the shapes of the roads so measuring the distance on the map is best done with string or a special map measuring wheel. Map 2 is a route planning map with connecting roads shown as straight lines. Children find the real lengths of different routes between two towns using the scale.

Extra Help
A piece of thread or thin cord will be useful for the children to use to measure distances along roads on maps.

Further extension
Children could find different road atlases and see if the scales are accurate by measuring the road between two towns and use an online journey planner to check the real distance.

Information
Published map scales are normally metric – 1:1250, 1:10 000, 1:25 000, 1:50 000, 1:250 000, 1: 625 000 and 1:1 000 000. An imperial scale of 1 inch:1 mile is 1:63 360 which is often used on historical maps. The second link below gives examples of these different scales

Be aware

- Children may become confused between large and small scales. Large-scale maps show more detail such as buildings. Small-scale maps show less detail; often the main features shown are roads.

Outcomes

- I can use ratio to work out distances using a scale on a map.

Supporting resources

Children can try this interactive activity to help with understanding scale:
- http://shop.sherston.com/freebees/act/CaptCactivity/loadcaptc.htm

Children can check real road distances here:
- http://maps.google.co.uk/maps?hl=en&tab=wl

Challenge Plan: Year 6

E3: understanding proportion; solving problems involving ratio and proportion; recognising prime numbers; factorising into prime factors

Summary

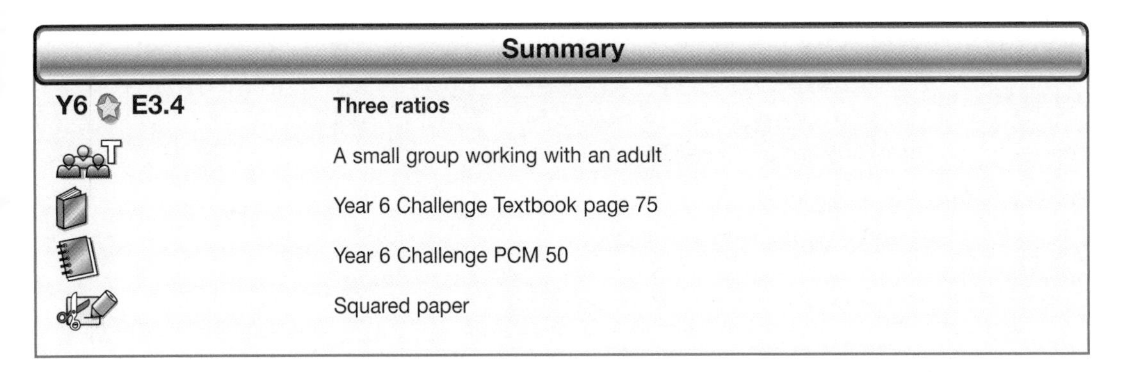

Y6 E3.4 **Three ratios**

A small group working with an adult

Year 6 Challenge Textbook page 75

Year 6 Challenge PCM 50

Squared paper

Abacus Evolve objectives

- **Y6-7** Understand the concept of ratio and use ratio notation
- **Y6-7** Reduce a ratio to its simplest form, e.g. 12:9 = 4:3
- **Y6-7** Solve problems involving ratio and direct proportion

Framework objectives

- **Y6-7** *Use ratio notation, reduce a ratio to its simplest form and divide a quantity into two parts in a given ratio; solve simple problems involving ratio and direct proportion (e.g. identify the quantities needed to make a fruit drink by mixing water and juice in a given ratio)*
- **Y6-7** Solve problems by breaking down complex calculations into simpler steps; choose and use operations and calculation strategies appropriate to the numbers and context; try alternative approaches to overcome difficulties; present, interpret and compare solutions

Teacher notes

Preparation

Photocopy PCM 50, one copy per child.

Getting started

Children need to be confident in working with fractions and understanding equivalents with common denominators. Familiarise yourself with this array, which demonstrates $\frac{1}{4}$ and $\frac{1}{5}$ having a common denominator of 20.

$\frac{1}{4}$ $\frac{1}{5}$

$\frac{1}{4} + \frac{1}{5}$ top cell moved to remind us to count it twice

This model shows $\frac{1}{4} + \frac{1}{5}$. The top left cell appears in both the row and the column, so it must be counted twice. We can see that $\frac{1}{4}$ $(\frac{5}{20})$ + $\frac{1}{5}$ $(\frac{4}{20})$ is $\frac{9}{20}$.

Activity

- Ask children to show $\frac{1}{4}$ as a drawing. Establish that there are four equal pieces. Repeat with $\frac{1}{5}$.
- Model $\frac{1}{4}$ of 20 squares and $\frac{1}{5}$ of 20 squares. Model the $\frac{1}{5}$ in the opposite direction so gridlines cross.
- *How many pieces for* $\frac{1}{4}$*? For* $\frac{1}{5}$*? How many altogether?* $\frac{1}{4}$ $(\frac{5}{20})$ + $\frac{1}{5}$ $(\frac{4}{20})$ is $\frac{9}{20}$. *How many are left over?* Confirm this is $\frac{11}{20}$.
- Agree that 1 = the whole piece, and that all parts $\frac{1}{4} + \frac{1}{5} + \frac{11}{20}$ make $\frac{20}{20} = 1$.
- Discuss that the ratio is 5:4:11, totalling 20 in all.
- Ask children to do the same for $\frac{1}{3}$ and $\frac{1}{4}$ and model this with a 3 by 4 grid. $\frac{4}{12} + \frac{3}{12} = \frac{7}{12}$, leaving $\frac{5}{12}$.
- Discuss the ratio of the parts, 4:3:5, totalling 12 parts in all.
- Children work from Textbook page 75 and use PCM 50 to model fractions and equivalents and find missing ratios.

Be aware

- When using proportion to describe shares, children may not understand that the whole is 1. Emphasise that all proportions/fractions must add up to 1.

Outcomes

- I can add simple fractions to find the whole.
- I can recognise ratios from three proportions.

E3: understanding proportion; solving problems involving ratio and proportion; recognising prime numbers; factorising into prime factors

Summary

Y6 E3.5 — **Domino rectangles**

Individuals, pairs or groups working independently

Year 6 Challenge Textbook page 76

Dominoes or similar blocks two units long and one unit wide

Abacus Evolve objectives

- Recognise and explain patterns and relationships, generalise and predict

Framework objectives

- Represent and interpret sequences, patterns and relationships involving numbers and shapes; suggest and test hypotheses; construct and use simple expressions and formulae in words then symbols, e.g. the cost of c pens at 15 pence each is 15c pence
- Understand and use a variety of ways to criticise constructively and respond to criticism

Teacher notes

Activity

Children work from Textbook page 76. They must use dominoes (two squares joined together) to make other rectangles. The rule is that the rectangles they make must always be two squares high.

They are shown the one possible arrangement of a single domino, then the two possible arrangements of a pair of dominoes. They are then shown two possible arrangements of three dominoes, and challenged to find the other possible arrangements. They move on to looking at four dominoes, then five.

Up to five dominoes will give patterns that are manageable to find. Children fill in a table with the information they have discovered, then use this to look for patterns.

Children are asked to describe the patterns they see, and predict how many arrangements there would be for nine dominoes. If children can find all arrangements for up to seven dominoes they may spot the Fibonacci sequence.

Extra help

Draw out some of the arrangements for four, five, six and seven dominoes. Children can then look for the additional arrangements.

Further extension

How many different arrangements are there to make a 4 × 4 high square from eight dominoes?

Information

The Fibonacci sequence is the sequence where each number is the sum of the two numbers before it: 1, 1, 2, 3, 5, 8, 13, 21, …

Be aware

- The reason for the two-high rule is that once children get past five dominoes the number of possible arrangements would be unmanageable if they could arrange them in any way they chose.

Outcomes

- I can investigate domino arrangements which follow a specific rule.
- I can find ways of solving a problem.

Challenge Plan: Year 6

E3: understanding proportion; solving problems involving ratio and proportion; recognising prime numbers; factorising into prime factors

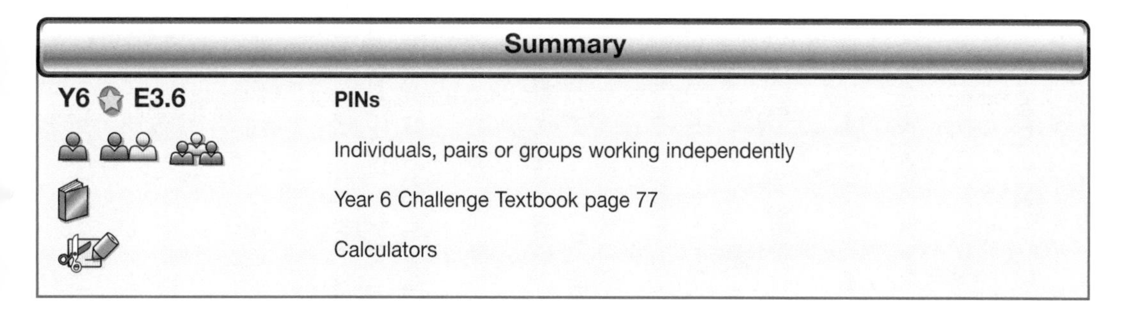

Summary

Y6 E3.6	**PINs**
	Individuals, pairs or groups working independently
	Year 6 Challenge Textbook page 77
	Calculators

Abacus Evolve objectives

- **Y6-7** Rehearse recognition of multiples of numbers up to and beyond the tenth multiple
- **Y6-7** Recognise prime numbers, and test by checking for divisibility
- **Y6-7** Find the factors of a number by checking for divisibility by primes

Framework objectives

- **Y6-7** Recognise and use multiples, factors, divisors, common factors, highest common factors and lowest common multiples in simple cases
- **Y6-7** Solve problems by breaking down complex calculations into simpler steps; choose and use operations and calculation strategies appropriate to the numbers and context; try alternative approaches to overcome difficulties; present, interpret and compare solutions

Teacher notes

Preparation
A calculator with a square root key will be useful.

Getting started
Check that children are confident in finding and recognising factors, square numbers, cubed numbers and prime numbers.

Activity
Children work from Textbook page 77. They match 4-digit PINs with corresponding mathematical properties. There are some red herrings which will have to be eliminated. When finding factors of a number children need to make sure they include 1 and the number itself or they will not find the correct PIN.

Extra help
Give children a list of prime numbers to help them complete this activity.

If you have time
Ask children to come up with their own ways of remembering a 4-digit number. See if the rest of the group can guess the number.

Be aware

- A common error is to forget that 2 is a prime number, as all the other prime numbers are odd. The number 1 and the number itself are often omitted from a list of factors of a number.

Outcomes

- I can work out other numbers by using number facts such as primes, squares, cubes and factors.

Year 6 Autumn Assessment Activity

Moving a cross

Assessment Foci: L5/6 Using and applying mathematics (Problem solving; Communicating; Reasoning); L5 Number (Numbers and the number system; Algebra)
Resources: PCMs A–E; scissors; squared paper

Lesson 1 – preparation – 1 hour

Part 1 – introduction – 20 minutes
Give children PCMs A, B and C. Ask them to cut out the cross template on PCM B, cutting out the cross shape at the centre. Ask them to position the cross template over the first number grid (10 × 10) on PCM A, and adjust the position so that five numbers can be seen in the cross. *The number at the centre of the cross is called the 'cross number'.* Ask pairs to complete the first recording table on PCM C (just the rows for numbers 12–16), using the 10 × 10 number grid on PCM A. Encourage pairs to explore the patterns they see. *How do the numbers in each row of the table relate to the cross number? Can you predict the other numbers if the cross number is 34? Choose a cross number of your own and predict the other numbers. Then use the template to see if you were right.*

Extension: ask children to use the 10 × 8 number grid on PCM A and explore the patterns generated. They can record their results on squared paper or use a second copy of PCM C. Alternatively, encourage them to explore patterns when they move the cross diagonally across the grid.

Part 2 – development – 30 minutes
Briefly discuss with children what they have done so far.

Now we are going to add the numbers: for each cross number, add left and right, top and bottom, all four outer numbers, then all five numbers. Children record their results in the second recording table on PCM C and explore the patterns. *Can you predict the totals if the cross number is 28? How does the grid size affect the patterns and rules?*

Extension: children can investigate the effect of different sized crosses. Some children may be able to express the patterns they see algebraically.

Part 3 – Plenary – 10 minutes
Discuss the patterns children have found and the reasons behind them. Briefly introduce the question of whether the size/shape of the cross will affect the patterns seen. The arms of the cross should be equal in length.

Lesson 2 – investigation – 1 hour

Part 1 – introduction – 10 minutes
Discuss the effects of changing the size of the cross as mentioned at the end of lesson 1. *Does the size of the cross affect the sum of the left number and right number? What about the top number and the bottom number? Why is this? What happens if you add up all the numbers in the cross?*

Now introduce the T-shapes on PCM B. *The 'T number' is the number at the base of the T.*

Part 2 – investigation – 35 minutes
Children record the numbers and sums for several T numbers on PCM D. Start with the short T template and the 10 × 10 number grid.

What happens if we move the T-shape across one? What happens if we move it down one? Why is this? Can you predict the other numbers if the T-number is 25? 100? A T number of your own?

Children then move on to consider the effects of using a 10 × 8 or other sized number grid. Again, they can record their results on squared paper or use a second copy of PCM D.

Children repeat the task using the long T template.

Is there a connection between the T number and the top middle number? What happens to the total if we move the T-shape across one? What happens if we move it down one? Why is this? Can you predict the other numbers if the T-number is 25? 100? A T number of your own?

Extension: ask children to explore the patterns associated with other shapes.

Part 3 – conclusions – 15 minutes
Children write a final report of their investigation, showing their journey and findings along the way, with any conclusions or fresh ideas.

Ask children to complete the self-assessment sheet on PCM E.

Moving a cross

Objectives

These are the objectives that could be met by children doing this Assessment Activity.

Strand	Abacus Evolve objectives	Framework objectives
Using and applying mathematics	**Y6** Make and investigate a general statement about familiar numbers or shapes by finding examples that satisfy it **Y6** Recognise and explain patterns and relationships, generalise and predict **Y6** Develop from explaining a generalised relationship in words to express it in a formula using letters as symbols **Y6** Recognise and extend number sequences **Y6–7** Begin to find a rule for the nth term of simple sequences	**Y6** Tabulate systematically the information in a problem or puzzle; identify and record the steps or calculations needed to solve it, using symbols where appropriate; interpret solutions in the original context and check their accuracy **Y6** Suggest, plan and develop lines of enquiry; collect, organise and represent information, interpret results and review methods; identify and answer related questions **Y6** Represent and interpret sequences, patterns and relationships involving numbers and shapes; suggest and test hypotheses; construct and use simple expressions and formulae in words then symbols, e.g. the cost of c pens at 15 pence each is 15c pence **Y6** Explain reasoning and conclusions, using words, symbols or diagrams as appropriate **Y6–7** Generate sequences and describe the general term; use letters and symbols to represent unknown numbers or variables; represent simple relationships as graphs

Moving a cross

Answers

Note: these answers are not exhaustive.

Preparation

Part 1 – introduction

PCM C Moving a cross (10 × 10 number grid):

Cross number	Top number	Left number	Right number	Bottom number
12	2	11	13	22
13	3	12	14	23
14	4	13	15	24
15	5	14	16	25
16	6	15	17	26
34	24	33	35	44
n	$n - 10$	$n - 1$	$n + 1$	$n + 10$

Part 2 – development

PCM C Cross totals (10 × 10 number grid):

Cross number	Left + right	Top + bottom	Total of outer four numbers	Total of all five numbers
12	24	24	48	60
13	26	26	52	65
14	28	28	56	70
15	30	30	60	75
16	32	32	64	80
28	56	56	112	140
n	$2n$	$2n$	$4n$	$5n$

left + right $= (n - 1) + (n + 1)$
$= 2n$
top + bottom $= (n - \textit{grid width}) + (n + \textit{grid width})$
$= 2n$

Investigation

Part 1 – introduction

When the 'arms' of the cross are lengthened, the bottom and right numbers will be increased, but the top and left numbers will be decreased. This means that *top + bottom* and *left + right* will always equal $2n$. Similarly, the total of the outer four numbers will always equal $4n$. However, the total of all the numbers in the cross will increase, because the cross contains more numbers. The total for a 5 by 5 cross (9 squares) is $9n$; the total for a 6 by 6 cross (13 squares) is $13n$; and so on.

Part 2 – investigation

PCM D Short T (10 × 10 number grid):

T number	Number above T number	Left top number	Right top number	Total of all four numbers
12	2	1	3	18
13	3	2	4	22
14	4	3	5	26
15	5	4	6	30
25	15	14	16	70
100	90	89	91	370
n	$n - 10$	$n - 11$	$n - 9$	$4n - 30$

As the short T moves across one square, the total of all four numbers increases by 4 (each square increases by 1 and $4 \times 1 = 4$). As the T moves down one square, the total increases by 40 (each square increases by 10 and $4 \times 10 = 40$; note that this changes according to the grid width).

PCM D Long T (10 × 10 number grid):

T number	Number above T number	Middle top number	Left top number	Right top number	Total of all five numbers
n	$n - 10$	$n - 20$	$n - 21$	$n - 19$	$5n - 70$

As the long T moves across one square, the total of all five numbers increases by 5. As the T moves down one square, the total increases by 50 (for a 10 × 10 number grid).

Year 6 Spring Assessment Activity

Domino products

Assessment Foci: L5/6 Using and applying mathematics (Problem solving; Communicating; Reasoning)
Resources: PCMs E–G; digit cards 1–9; squared paper

Lesson 1 – preparation – 1 hour

Part 1 – introduction – 15 minutes
Give children PCM F. *A 2 by 2 square could be seen as containing four dominoes: two across and two down.* Children randomly select four digit cards from a 1–9 set and arrange them in a 2 by 2 square. They calculate the product of each domino. They then find the total of the two 'across' products, the total of the two 'down' products, then add the two totals.

Discuss children's squares as a class:
- What is the difference between your 'across' total and your 'down' total?
- Whose set of digits has the smallest difference?
- Whose set of digits has the largest difference?
- *Who has the smallest/largest overall total?*

Part 2 – development – 35 minutes
Ask children to explore as fully as possible some or all of the following questions:
- *Which set of digits would have the smallest difference?*
- *Which set of digits would have the largest difference?*
- *What is the maximum possible overall total?*
- *What is the minimum possible overall total?*

Encourage children to work as systematically as possible, using squared paper to record their trials. Final answers can be recorded on PCM F.

Extension: ask children to try out some patterns of their own, finding all the dominoes and their products. Possible arrangements include:

Part 3 – plenary – 10 minutes
Draw the children together to compare their findings. What have they found out? What other ideas have they had?

Lesson 2 – investigation – 1 hour

Part 1 – introduction – 10 minutes
Give children PCM G. Explain that all the numbers 1 to 9 will be used in each 3 by 3 square. *How many dominoes can you see?* (six across and six down)

Children make a square of their own. They calculate the products and add them to find the totals across and down, and the overall total.

Part 2 – investigation – 35 minutes
Children work individually to answer the following questions:
- Which arrangements of the nine digits would have the smallest difference?
- Which arrangements of the nine digits would have the largest difference?
- What is the maximum possible overall total?
- What is the minimum possible overall total?

As before, children should work as systematically as possible, using squared paper to record their trials. Final answers can be recorded on PCM G

Extension: challenge children to explore a 4 by 4 square, using two sets of the numbers 2 to 9 to fill the sixteen spaces.

Part 3 – conclusions – 15 minutes
Children write a final report of their investigation, showing their journey and findings along the way, with any conclusions or fresh ideas.

Ask children to complete the self-assessment sheet on PCM E.

Year 6 Spring Assessment Activity

Domino products

Objectives

These are the objectives that could be met by children doing this Assessment Activity.

Strand	Abacus Evolve objectives	Framework objectives
Using and applying mathematics	**Y6** Make and investigate a general statement about familiar numbers or shapes by finding examples that satisfy it **Y6** Recognise and explain patterns and relationships, generalise and predict	**Y6** Tabulate systematically the information in a problem or puzzle; identify and record the steps or calculations needed to solve it, using symbols where appropriate; interpret solutions in the original context and check their accuracy **Y6** Suggest, plan and develop lines of enquiry; collect, organise and represent information, interpret results and review methods; identify and answer related questions **Y6** Represent and interpret sequences, patterns and relationships involving numbers and shapes; suggest and test hypotheses; construct and use simple expressions and formulae in words then symbols, e.g. the cost of c pens at 15 pence each is 15c pence **Y6** Explain reasoning and conclusions, using words, symbols or diagrams as appropriate

Domino products

Answers

Note: these answers are not exhaustive.

Preparation

Part 2 – development

- ***Which set of digits would have the smallest difference?***

The smallest difference is 1; several sets achieve this. There must be a difference of 1 between the first and fourth number and also between the middle two numbers. For example:

6	3
2	5

Across: 18 + 10 = 28
Down: 12 + 15 = 27
Difference: 28 − 27 = 1

8	4
5	7

Across: 32 + 35 = 67
Down: 40 + 28 = 68
Difference: 68 − 67 = 1

This may generate another question: is it possible to arrange four digits so that the two totals are equal? The answer to this is no, it is not possible.

- ***Which set of digits would have the largest difference?***

The largest difference is 49. This time the first and last numbers, and the middle two, must be as different as possible (i.e. two pairs with a difference of 7: 1 and 8; 2 and 9). For example:

1	9
2	8

Across: 9 + 16 = 25
Down: 2 + 72 = 74
Difference: 72 − 25 = 49

- ***What is the maximum possible overall total? What is the minimum?***

The maximum possible overall total is 224. It is achieved using the four largest numbers (6, 7, 8 and 9) arranged to give the largest possible differences (two pairs with a difference of 2: 6 and 8; 7 and 9).

The minimum possible overall total is 21. It is achieved using the four smallest numbers (1, 2, 3, 4) arranged to give the smallest possible differences (two pairs with a difference of 1: 1 and 2; 3 and 4).

6	9
7	8

Across: 54 + 56 = 110
Down: 42 + 72 = 114
Total: 110 + 114 = 224

1	4
3	2

Across: 4 + 6 = 10
Down: 3 + 8 = 11
Total: 10 + 11 = 21

Investigation

Part 2 – investigation

- ***Which arrangements would have the smallest difference?***

It is possible to make an arrangement with identical totals. For example:

1	7	2
6	3	9
4	8	5

Across:
7 + 14 = 21
18 + 27 = 45
32 + 40 = 72
Total = 138

Down:
6 + 24 = 30
21 + 24 = 45
18 + 45 = 63
Total = 138

Difference = 0

- ***Which arrangements would have the largest difference?***

The maximum difference is unknown.

- ***What is the maximum possible overall total?***

To achieve the maximum, the 9 must be placed in the centre cell. Children may assume that the next four largest numbers (5, 6, 7 and 8) must surround it, with the other numbers filling the corner spaces. Within this limitation, 371 is the largest total possible. However, the actual maximum is 377.

6	8	4
7	9	5
2	3	1

Across:
48 + 32 = 80
63 + 45 = 108
6 + 3 = 9
Total = 197

Down:
42 + 14 = 56
72 + 27 = 99
20 + 5 = 25
Total = 180

Overall total = 377

- ***What is the minimum possible overall total?***

The minimum is 193.

9	2	7
1	5	4
8	3	6

Across:
18 + 14 = 32
5 + 20 = 25
24 + 18 = 42
Total = 99

Down:
9 + 8 = 17
10 + 15 = 25
28 + 24 = 52
Total = 94

Overall total = 193

Year 6 Summer Assessment Activity

Polygons in squares

Assessment Foci: L5/6 Using and applying mathematics (Problem solving; Communicating; Reasoning); L5 Number (Fractions, decimals, percentages, ratio and proportion); L5 Shape, space and measures (Properties of shape; Properties of position and movement)
Resources: PCMs E and H–J; rulers

Lesson 1 – preparation – 1 hour

Part 1 – introduction - 15 minutes

Give children PCM H, which provides some 8-point squares. *You are going to make shapes by joining three of the eight points on the squares. Try to answer these questions:*

- *How many different shapes can you make?*
- *How can you be sure you have found them all?*
- *What fraction of the square is each of these polygons?*
- *What fractions of the square are the shapes outside each polygon?*
- *Does each set of fractions add up to 1?*

Now ask children to answer the same questions for shapes made by joining four of the eight points on the squares.
Finally, identify those polygons where each side cuts across the square (rather than following a side of the square).

Part 2 – development – 30 minutes

Give children PCM I, which provides some 12-point squares. Challenge children to make as many polygons as they can, joining any number of points. The only rule is that each side of the polygon must cut across the outer square (rather than following a side of the square).
Ask children to label each of their polygons with the shape name. They should find what fraction of the square's area is inside the polygon, and what fractions are outside the polygon, checking that these add up to 1.

Part 3 – plenary – 15 minutes

Ask children to share the polygons they made on the 12-point squares. Pool all the polygons. Identify ones that are identical and put aside the duplicates. Identify ones that are rotations or reflections of others and put them aside. How many different polygons has the group made?

Lesson 2 – investigation – 1 hour

Part 1 – introduction – 10 minutes

Remind children of the questions they answered in Lesson 1 and the lines of investigation they used to do so. Give them PCM J and explain that in this lesson they are going to work with 16-point squares.

Demonstrate joining the mid-point of each side to make a square within a square.

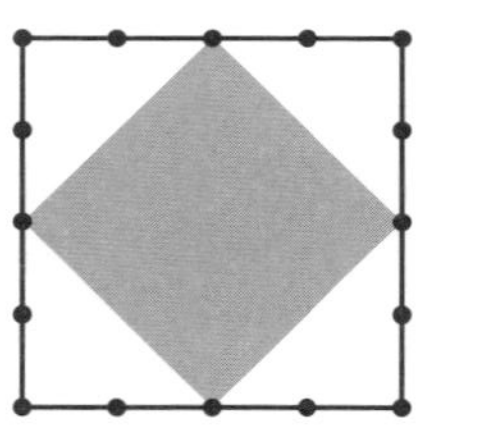

Support children in deducing that this has half the area of the outer square. Each of the four outer triangle pieces should then be deduced as $\frac{1}{8}$ of the outer square. So the outcomes and checking equation are:
The polygon is a square of area $\frac{1}{2}$.
The large square is composed of $\frac{1}{2} + (4 \times \frac{1}{8}) = 1$.

Part 2 – investigation – 35 minutes

Children find all possible polygons that satisfy the rule that each side of the polygon must cut across the outer square. They name the polygons and work out the fraction areas of the polygons and the spaces around them, checking that these add up to 1.

Part 3 – conclusions – 15 minutes

Children write a final report of their investigation, showing their journey and findings along the way, with any conclusions or fresh ideas.
Ask children to complete the self-assessment sheet on PCM E.

Polygons in squares

Objectives

These are the objectives that could be met by children doing this Assessment Activity.

Strand	Abacus Evolve objectives	Framework objectives
Using and applying mathematics	**Y6** Make and investigate a general statement about familiar numbers or shapes by finding examples that satisfy it **Y6** Recognise and explain patterns and relationships, generalise and predict	**Y6** Tabulate systematically the information in a problem or puzzle; identify and record the steps or calculations needed to solve it, using symbols where appropriate; interpret solutions in the original context and check their accuracy **Y6** Suggest, plan and develop lines of enquiry; collect, organise and represent information, interpret results and review methods; identify and answer related questions **Y6** Represent and interpret sequences, patterns and relationships involving numbers and shapes; suggest and test hypotheses; construct and use simple expressions and formulae in words then symbols, e.g. the cost of c pens at 15 pence each is 15c pence **Y6** Explain reasoning and conclusions, using words, symbols or diagrams as appropriate
Counting and understanding number	**Y6** Consolidate recognition of equivalent fractions **Y6** Reduce a fraction to its simplest form by cancelling common factors in the numerator and denominator **Y6** Recognise relationships between fractions, e.g. $\frac{1}{16}$ is half of $\frac{1}{8}$	**Y6** Express a larger whole number as a fraction of a smaller one e.g. recognise that 8 slices of a 5-slice pizza represents $\frac{8}{5}$ or $1\frac{3}{5}$ pizzas; simplify fractions by cancelling common factors; order a set of fractions by converting them to fractions with a common denominator
Understanding shape	**Y6** Use the terms 'parallelogram', 'rhombus' and 'trapezium' **Y6** Begin to know the properties of parallelograms, rhombuses and trapezia **Y6** Begin to use the term 'kite' **Y6** Accurately make and draw shapes **Y6–7** Continue to recognise the properties of different types of triangle, including right-angled, equilateral and isosceles triangles **Y6–7** Continue to recognise the properties of different types of quadrilateral, including kites and arrowheads	**Y6** Describe, identify and visualise parallel and perpendicular edges or faces and use these properties to classify 2D shapes and 3D solids **Y6** Make and draw shapes with increasing accuracy and apply knowledge of their properties **Y6–7** Extend knowledge of properties of triangles and quadrilaterals and use these to visualise and solve problems, explaining reasoning with diagrams

Year 6 Summer Assessment Activity

Polygons in squares

Answers – preparation

Note: these answers are not exhaustive.

Part 1 – introduction

There are nine triangles and nine quadrilaterals that can be made on an 8-point square.

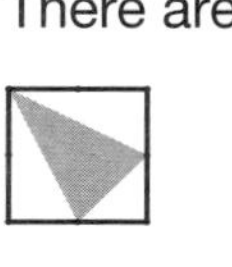
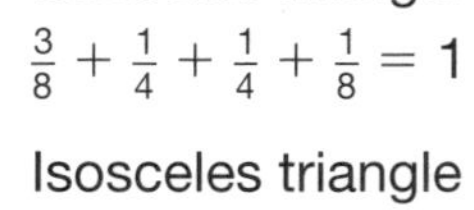

Isosceles triangle ($\frac{3}{8}$)
$\frac{3}{8} + \frac{1}{4} + \frac{1}{4} + \frac{1}{8} = 1$

Isosceles triangle ($\frac{1}{2}$)
$\frac{1}{2} + \frac{1}{4} + \frac{1}{4} = 1$

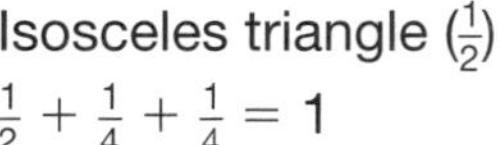
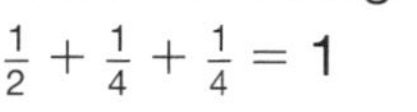

Scalene right-angled triangle ($\frac{1}{4}$)
$\frac{1}{4} + \frac{1}{4} + \frac{1}{2} = 1$

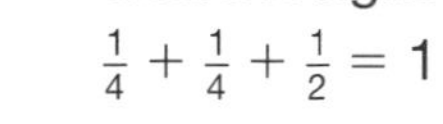

Square ($\frac{1}{2}$)
$\frac{1}{2} + \frac{1}{8} + \frac{1}{8} + \frac{1}{8} + \frac{1}{8} = 1$

Parallelogram ($\frac{1}{2}$)
$\frac{1}{2} + \frac{1}{4} + \frac{1}{4} = 1$

Trapezium ($\frac{3}{8}$)
$\frac{3}{8} + \frac{1}{8} + \frac{1}{2} = 1$

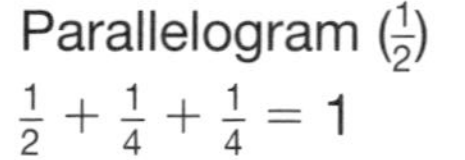
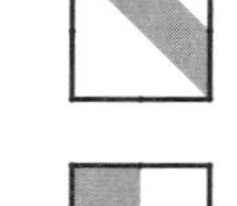

Isosceles right-angled triangle ($\frac{1}{4}$)
$\frac{1}{4} + \frac{1}{8} + \frac{1}{8} + \frac{1}{2} = 1$

Scalene triangle ($\frac{1}{4}$)
$\frac{1}{4} + \frac{1}{4} + \frac{1}{2} = 1$

Isosceles right-angled triangle ($\frac{1}{8}$)
$\frac{1}{8} + \frac{7}{8} = 1$

Kite ($\frac{1}{2}$)
$\frac{1}{2} + \frac{1}{4} + \frac{1}{4} = 1$

Isosceles trapezium ($\frac{3}{8}$)
$\frac{3}{8} + \frac{1}{8} + \frac{1}{2} = 1$

Rectangle ($\frac{1}{2}$)
$\frac{1}{2} + \frac{1}{2} = 1$

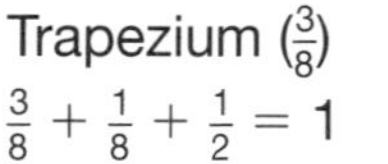
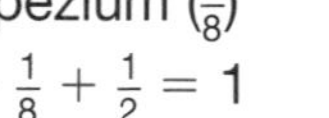
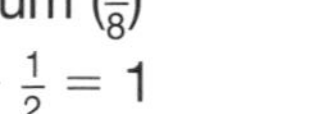
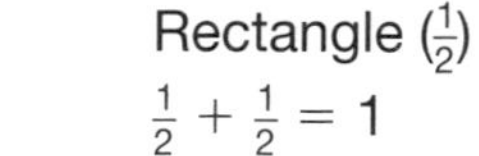

Scalene right-angled triangle ($\frac{1}{4}$)
$\frac{1}{4} + \frac{3}{4} = 1$

Scalene triangle ($\frac{1}{8}$)
$\frac{1}{8} + \frac{1}{8} + \frac{3}{4} = 1$

Isosceles right-angled triangle ($\frac{1}{2}$)
$\frac{1}{2} + \frac{1}{2} = 1$

Quadrilateral ($\frac{1}{2}$)
$\frac{1}{2} + \frac{1}{4} + \frac{1}{8} + \frac{1}{8} = 1$

Trapezium ($\frac{3}{4}$)
$\frac{3}{4} + \frac{1}{4} = 1$

Quadrilateral ($\frac{5}{8}$)
$\frac{5}{8} + \frac{1}{8} + \frac{1}{4} = 1$

Only the first two triangles and the first square have sides that all cut across the square.

Part 2 – development

On a 12-point square, there are seven triangles and four quadrilaterals whose sides all cut across the square.

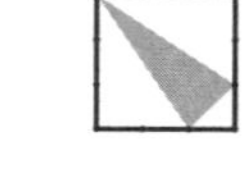
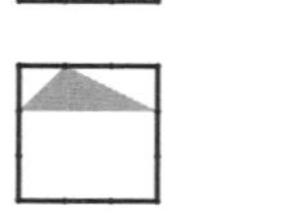

Isosceles triangle ($\frac{4}{9}$)
$\frac{4}{9} + \frac{1}{6} + \frac{1}{6} + \frac{2}{9} = 1$

Scalene right-angled triangle ($\frac{5}{18}$)
$\frac{5}{18} + \frac{1}{2} + \frac{1}{9} + \frac{1}{9} = 1$

Scalene right-angled triangle ($\frac{2}{9}$)
$\frac{2}{9} + \frac{1}{18} + \frac{1}{2} + \frac{2}{9} = 1$

Isosceles trapezium ($\frac{1}{2}$)
$\frac{1}{2} + \frac{1}{18} + (2 \times \frac{1}{9}) + \frac{2}{9} = 1$

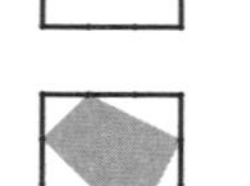
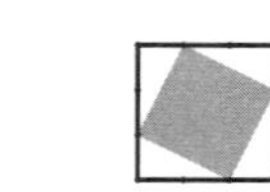

Scalene triangle ($\frac{7}{18}$)
$\frac{7}{18} + \frac{1}{3} + \frac{1}{6} + \frac{1}{9} = 1$

Scalene triangle ($\frac{1}{3}$)
$\frac{1}{3} + \frac{1}{3} + \frac{2}{9} + \frac{1}{9} = 1$

Square ($\frac{5}{9}$)
$\frac{5}{9} + (4 \times \frac{1}{9}) = 1$

Rectangle ($\frac{4}{9}$)
$\frac{4}{9} + (2 \times \frac{2}{9}) + (2 \times \frac{1}{18}) = 1$

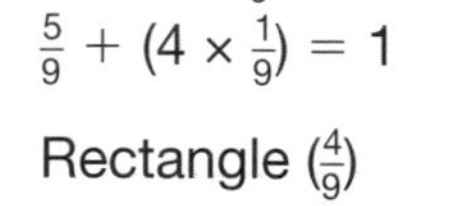

Isosceles triangle ($\frac{5}{18}$)
$\frac{5}{18} + \frac{1}{3} + \frac{1}{18} + \frac{1}{3} = 1$

Scalene triangle ($\frac{1}{6}$)
$\frac{1}{6} + \frac{2}{3} + \frac{1}{9} + \frac{1}{18} = 1$

Quadrilateral ($\frac{1}{2}$)
$\frac{1}{2} + \frac{2}{9} + \frac{1}{18} + (2 \times \frac{1}{9}) = 1$

Polygons in squares

Answers – investigation

On a 16-point square, 14 triangles and 16 quadrilaterals fit the rule.

Note: these answers are not exhaustive.

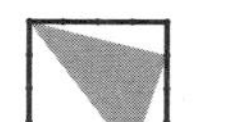
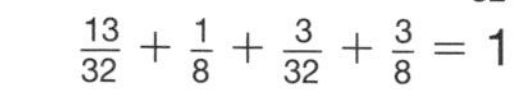

Scalene triangle $(\frac{13}{32})$

$\frac{13}{32} + \frac{1}{8} + \frac{3}{32} + \frac{3}{8} = 1$

Right-angled triangle $(\frac{5}{16})$

$\frac{5}{16} + \frac{1}{4} + \frac{1}{16} + \frac{3}{8} = 1$

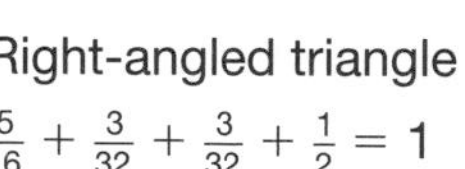

Right-angled triangle $(\frac{5}{16})$

$\frac{5}{16} + \frac{3}{32} + \frac{3}{32} + \frac{1}{2} = 1$

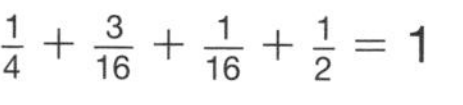

Scalene triangle

$\frac{1}{4} + \frac{3}{16} + \frac{1}{16} + \frac{1}{2} = 1$

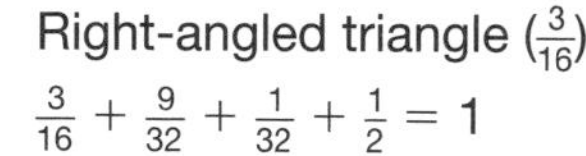

Right-angled triangle $(\frac{3}{16})$

$\frac{3}{16} + \frac{9}{32} + \frac{1}{32} + \frac{1}{2} = 1$

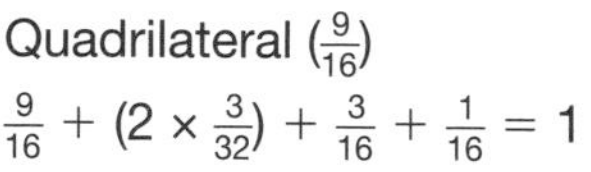

Quadrilateral $(\frac{9}{16})$

$\frac{9}{16} + (2 \times \frac{3}{32}) + \frac{3}{16} + \frac{1}{16} = 1$

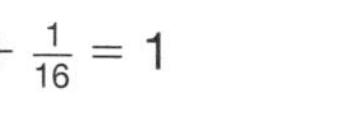

Rectangle $(\frac{1}{2})$

$\frac{1}{2} + (2 \times \frac{1}{16}) + (2 \times \frac{3}{16}) = 1$

Quadrilateral $(\frac{1}{2})$

$\frac{1}{2} + \frac{3}{32} + \frac{9}{32} + (2 \times \frac{1}{16}) = 1$

Quadrilateral $(\frac{17}{32})$

$\frac{17}{32} + \frac{3}{16} + \frac{1}{8} + \frac{1}{16} + \frac{3}{32} = 1$

Quadrilateral $(\frac{7}{16})$

$\frac{7}{16} + \frac{1}{32} + \frac{3}{16} + \frac{1}{16} + \frac{9}{32} = 1$

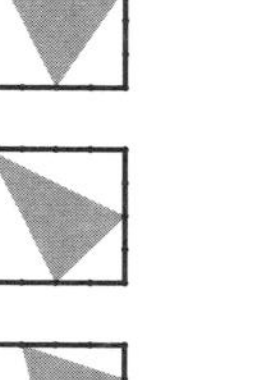

Scalene triangle $(\frac{7}{16})$

$\frac{7}{16} + \frac{1}{4} + 1/8 + \frac{3}{16} = 1$

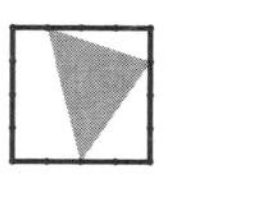

Isosceles triangle $(\frac{3}{8})$

$\frac{3}{8} + \frac{1}{4} + \frac{1}{8} + \frac{1}{4} = 1$

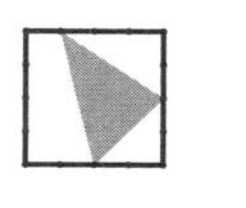

Scalene triangle $(\frac{11}{32})$

$\frac{11}{32} + \frac{3}{32} + \frac{3}{16} + \frac{3}{8} = 1$

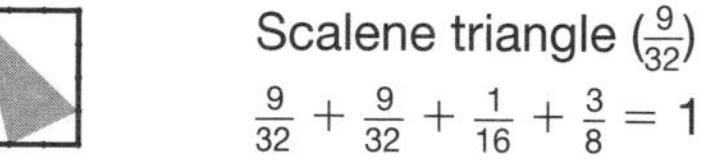
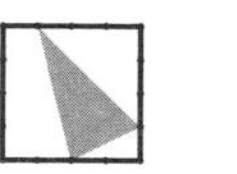

Scalene triangle $(\frac{5}{16})$

$\frac{5}{16} + \frac{3}{16} + \frac{1}{8} + \frac{3}{8} = 1$

Scalene triangle $(\frac{9}{32})$

$\frac{9}{32} + \frac{9}{32} + \frac{1}{16} + \frac{3}{8} = 1$

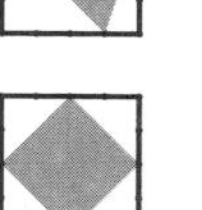
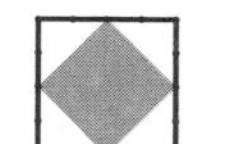

Quadrilateral $(\frac{1}{2})$

$\frac{1}{2} + (2 \times \frac{3}{32}) + \frac{9}{32} + \frac{1}{32} = 1$

Square $(\frac{1}{2})$

$\frac{1}{2} + (4 \times \frac{1}{8}) = 1$

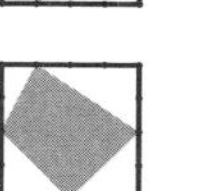
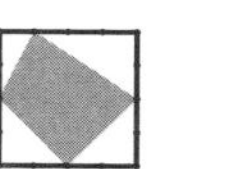

Isosceles trapezium $(\frac{1}{2})$

$\frac{1}{2} + (2 \times \frac{3}{32}) + \frac{9}{32} + \frac{1}{32} = 1$

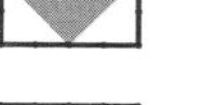

Quadrilateral $(\frac{1}{2})$

$\frac{1}{2} + \frac{3}{16} + (2 \times \frac{1}{8}) + \frac{1}{16} = 1$

Quadrilateral $(\frac{1}{2})$

$\frac{1}{2} + \frac{1}{32} + (2 \times \frac{3}{32}) + \frac{9}{32} = 1$

Isosceles triangle $(\frac{15}{32})$

$\frac{15}{32} + \frac{1}{8} + \frac{9}{32} + \frac{1}{8} = 1$

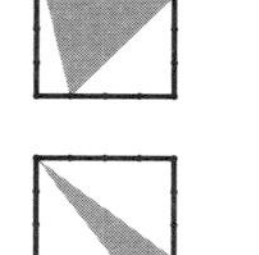
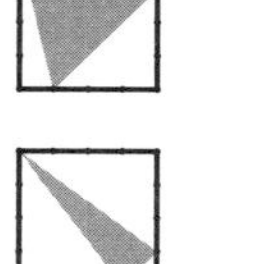
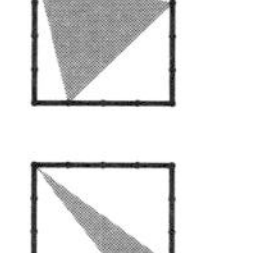

Isosceles triangle $(\frac{7}{32})$

$\frac{7}{32} + \frac{3}{8} + \frac{1}{32} + \frac{3}{8} = 1$

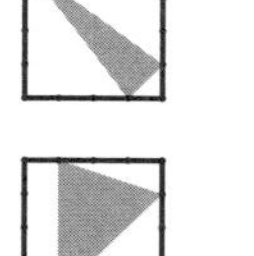
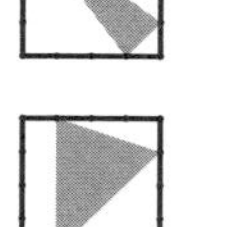

Scalene triangle $(\frac{3}{8})$

$\frac{3}{8} + \frac{3}{32} + \frac{9}{32} + \frac{1}{4} = 1$

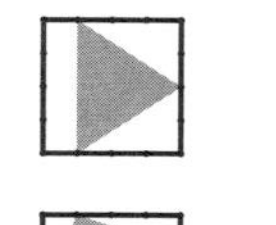
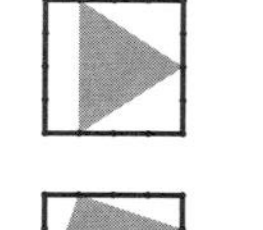

Isosceles triangle $(\frac{3}{8})$

$\frac{3}{8} + \frac{3}{16} + \frac{3}{16} + \frac{1}{4} = 1$

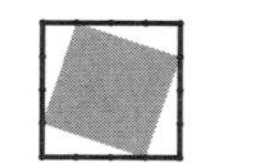

Square $(\frac{5}{8})$

$\frac{5}{8} + (4 \times \frac{3}{32}) = 1$

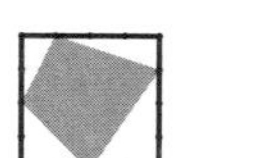

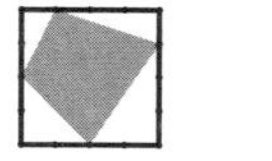

Quadrilateral $(\frac{17}{32})$

$\frac{17}{32} + \frac{3}{32} + \frac{3}{16} + \frac{1}{8} + \frac{1}{16} = 1$

Trapezium $(\frac{1}{2})$

$\frac{1}{2} + \frac{3}{32} + (2 \times \frac{3}{16}) + \frac{1}{32} = 1$

Quadrilateral $(\frac{7}{16})$

$\frac{7}{16} + \frac{3}{16} + \frac{1}{16} + \frac{9}{32} + \frac{1}{32} = 1$

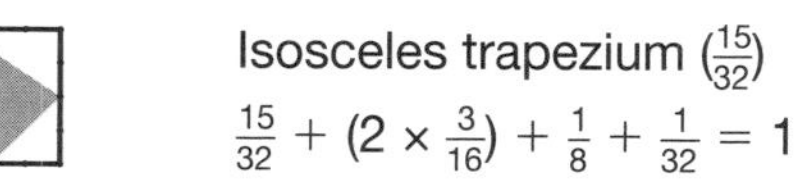
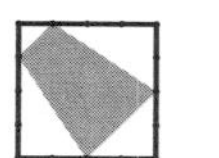
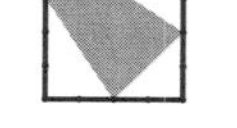

Isosceles trapezium $(\frac{15}{32})$

$\frac{15}{32} + (2 \times \frac{3}{16}) + \frac{1}{8} + \frac{1}{32} = 1$

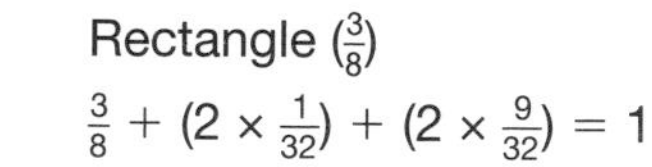

Rectangle $(\frac{3}{8})$

$\frac{3}{8} + (2 \times \frac{1}{32}) + (2 \times \frac{9}{32}) = 1$

Notice that all the fractions are in the $\frac{1}{2}, \frac{1}{4}, \frac{1}{8}, \frac{1}{16}, \frac{1}{32}$ family.

PCM Contents

What are you worth?

Here are the details of all the British coins in circulation.

Value	Weight in grams	Diameter in mm	Thickness in mm	Number in circulation
£2	12·0	28·4	2·50	268 million
£1	9·5	22·5	3·15	1452 million
50p	8·0	27·3	1·78	696 million
20p	5·0	21·4	1·70	2190 million
10p	6·5	24·5	1·85	1587 million
5p	3·3	18·0	1·70	3659 million
2p*	7·1	25·9	1·85 or 2·03	6421 million
1p*	3·6	20·3	1·52 or 1·65	10 576 million

*There are two different coins in circulation: bronze and copper plated steel

Let's cook

Shortbread

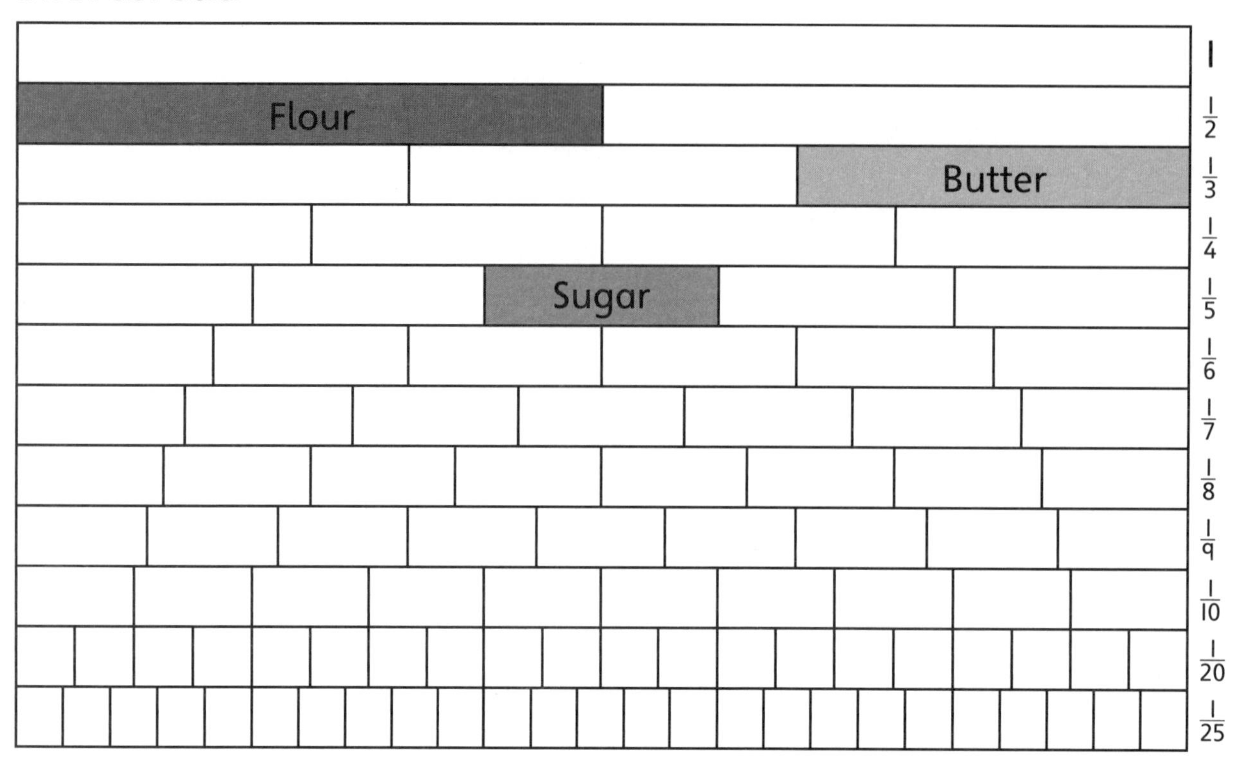

Fraction wall

Soup

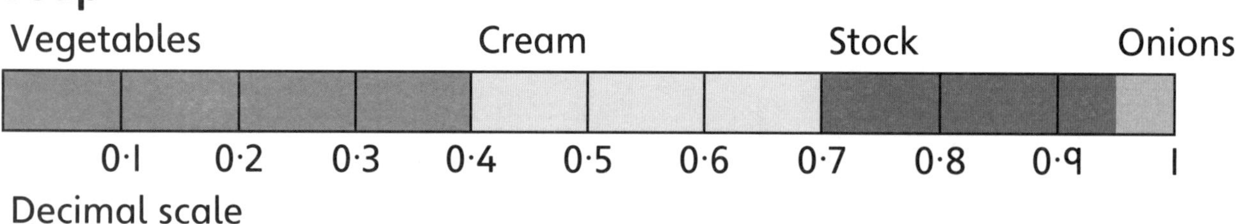

Decimal scale

Pizza

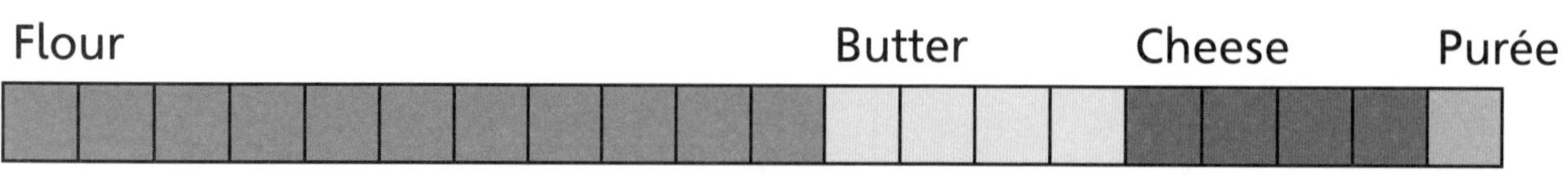

Percentage scale

Casting out 9s

Check these answers using the 'casting out 9s' methods shown on Textbook page 6. Show your workings in the boxes.

1 6752 + 2356 = 9180

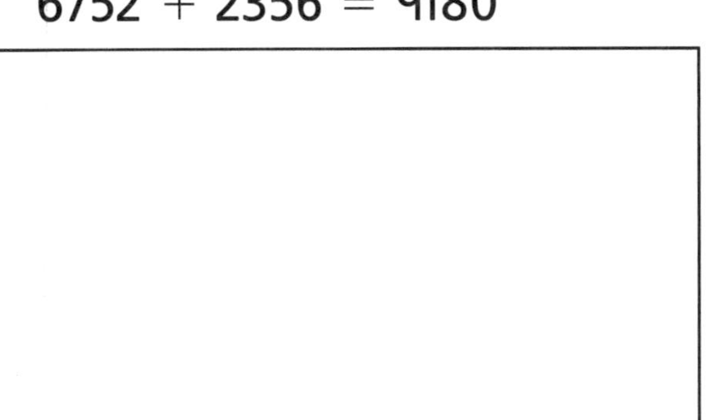

2 9634 + 3826 = 13 460

3 9234 − 3647 = 5767

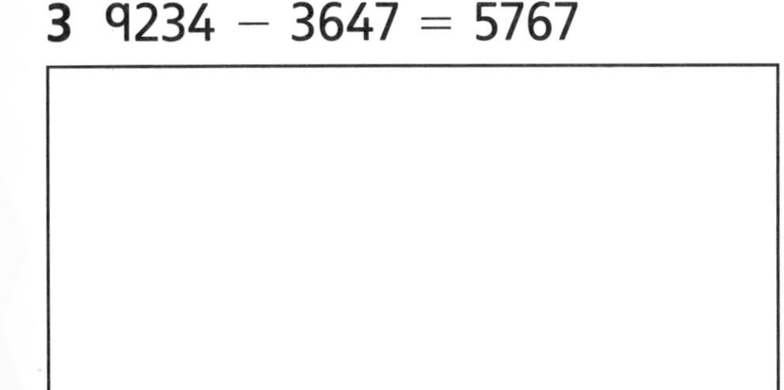

5 83 746 − 2947 = 80 799

5 683 × 428 = 292 324

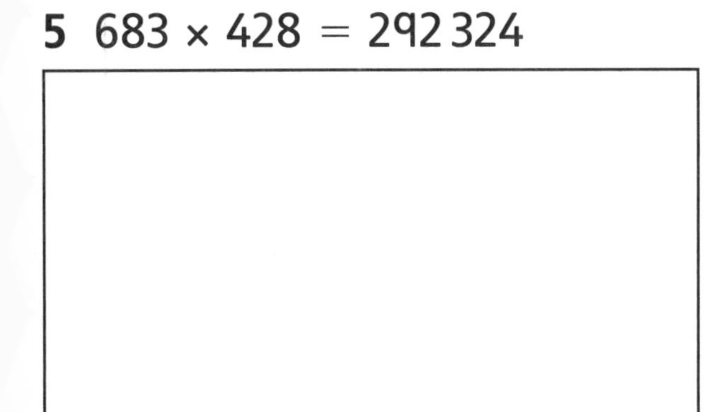

6 500 × 4500 = 2 250 000

7 672 ÷ 24 = 28

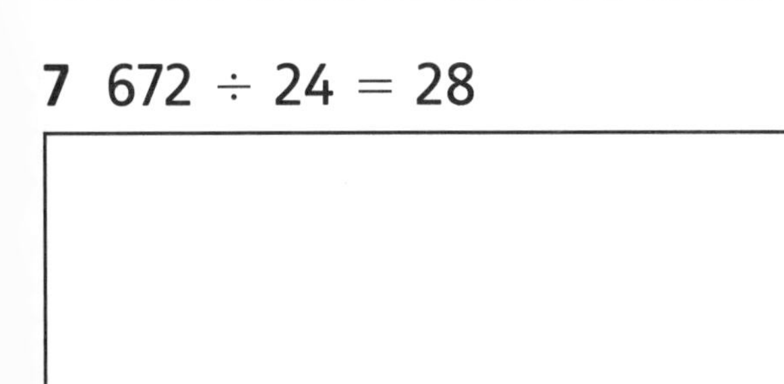

8 525 ÷ 21 = 25

Now check all the answers using a calculator.

Finding percentages

The following information might help you to calculate percentage increases and decreases.

To find	As a fraction	Divide by	Then
1%	$\frac{1}{100}$	100	
5%	$\frac{5}{100} = \frac{1}{20}$	20	
	or Find 10% and halve it	10 and then by 2	
10%	$\frac{10}{100} = \frac{1}{10}$	10	
15%	$\frac{15}{100} = \frac{3}{20}$	20	×3
	or Add together 5% and 10%		
20%	$\frac{20}{100} = \frac{1}{5}$	5	
25%	$\frac{25}{100} = \frac{1}{4}$	4	
	or Find 50% and halve it	2 and 2 again	
30%	$\frac{30}{100} = \frac{3}{10}$	10	×3
50%	$\frac{50}{100} = \frac{1}{2}$	2	
75%	$\frac{75}{100} = \frac{3}{4}$	4	×3
100%	$\frac{100}{100} = 1$	1	

Pay rise

Last year Class 6C were paid the following average amounts for the jobs they did at home.

Job	Pay	Job	Pay
Window cleaning	£5·50	Bed making	£3·30
Car washing	£10·50	Cleaning	£5·00
Cat grooming	£4·40	Gardening	£8·60
Vacuuming	£3·40	Feeding the chickens	£7·70
Babysitting	£6·60	Dog walking	£10·30

This year there was a pay rise for some jobs, but a decrease for other jobs.

The pay for **bed making** and **cleaning** increased by **5%**.

The pay for **window cleaning**, **vacuuming** and **babysitting** fell by **10%**.

The pay for **cat grooming** increased by **30%**.

The pay for **car washing** and **feeding the chickens** fell by **15%**.

The pay for **gardening** fell by **25%**.

The pay for **dog walking** fell by **20%**.

1 Fill in this table with the new rates.

Job	New pay	Job	New pay
Window cleaning		Bed making	
Car washing		Cleaning	
Cat grooming		Gardening	
Vacuuming		Feeding the chickens	
Babysitting		Dog walking	

Naming numbers

Use the clues to work out the numbers. What is the total of all the numbers?

1 The product of the first two prime numbers.

2 The total of the first four prime numbers.

3 A prime number less than 20 with a digit total of 8.

4 A square number greater than 25 which is the sum of two prime numbers less than 30.

5 A number less than 20 which is the product of two odd prime numbers.

6 An odd number less than 40 but greater than 35 which is the product of two prime numbers.

7 Two numbers which cannot be digital roots of prime numbers.

8 The smallest prime factor of 33.

9 The largest prime factor of 45.

10 A prime number which is a factor of 12 and 21.

11 The smallest common multiple of 3 and 4.

12 A number less than 50 with the prime factors 2, 3 and 5.

13 A 2-digit number which is a multiple of 3, 4 and 5.

14 A number greater than 40 which gives 6 when divided by a prime number less than 10.

Total

Gate shapes

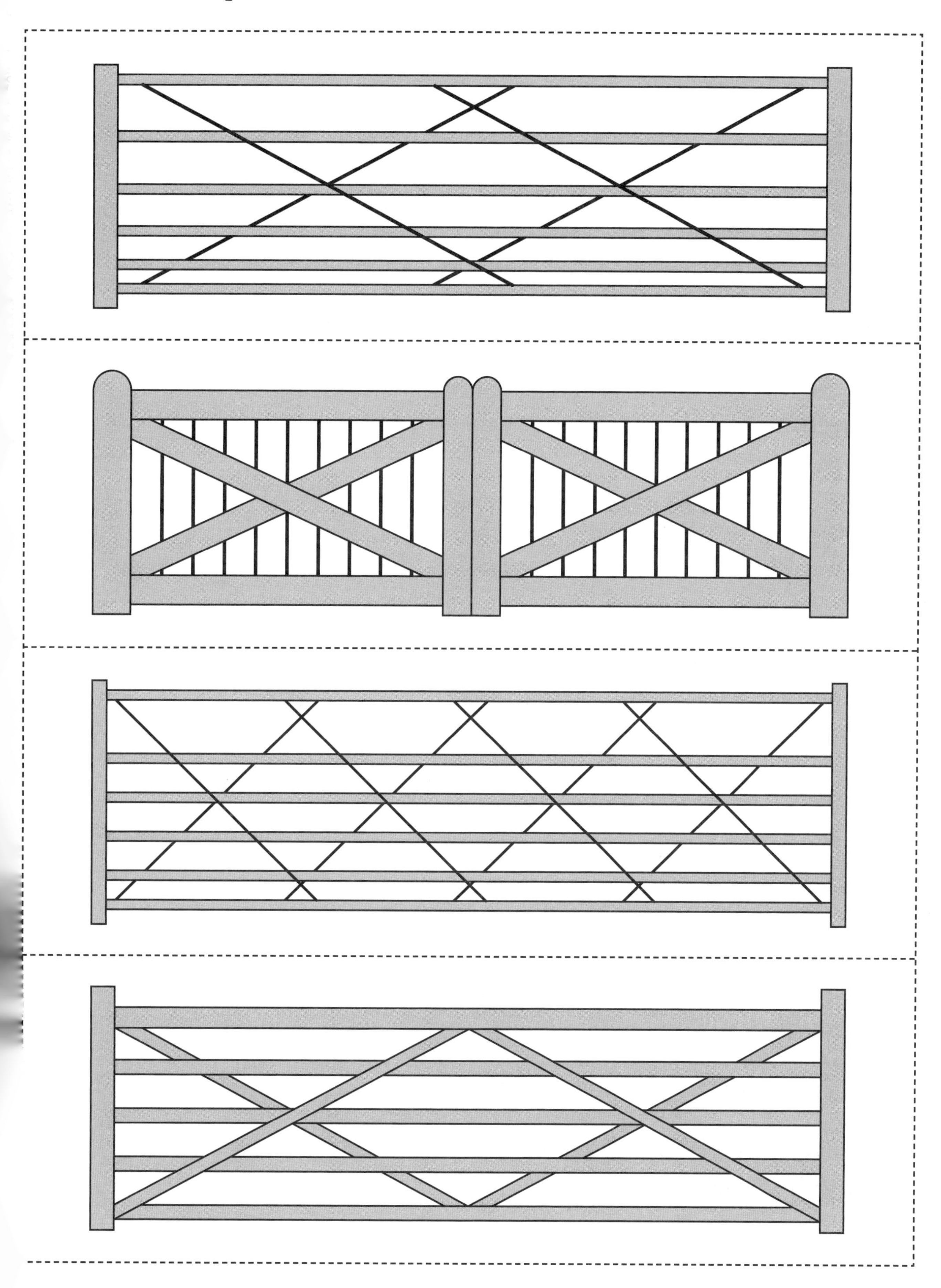

Match the properties: number cards

Rules

- You need the number cards from PCM 8, the picture cards from PCM 9 and the word cards from PCM 10.
- Shuffle all the cards and deal them out. Put your pile of cards in front of you.
- Take turns to turn over your top card.
- If you can see two or more cards that are linked, call out *Snap!* Then explain why the cards are linked.
- For example: *60 and equilateral triangle are linked because the angles are all 60°.*
- If your explanation is correct you can keep the cards that are linked.
- The first player to get all the cards wins!

1	2	3	4
5	6	7	8
9	10	11	12
20	60	90	108

Match the properties: picture cards

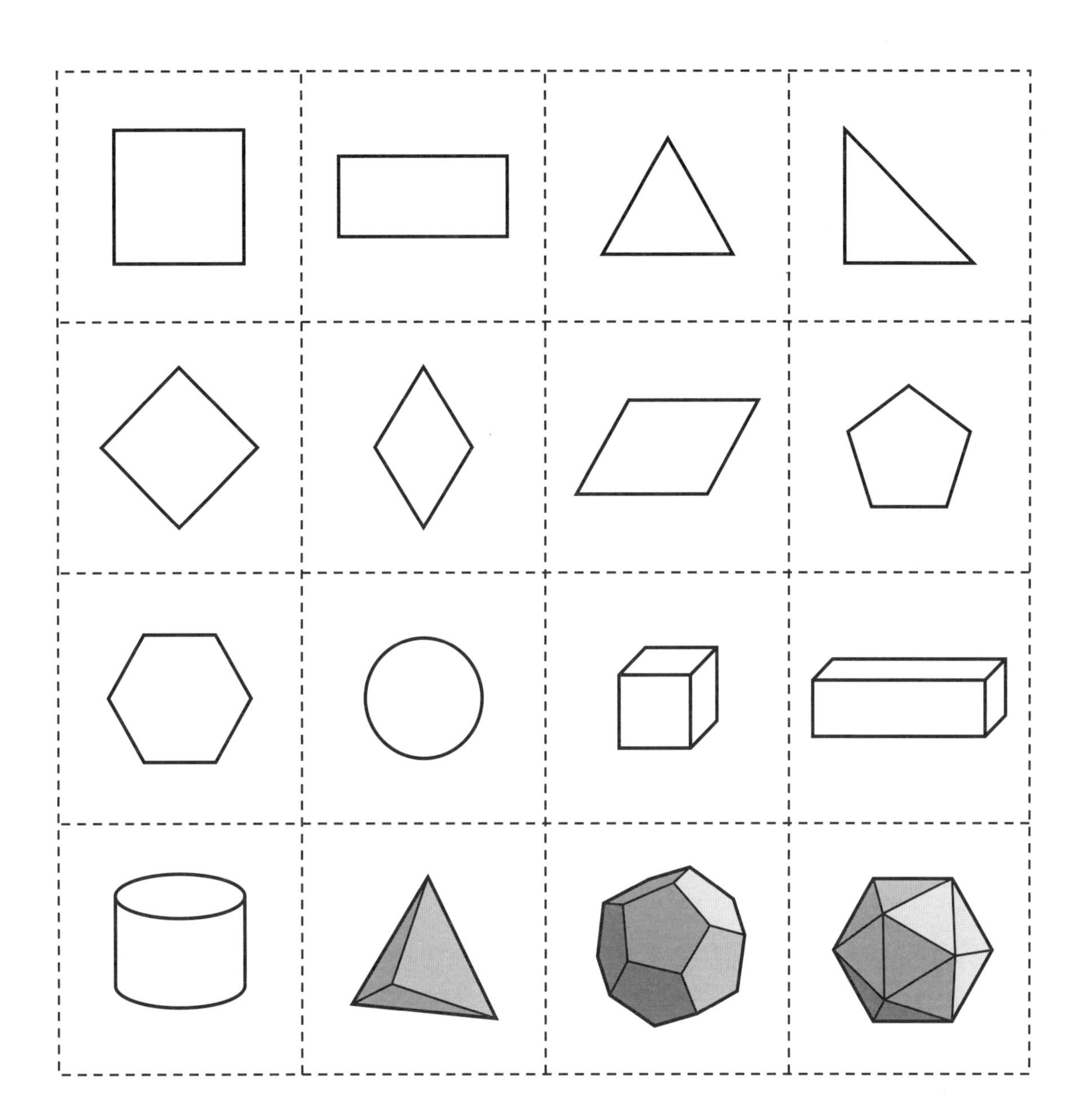

Match the properties: word cards

rhombus	cube	cuboid	cylinder
icosahedron	dodecahedron	tetrahedron	Platonic
parallel	perpendicular	equilateral	face
edge	adjacent	vertex	right angle

Spelling scores 1

Scores from 80 children in a spelling test on Monday

6	8	11	9	13
15	7	9	12	14
11	15	17	11	10
9	8	12	13	7
8	6	9	11	12
9	13	16	15	12
11	11	13	9	6
5	17	18	1	11
12	15	20	18	12
10	10	8	14	11
9	8	12	15	17
7	5	8	12	14
10	8	17	15	14
19	14	6	8	10
3	8	10	12	16
9	7	8	13	2

Spelling scores 2

Scores from 80 children in a spelling test on Friday

9	11	14	12	15
15	9	7	11	17
13	19	18	14	6
14	17	18	16	11
18	16	9	17	15
15	17	15	17	16
11	14	16	14	8
8	18	19	4	10
14	17	20	20	16
12	16	12	14	11
9	6	13	16	19
17	5	12	15	15
16	9	19	15	17
20	11	8	11	10
1	16	12	17	18
11	12	9	14	3

Angles in quadrilaterals

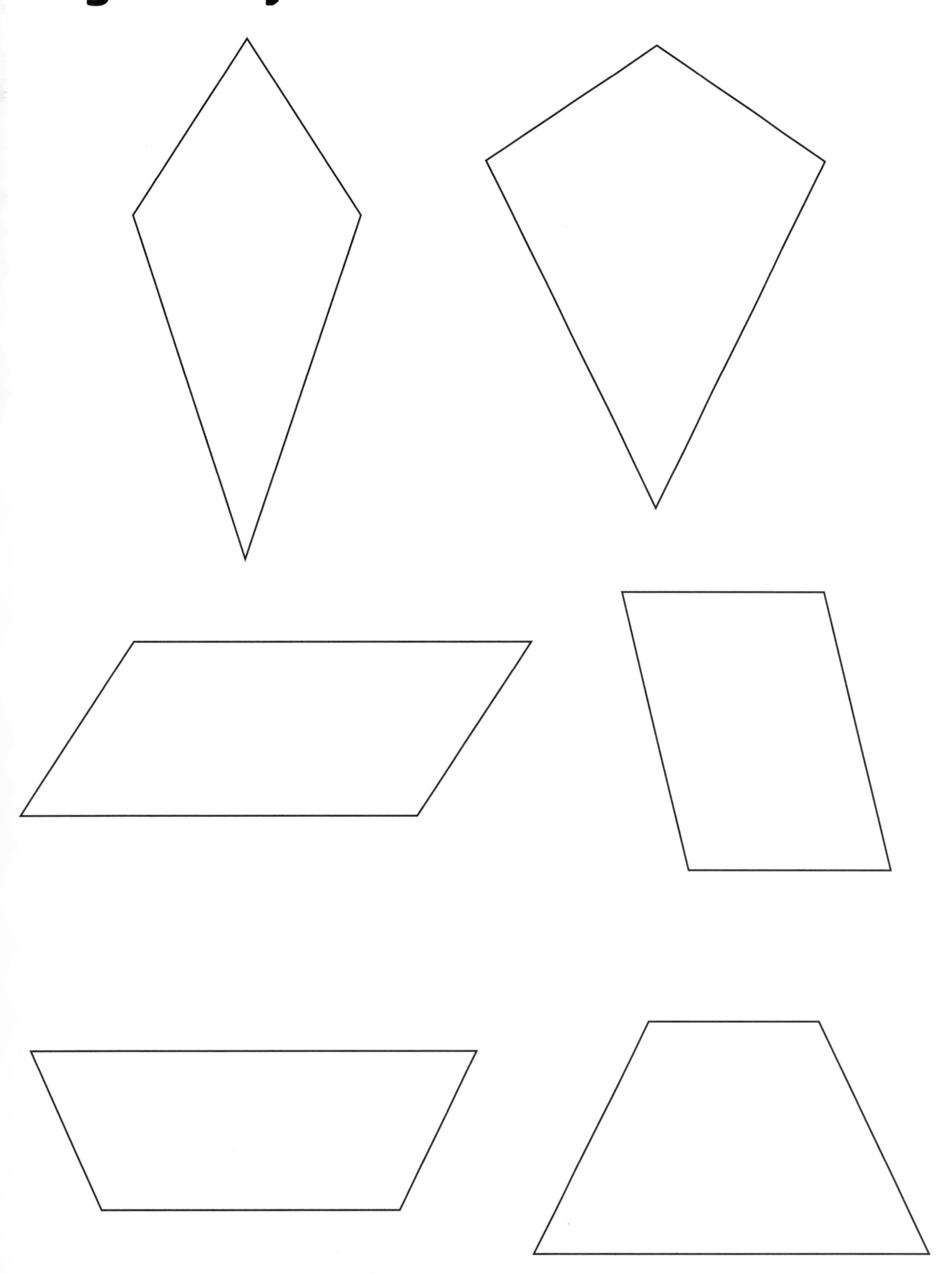

Finding differences: rules

Game rules

Spin the spinner on PCM 15 four times. Record the numbers as A, B, C and D.
Find the difference between A and B. Find the difference between C and D.
Then find the difference between the differences.
Whoever has the highest difference between the differences wins the round.

Round 1	A ______	B ______	Difference? ______
	C ______	D ______	Difference? ______
			Difference between the differences? ______
Round 2	A ______	B ______	Difference? ______
	C ______	D ______	Difference? ______
			Difference between the differences? ______
Round 3	A ______	B ______	Difference? ______
	C ______	D ______	Difference? ______
			Difference between the differences? ______
Round 4	A ______	B ______	Difference? ______
	C ______	D ______	Difference? ______
			Difference between the differences? ______
Round 5	A ______	B ______	Difference? ______
	C ______	D ______	Difference? ______
			Difference between the differences? ______

Swap sheets and check each other's answers.

Finding differences: spinner

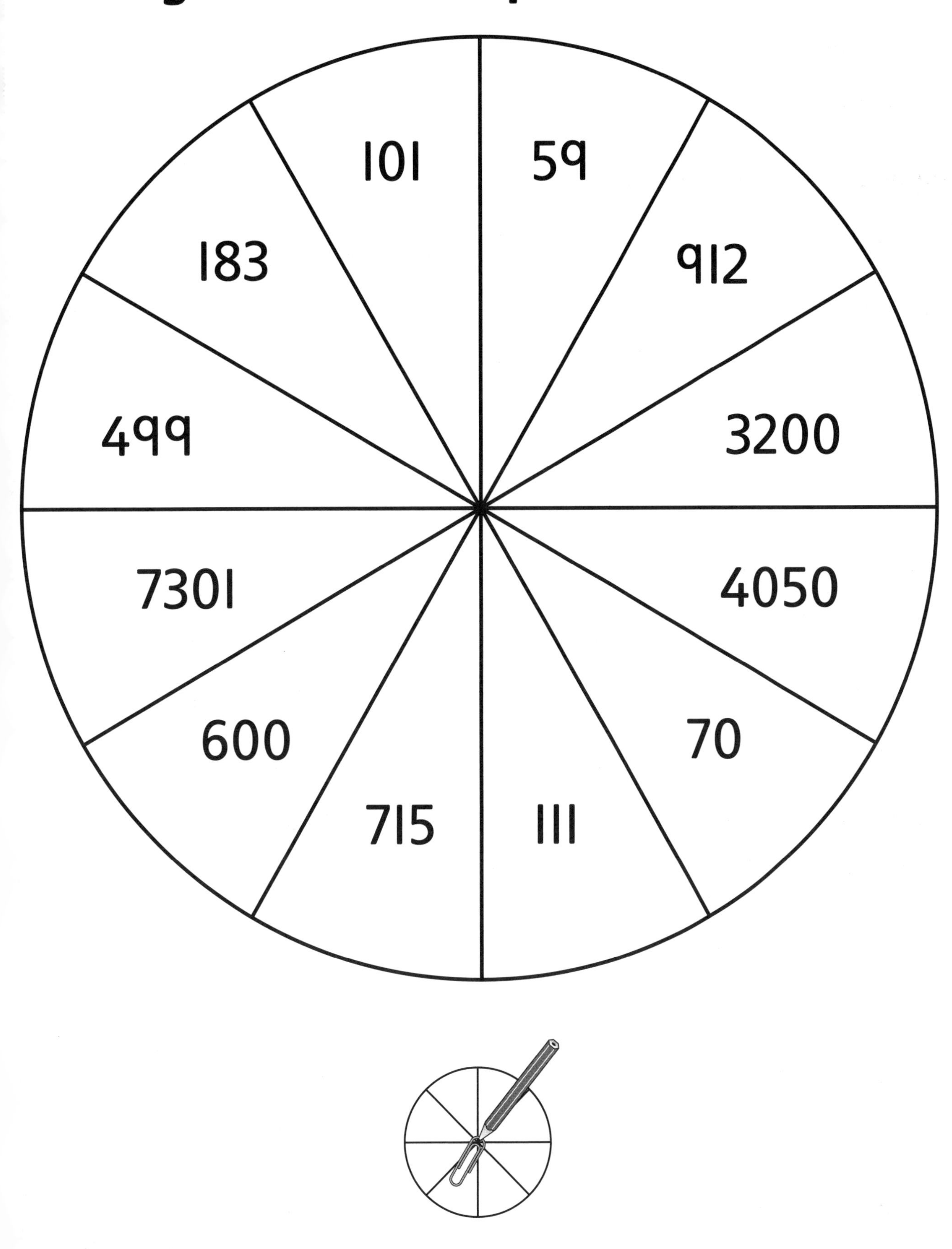

Fair shares

6 pizzas between 5 people ______ each

1 pizza costs £2·50 Cost: ______ each

8 sausages between 6 people ______ each

8 sausages cost £1·99 Cost: ______ each

12 cakes between 9 children ______ each

4 cakes cost 75p Cost: ______ each

200 g of chocolate between 12 people ______ each

200 g of chocolate costs £1·80 Cost: ______ each

12 m of ribbon cut into 5 strips ______ each

1 m of ribbon costs 25p Cost: ______ each

10 apples between 7 children ______ each

1 apple costs 49p Cost: ______ each

20 sandwiches between 11 people ______ each

2 sandwiches cost £1·60 Cost: ______ each

16 sweets between 5 people ______ each

1 sweet costs 4p Cost: ______ each

9 cans between 8 people ______ each

6 cans cost £2·45 Cost: ______ each

£150 shared between 8 people ______ each

Egyptian fractions

	Egyptian fraction		Egyptian fraction		Egyptian fraction
$\frac{2}{3}$	$\frac{1}{2} + \frac{1}{6}$	$\frac{6}{7}$	$\frac{1}{2} + \frac{1}{3} + \frac{1}{42}$	$\frac{2}{10}$	$\frac{1}{5}$
$\frac{2}{4}$	$\frac{1}{2}$	$\frac{2}{8}$	$\frac{1}{4}$	$\frac{3}{10}$	$\frac{1}{4} + \frac{1}{20}$ or $\frac{1}{5} + \frac{1}{10}$
$\frac{3}{4}$	$\frac{1}{2} + \frac{1}{4}$	$\frac{3}{8}$	$\frac{1}{3} + \frac{1}{24}$ or $\frac{1}{4} + \frac{1}{8}$	$\frac{4}{10}$	$\frac{1}{3} + \frac{1}{15}$
$\frac{2}{5}$	$\frac{1}{3} + \frac{1}{15}$	$\frac{4}{8}$	$\frac{1}{2}$	$\frac{5}{10}$	$\frac{1}{2}$
$\frac{3}{5}$	$\frac{1}{2} + \frac{1}{10}$	$\frac{5}{8}$	$\frac{1}{2} + \frac{1}{8}$	$\frac{6}{10}$	$\frac{1}{2} + \frac{1}{10}$
$\frac{4}{5}$	$\frac{1}{2} + \frac{1}{4} + \frac{1}{20}$	$\frac{6}{8}$	$\frac{1}{2} + \frac{1}{4}$	$\frac{7}{10}$	$\frac{1}{2} + \frac{1}{5}$
$\frac{2}{6}$	$\frac{1}{3}$	$\frac{7}{8}$	$\frac{1}{2} + \frac{1}{4} + \frac{1}{8}$	$\frac{8}{10}$	$\frac{1}{2} + \frac{1}{4} + \frac{1}{20}$
$\frac{3}{6}$	$\frac{1}{2}$ or $\frac{1}{3} + \frac{1}{6}$	$\frac{2}{9}$	$\frac{1}{5} + \frac{1}{45}$	$\frac{9}{10}$	$\frac{1}{2} + \frac{1}{3} + \frac{1}{15}$
$\frac{4}{6}$	$\frac{2}{3}$	$\frac{3}{9}$	$\frac{1}{3}$	$\frac{2}{11}$	$\frac{1}{6} + \frac{1}{66}$
$\frac{5}{6}$	$\frac{1}{2} + \frac{1}{3}$	$\frac{4}{9}$	$\frac{1}{3} + \frac{1}{9}$	$\frac{3}{11}$	$\frac{1}{4} + \frac{1}{44}$
$\frac{2}{7}$	$\frac{1}{4} + \frac{1}{28}$	$\frac{5}{9}$	$\frac{1}{2} + \frac{1}{18}$	$\frac{4}{11}$	$\frac{1}{3} + \frac{1}{33}$
$\frac{3}{7}$	$\frac{1}{3} + \frac{1}{11} + \frac{1}{231}$	$\frac{6}{9}$	$\frac{2}{3}$	$\frac{5}{11}$	$\frac{1}{3} + \frac{1}{9} + \frac{1}{99}$
$\frac{4}{7}$	$\frac{1}{2} + \frac{1}{14}$	$\frac{7}{9}$	$\frac{1}{2} + \frac{1}{4} + \frac{1}{36}$	$\frac{6}{11}$	$\frac{1}{2} + \frac{1}{22}$
$\frac{5}{7}$	$\frac{1}{2} + \frac{1}{5} + \frac{1}{70}$	$\frac{8}{9}$	$\frac{1}{2} + \frac{1}{3} + \frac{1}{18}$	$\frac{7}{11}$	$\frac{1}{2} + \frac{1}{8} + \frac{1}{88}$

Tides

Use the rule of twelfths to complete the table.

Three hours after high water, the water will have dropped $\frac{1}{12} + \frac{2}{12} + \frac{3}{12} = \frac{6}{12} = \frac{1}{2}$ of the total range.

Two hours after low water, the water will have risen $\frac{1}{12} + \frac{2}{12} = \frac{3}{12} = \frac{1}{4}$ of the total range.

Port	High water (m)	Low water (m)	Tidal range (m)	Water height 2 hours after low water (m)	Water height 3 hours after high water (m)
Belfast	6·0	3·7		4·275	
Liverpool	9·5	0·8			5·15
Portland	2·0	0·2		0·65	
London Bridge	6·8	0·8		2·3	
Milford Haven	7·1	0·7		2·3	
Barrow	9·4		8·0	3·4	
Lerwick		0·7	1·6		1·5
Tyne		0·3	5·1	1·575	
Avonmouth		1·5	11·8		7·4
Shoreham	6·3		5·7		3·45

Planets in our Solar System

Planet	Diameter (km)	To nearest 1000 km	Distance from Sun (millions of km)	To nearest 10 million km	How many times bigger or smaller than Earth	To nearest tenth	Time to travel around Sun (Earth days/ years)	To nearest 100 days
Mercury	4880		57·9		0·38		87·96 days	
Venus	12 104		108·2		0·95		224·68 days	
Earth	12 756		149·6		1·00		365·26 days	
Mars	6788		228·0		0·53		686·98 days	
Jupiter	142 740		778·4		11·19		11·68 years	
Saturn	120 034		1424·6		9·41		29·46 years	
Uranus	51 152		2873·5		4·01		84·07 years	
Neptune	49 620		4501·0		3·89		164·81 years	

Place-value board

Thousandths 0·001	
Hundredths 0·01	
Tenths 0·1	
Units 1	
Tens 10	
Hundreds 100	
Thousands 1000	

Which calculation?

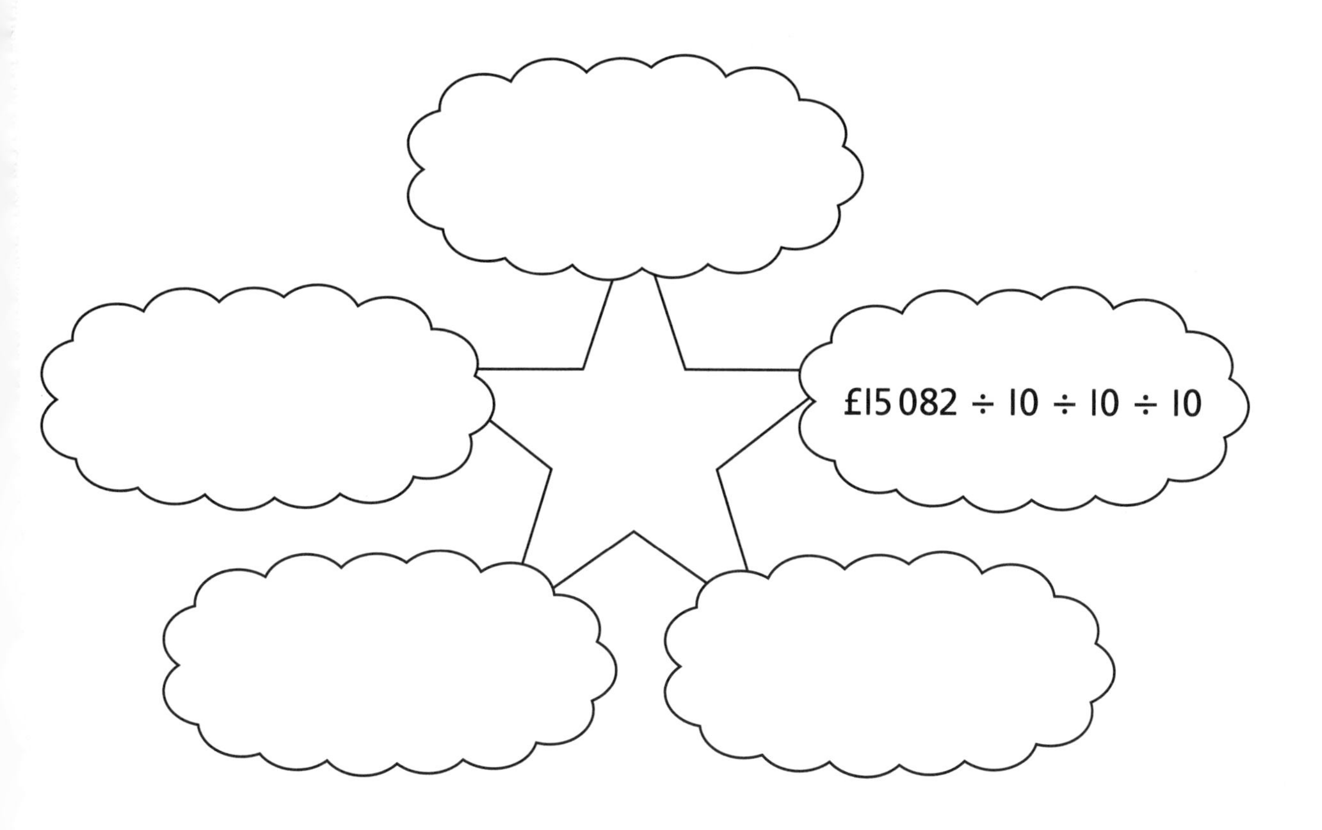

Where does the number go?

6·01   8·04   7·65   6·7   7·23   5·99   7·61   6·1

1 Only five of these numbers go on the number line. Which five? Write them in the correct boxes.

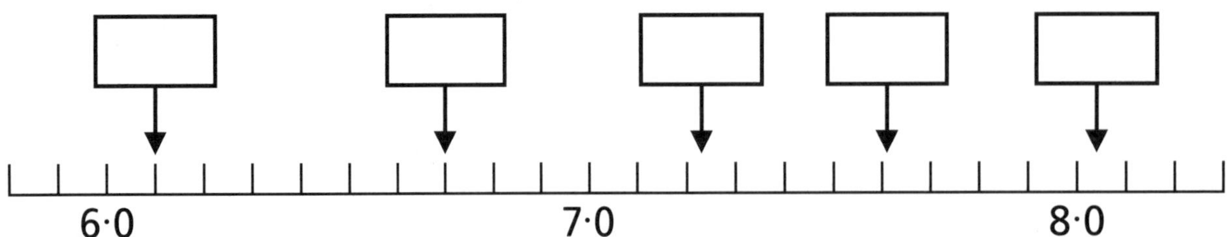

2 This number line is divided into tenths. Write the number each marker is pointing to, to the nearest hundredth.

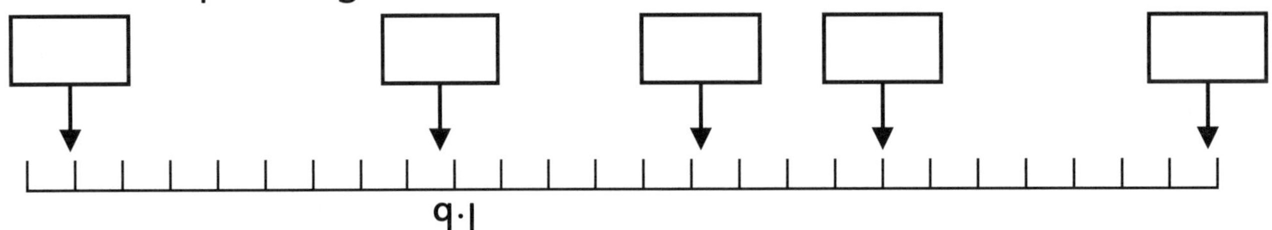

3 Write the numbers the markers are pointing at. Then use the number line to work out where each marker would be if it was moved on by 0·75. Fill in the blanks in the calculations.

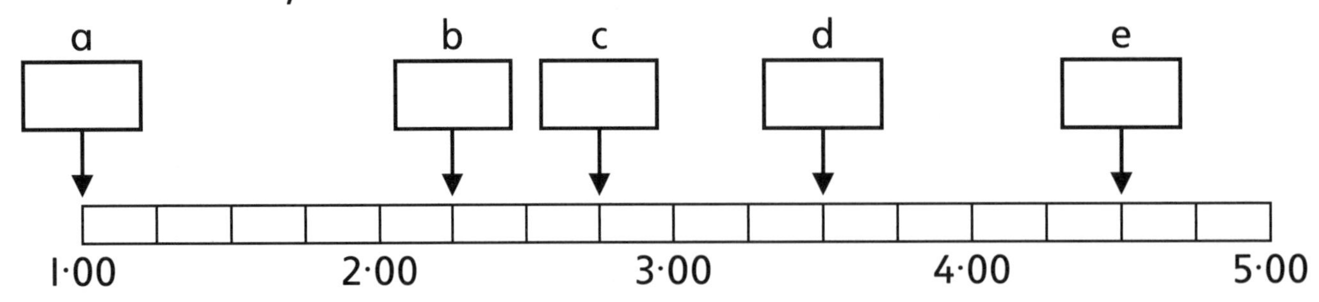

a ________ +0·75 = ________

b ________ +0·75 = ________

c ________ +0·75 = ________

d ________ +0·75 = ________

e ________ +0·75 = ________

Powers of numbers: n^2 to n^7

n	n^2	n^3	n^4	n^5	n^6	n^7
1	1	1	1	1	1	1
2	4	8	16	32	64	128
3	9	27	81	243	729	2187
4						
5	25	125	625	3125	15 625	78 125
6	36	216	1296	7776	46 656	279 936
7					117 649	823 543
8	64	512	4096	32 768	262 144	2 097 152
9	81	729	6561	59 049	531 441	4 782 969
10	100	1000	10 000			
11	121	1331	14 641	161 051	1 771 561	19 487 171
12	144	1728	20 736	248 832	2 985 984	35 831 808
13			28 561	371 293	4 826 809	62 748 517
14			38 416	537 824	7 529 536	105 413 504
15			50 625	759 375	11 390 625	170 859 375
16			65 536	1 048 576	16 777 216	268 435 456
17			83 521	1 419 857	24 137 569	410 338 673
18			104 976	1 889 568	34 012 224	612 220 032
19			130 321	1 476 099	47 045 881	893 871 739
20			160 000	3 200 000	64 000 000	1 280 000 000

Powers of numbers: n^8 to n^{10}

n	n^8	n^9	n^{10}
1	1	1	1
2	256	512	1024
3	6561	19 683	59 049
4			
5	390 625	1 953 125	9 765 625
6	1 679 616	10 077 696	60 466 176
7	5 764 801	40 353 607	282 475 249
8	16 777 216	134 217 728	1 073 741 824
9	43 046 721	387 420 489	3 486 784 401
10			
11	214 358 881	2 357 947 691	25 937 424 601
12	429 981 696	5 159 780 352	61 917 364 224
13	815 730 721	10 604 499 373	137 858 491 849
14	1 475 789 056	20 661 046 784	289 254 654 976
15	2 562 890 625	38 443 359 375	576 650 390 625
16	4 294 967 296	68 719 476 736	1 099 511 627 776
17	6 975 757 441	118 587 876 497	2 015 993 900 449
18	11 019 960 576	198 359 290 368	3 570 467 226 624
19	16 983 563 041	322 687 697 779	6 131 066 257 801
20	25 600 000 000	512 000 000 000	10 240 000 000 000

Powers of numbers: digital roots

Find the digital root of each number.

n	Digital root	n^2	Digital root	n^3	Digital root	n^4	Digital root	n^5	Digital root
1		1		1		1		1	
2		4		8		16		32	
3		9		27		81		243	
4		16		64		256		1024	
5		25		125		625		3125	
6		36		216		1296		7776	
7		49		343		2401		16 807	
8		64		512		4096		32 768	
9		81		729		6561		59 049	
10		100		1000		10 000		100 000	
11		121		1331		14 641		161 051	
12		144		1728		20 736		248 832	
13		169		2197		28 561		371 293	
14		196		2744		38 416		537 824	
15		225		3375		50 625		759 375	
16		256		4096		65 536		1 048 576	
17		289		4913		83 521		1 419 857	
18		324		5832		104 976		1 889 568	
19		361		6859		130 321		2 476 099	
20		400		8000		160 000		3 200 000	

Coordinates

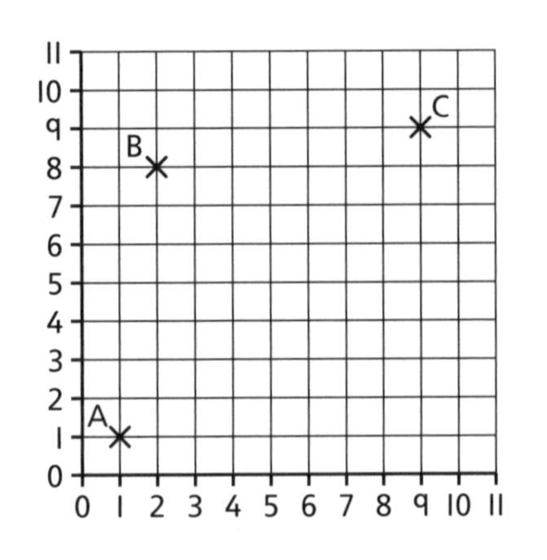

1 A, B and C are vertices of a symmetrical quadrilateral. Label missing vertex D.

2 Give the coordinates of the four vertices.

A ______________ B ______________

C ______________ D ______________

3 Join the corners and name the shape.

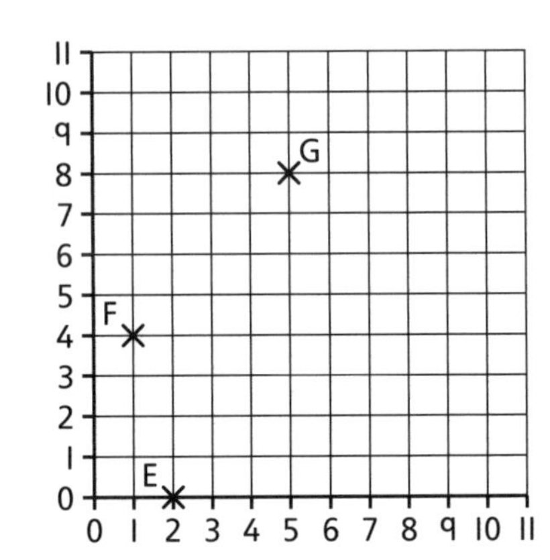

4 E, F and G are vertices of an isosceles trapezium. Label missing vertex H.

5 Give the coordinates of the four vertices.

E ______________ F ______________

G ______________ H ______________

6 Join the vertices and draw the line of symmetry.

7 Mark these points on the grid and join them.
(4, 1) (0, 8) (4, 4) (8, 8)

8 Name the shape. 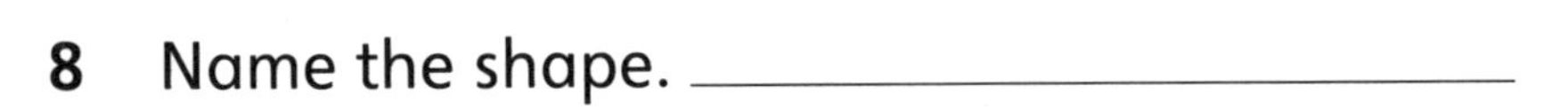

9 Draw the lines of symmetry.

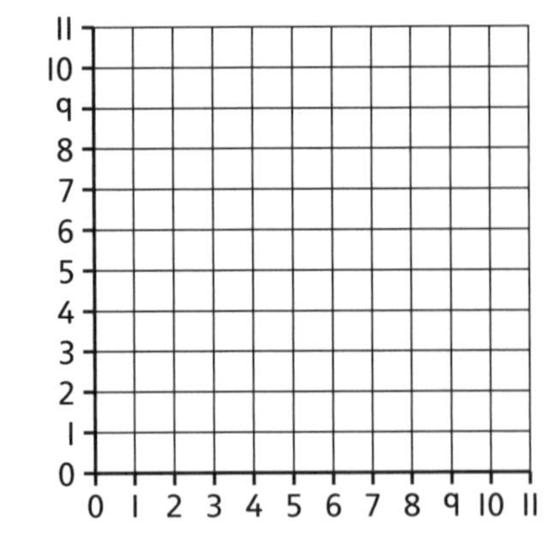

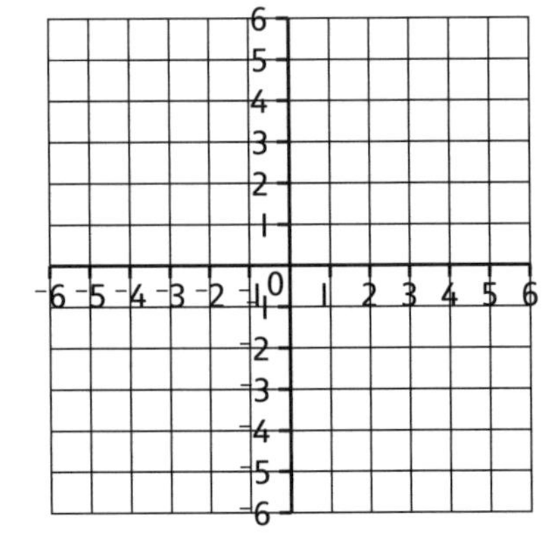

10 Mark these points on the grid and join them.
(0, 0) (4, 0) (0, 5)

11 Name the shape. ______________

12 Reflect the shape in the vertical axis.
Reflect both shapes in the horizontal axis.

13 Name the new shape. ______________

14 Mark and join the mid points of each side.

Seeing shapes: shape words

adjacent angle acute obtuse

right reflex face concave convex

angles at a point angles on a straight line

diagonal horizontal vertical identical

intersect opposite sides opposite angles

parallel perpendicular polygon

pentagon hexagon octagon

quadrilateral arrowhead kite parallelogram

rectangle hemisphere prism

square-based pyramid pyramid

sphere tetrahedron 3D triangle

equilateral isosceles scalene

right-angled vertex vertices

Average word lengths

For each article find the mean, mode and median word length.

Draw a graph to represent each set of data.
What type of graph will be most useful? Will you need to group your data? Will it help to draw a frequency table first?
What type of average can be found using your graphs?

TOTTENHAM have been knocked out of the FA Cup in the fourth round, following their 2–1 defeat by Manchester United. In the first half of the match, spectators were treated to a decent game. The second half was in great contrast to this, with both teams looking suspiciously as though they were trying to avoid a replay.

Prior to the match, there were widespread rumours that two reserve teams would be participating. Harry Redknapp, manager of Tottenham, had even promised to field his weakest possible team. As it turned out, however, both managers named perfectly respectable line-ups. The only questionable decisions were Redknapp keeping Jermain Defoe on the bench for Tottenham, and Sir Alex Ferguson giving Fabio da Silva his debut for United.

The match appeared to be going Tottenham's way when Roman Pavlyuchenko scored within the first five minutes. The remainder of the first half made for exciting viewing, as United fought back with goals from Paul Scholes and Dimitar Berbatov. Spurs seemed to have lost the will to fight in the second half, and the match fizzled out rather disappointingly.

Spurs are out of the FA Cup after losing 2–1 to Man United. Harry Redknapp's team were cheering when Roman Pavlyuchenko scored a header early on, but United hit back with a goal by Paul Scholes in the 35th minute, and one more by Dimitar Berbatov 90 seconds later.

Spurs didn't seem to be trying after that, and the second half was awful. United seemed happy to coast through the rest of the game and Spurs gave them no trouble at all.

Dinner out

Cold starters

Prawn cocktail	£4·95
Ham and melon	£5·50
Three coloured salad (V)	£5·50
Pink prawns	£5·50
Crab salad	£5·95
Seafood salad	£5·50

Hot starters

Sardines	£4·95
Garlic mushrooms (V)	£4·95
Mussels	£5·50
French cheese (V)	£4·95
Fried squid	£4·95

Salads

Tuna and bean salad	£8·95
Smoked chicken salad	£8·95
Chef's special (V)	£9·95
Greek salad (V)	£8·95

Pasta

Lasagne	£7·50
Spaghetti Bolognese	£7·50
Mushroom pasta (V)	£7·95
Spaghetti with bacon	£7·50

Meats

Rack of ribs	£9·65
Sirloin steak	£12·95
Lamb shank	£10·95
Grilled chop	£12·95
Lamb cutlets	£11·95

Chicken and duck

Grilled chicken with lime	£9·50
Cajun chicken	£9·50
Chicken with mushrooms	£9·95
Duck with orange	£12·95

Fish

Swordfish	£11·95
Trout	£10·95
Salmon	£11·95
King prawns	£12·95
Scampi	£11·95

Side orders

Garlic bread (V)	£1·90
Mixed salad (V)	£2·95
Onion rings (V)	£2·95
Mixed vegetables (V)	£2·95
Chips (V)	£1·90
Rice (V)	£2·50

Desserts

Fruit salad (V)	£2·55
Ice cream (V)	£2·75
Crème caramel (V)	£2·75
Chocolate sponge (V)	£2·95
Apple pie and cream (V)	£3·20

Drinks

Diet cola	£1·30
Lemonade	£1·25
Fresh orange juice	£2·25
Fresh apple juice	£2·20
Mixed fruit crush	£2·70
Sparkling water	£0·95

All our main courses are served with chips and fresh vegetables or salad

Addition walls

Add each pair of next-door numbers and put the answer in the space above.
Use column addition to work out the totals. Carry on until the top brick is filled.

1 What is the top number?

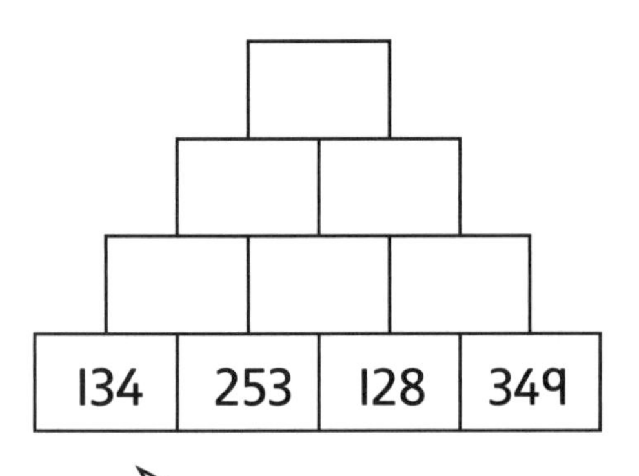

2 Rearrange the four starting numbers to give a larger top number.

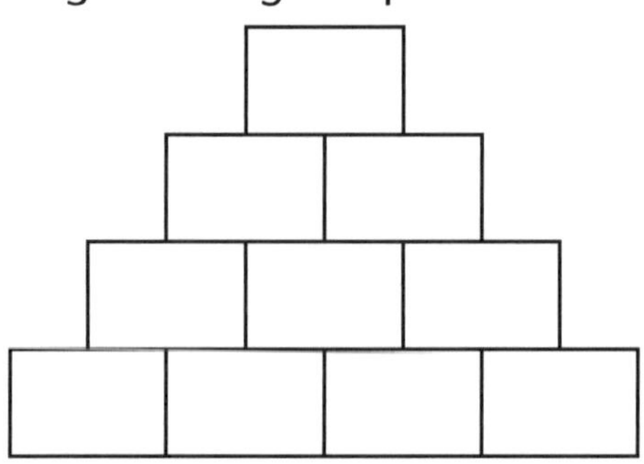

Did you estimate the answers before working them out?

Start with the numbers 188, 227, 107 and 335.

3 Where would you place them to get the largest top number?

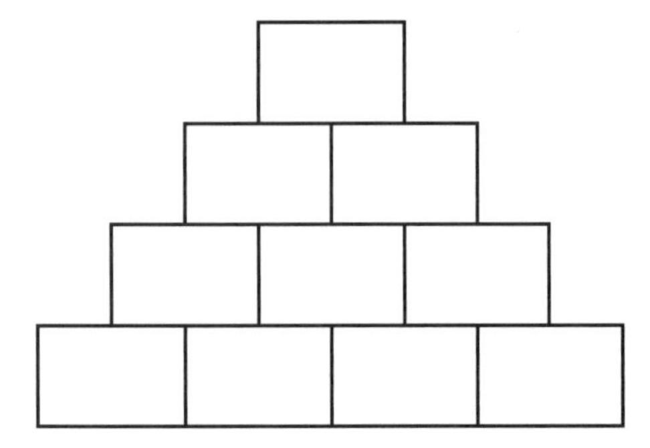

4 Where would you place them to get the smallest top number?

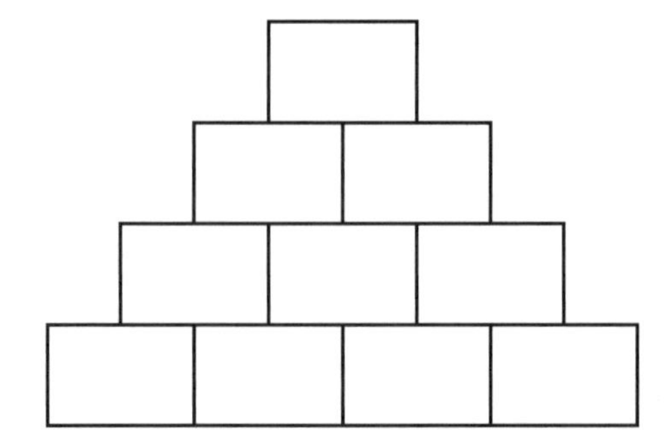

Start with the numbers 97, 176, 217, 98 and 189.

5 Where would you place them on this wall to get the largest top number?

Did you find any rules to help you make the largest top number?

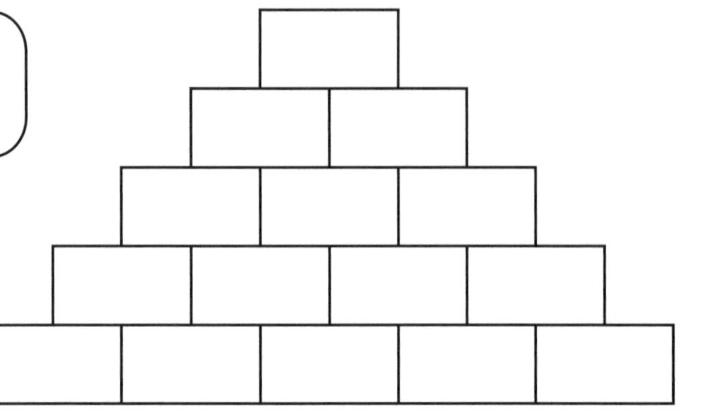

Fill it up

Car A

Fuel capacity 75 litres

Fuel gauge $\frac{1}{2}$ full

Petrol consumption 7 miles per litre

Car B

Fuel capacity 60 litres

Fuel gauge 0.25 full

Petrol consumption 35 miles per gallon

Car C

Fuel capacity 45 litres

Fuel gauge $\frac{1}{3}$ full

Petrol consumption 45 miles per gallon

Car D

Fuel capacity 20 gallons

Fuel gauge $\frac{5}{8}$ full

Petrol consumption 5 kilometres per litre

Car E

Fuel capacity 55 litres

Fuel gauge $\frac{7}{10}$ full

Petrol consumption 12 miles per litre

Car F

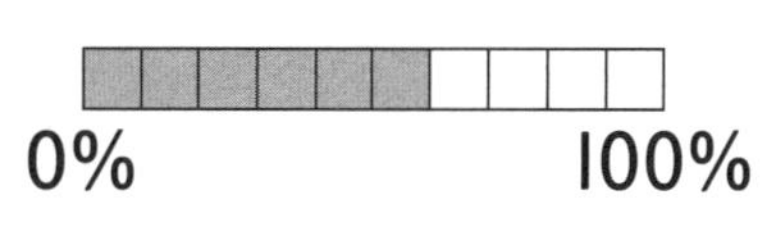

Fuel capacity 12 gallons

Fuel gauge 60% full

Petrol consumption 56 kilometres per gallon

Decimal dominoes 1

0·05	$\frac{20}{100}$	$\frac{19}{20}$	45%
20%	0·8	$\frac{9}{20}$	30%
80%	$\frac{1}{2}$	0·3	75%
50%	$\frac{35}{100}$	$\frac{3}{4}$	$\frac{95}{100}$
35%	$\frac{13}{20}$	0·95	$\frac{25}{100}$

Decimal dominoes 2

65%	0·25	25%	$\frac{11}{20}$
15%	40%	0·15	5%
$\frac{40}{100}$	70%	$\frac{60}{100}$	$\frac{15}{100}$
0·7	0·35	$\frac{75}{100}$	60%
$\frac{7}{20}$	55%	$\frac{45}{100}$	0·75

Decimal dominoes 3

$\frac{55}{100}$	$\frac{100}{100}$	$\frac{10}{100}$	0·45
1	$\frac{3}{10}$	0·65	$\frac{1}{10}$
$\frac{1}{4}$	$\frac{80}{100}$	0·55	$\frac{9}{10}$
$\frac{4}{5}$	10%	90%	$\frac{2}{5}$
0·1	100%	0·4	$\frac{3}{5}$

Decimal dominoes 4

0·01	95%	0·6	$\frac{3}{20}$
$\frac{1}{100}$	85%	0·9	$\frac{65}{100}$
0·85	$\frac{1}{20}$	0·2	$\frac{90}{100}$
$\frac{5}{100}$	$\frac{17}{20}$	$\frac{50}{100}$	$\frac{1}{5}$
$\frac{85}{100}$	$\frac{7}{10}$	$\frac{70}{100}$	0·5

Flying high

This table shows the heights that six aircraft fly at.

Plane	Cruising height in feet	Cruising height in metres	Ground temperature at sea level	Approximate temperature outside plane
A	12 000		5°C	
B	20 000		5°C	
C	22 000		0°C	
D	38 000		10°C	
E	43 000		0°C	
F	48 000		10°C	
G	70 000		20°C	

1 Fill in the heights in metres.

1000 ft is approximately 305 m.

The temperature falls approximately 6·5°C for every 1000 m above sea level.

2 Fill in the approximate temperature outside each plane.

3 Look at this table. Work out the approximate temperature at the summit of each mountain if the temperature at sea level for each is 0°C.

Mountain	Height in feet	Height in metres	Approximate temperature at summit
Mount Everest	29 028		−57·5°C
K2	28 251		
Annapurna I	26 545		
Chimborazo	20 564		
Mount McKinley	20 321		
Mount Kilimanjaro	19 340		
Mount Ararat	16 853		
Mount Fuji	12 388		
Ben Nevis	4409		

Summer holiday

Item	Cost for one child	Cost for one adult	Cost for 2 adults and 4 children	Cost for 4 adults and 4 children
3 pairs of shorts				
5 T-shirts				
2 swimsuits				
I pair of beach shoes				
I pair of trousers				
4 shirts				
I suitcase				
I beach ball				
7 sets of underwear				
I pair of shoes				
2 books				
I magazine				
I wash bag				
I sunhat				
I beach towel				
I beach bag				
2 pairs of sunglasses				
I bottle of sun-block				
I bottle of after-sun				
I camera				
		Grand totals		

Well I never!

1 Take any 2-digit number. Write the digits in the boxes then do the calculation. Estimate the answer before you do the calculation.

□□ × 101 = ____________ Estimate: ____________

2 Now do the same with a different 2-digit number.

□□ × 101 = ____________ Estimate: ____________

3 Now multiply the same 2-digit numbers by 1001, then by 10 001 and 100 001. Estimate the answer before you do the calculation.

□□ × 1001 = ____________ Estimate: ____________

□□ × 1001 = ____________ Estimate: ____________

□□ × 10 001 = ____________ Estimate: ____________

□□ × 10 001 = ____________ Estimate: ____________

□□ × 100 001 = ____________ Estimate: ____________

□□ × 100 001 = ____________ Estimate: ____________

4 Take any 3-digit number and multiply it by 1001, 10 001 and 100 001.

5 Take any 4-digit number and multiply it by 10 001 and 100 001.

6 Take any 5-digit number and multiply it by 100 001.

7 What do you notice?

8 Can you suggest any rules for what you have found?

Pop tour: distance chart

This chart shows the distance in kilometres between each city on the tour

	Glasgow	Newcastle	Sheffield	Manchester	Liverpool	Bournemouth	Brighton	London	Plymouth	Nottingham	Cardiff	Birmingham
Birmingham	467	330	147	153	159	272	283	189	330	84	200	
Cardiff	641	516	333	327	333	264	319	244	243	270		200
Nottingham	454	255	72	130	180	328	306	206	408		270	84
Plymouth	780	656	473	467	473	203	401	383		408	243	330
London	648	453	270	335	341	172	85		383	206	244	189
Brighton	743	554	370	430	436	152		85	401	306	319	283
Bournemouth	731	569	386	418	424		152	172	203	328	264	272
Liverpool	352	277	125	55		424	436	341	473	180	333	159
Manchester	349	228	62		55	418	430	335	467	130	327	153
Sheffield	414	215		62	125	386	370	270	473	72	333	147
Newcastle	244		215	228	277	569	554	453	656	255	516	330
Glasgow		244	414	349	352	731	743	648	780	454	641	467

Pop tour: time chart

This chart shows how long in hours and minutes it takes to travel between each city on the tour.

	Glasgow	Newcastle	Sheffield	Manchester	Liverpool	Bournemouth	Brighton	London	Plymouth	Nottingham	Cardiff	Birmingham
Glasgow		2:53	4:53	3:42	3:53	7:34	7:40	6:52	7:59	5:04	6:36	4:49
Newcastle	**2:53**		2:24	2:40	3:07	6:05	5:52	4:59	6:49	2:55	5:26	3:32
Sheffield	4:53	**2:24**		7:34	7:40	6:52	7:59	5:04	6:36	4:49	3:32	1:38
Manchester	3:42	2:40	**7:34**		0:49	4:26	4:32	3:44	4:51	1:50	3:28	1:41
Liverpool	3:53	3:07	7:40	**0:49**		4:34	4:41	3:52	5:00	2:19	3:36	1:50
Bournemouth	7:34	6:05	6:52	4:26	**4:34**		2:11	2:06	2:41	3:38	2:53	2:55
Brighton	7:40	5:52	7:59	4:32	4:41	**2:11**		1:30	4:41	3:25	3:27	3:03
London	6:52	4:59	5:04	3:44	3:52	2:06	**1:30**		4:09	2:32	2:46	2:13
Plymouth	7:59	6:49	6:36	4:51	5:00	2:41	4:41	**4:09**		4:22	2:39	3:33
Nottingham	5:04	2:55	4:49	1:50	2:19	3:38	3:25	2:32	**4:22**		2:59	1:05
Cardiff	6:36	5:26	3:32	3:28	3:36	2:53	3:27	2:46	2:39	**2:59**		2:08
Birmingham	4:49	3:32	1:38	1:41	1:50	2:55	3:03	2:13	3:33	1:05	**2:08**	

Pop tour: map of Britain

Making a bird table

You will need the following pieces of wood.
All measurements are given as l × w × d

Plywood sheets
1 One feeding tray – 35 cm × 35 cm × 9 mm
2 Two roof side panels – 35 cm × 20 cm × 9 mm
3 Two side supports – 30 cm × 10 cm × 9 mm

Wooden strips
4 Four feeding tray edges – 33 cm × 10 mm × 10 mm

Wooden planks
5 Two roof end panels – identical triangles made from a piece of wood 20 cm × 20 cm × 18 mm

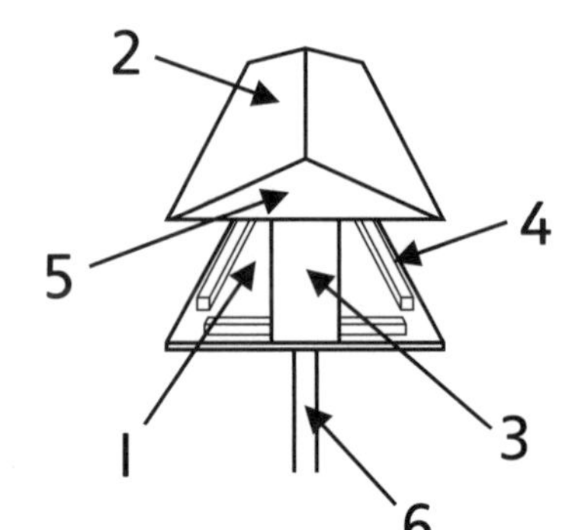

Wooden posts
6 One post – 150 cm × 44 mm × 44 mm

Additional materials
Panel pins, large nails, a hammer, wood glue

Assembly instructions
- Nail and glue the four wood strips (4) to the feeding tray (1).
- Nail and glue the middle of the tray (1) to the wooden post (6).
- Nail and glue the two roof side panels (2) to the two roof end panels (5).
- Nail and glue the side supports (3) to the roof end and panels and the feeding tray edges (4)

Sizes and prices of wood and other materials from the hardware shop

Item	Size	Cost
Plywood	l 2440 mm × w 1220 mm × d 9 mm	£12·88
Wooden strip	l 2100 mm × w 10 mm × d 10 mm	£1·43
Wooden plank	l 1750 mm × w 200 mm × d 18 mm	£11·98
Wooden post	l 3100 mm × w 44 mm × d 44 mm	£4·68
Additional materials	Assorted	£1·00

How much petrol?

Use the distance chart on PCM 39 to find the distance between the cities.

1 Calculate how many gallons of petrol The Gang use in a tour bus which runs for 48 km on 1 gallon of petrol. Give your answers to two decimal places.

2 1 gallon is 4·5 litres. Convert the number of gallons for each stage of the journey into litres.

3 How much will their total fuel cost if petrol costs £0·85 per litre?

Start: ***Glasgow***	Gallons	Litres	£
to Newcastle			
to Sheffield			
to Manchester			
to Liverpool			
to Bournemouth			
to Brighton			
to London			
to Plymouth			
to Nottingham			
to Cardiff			
to Birmingham			
TOTAL			

4 The band has a budget of £200 for fuel. Do they have enough to pay for all their petrol? If so, how much money do they have left over?

Probability game rules

Rules

Play in pairs. Each put your counter on Start, then take turns to move.

- Player A – move forward four spaces each turn.
- Player B – roll the dice and move forward by the number shown.

Continue until both players have reached Finish.
If you throw a higher number than you need to reach Finish that still means you have finished.

As you play, record the number of turns you take.
If both players finish in the same round, the game is a draw.

Play 10 times.

1 Record your scores in a table. Who won most often?

2 Is this a fair game?

3 What would happen if player A moved a different number of spaces each turn (such as 1, 2, 3, 5 or 6)?

4 How can you change the rules to make it fairer?

Probability game board

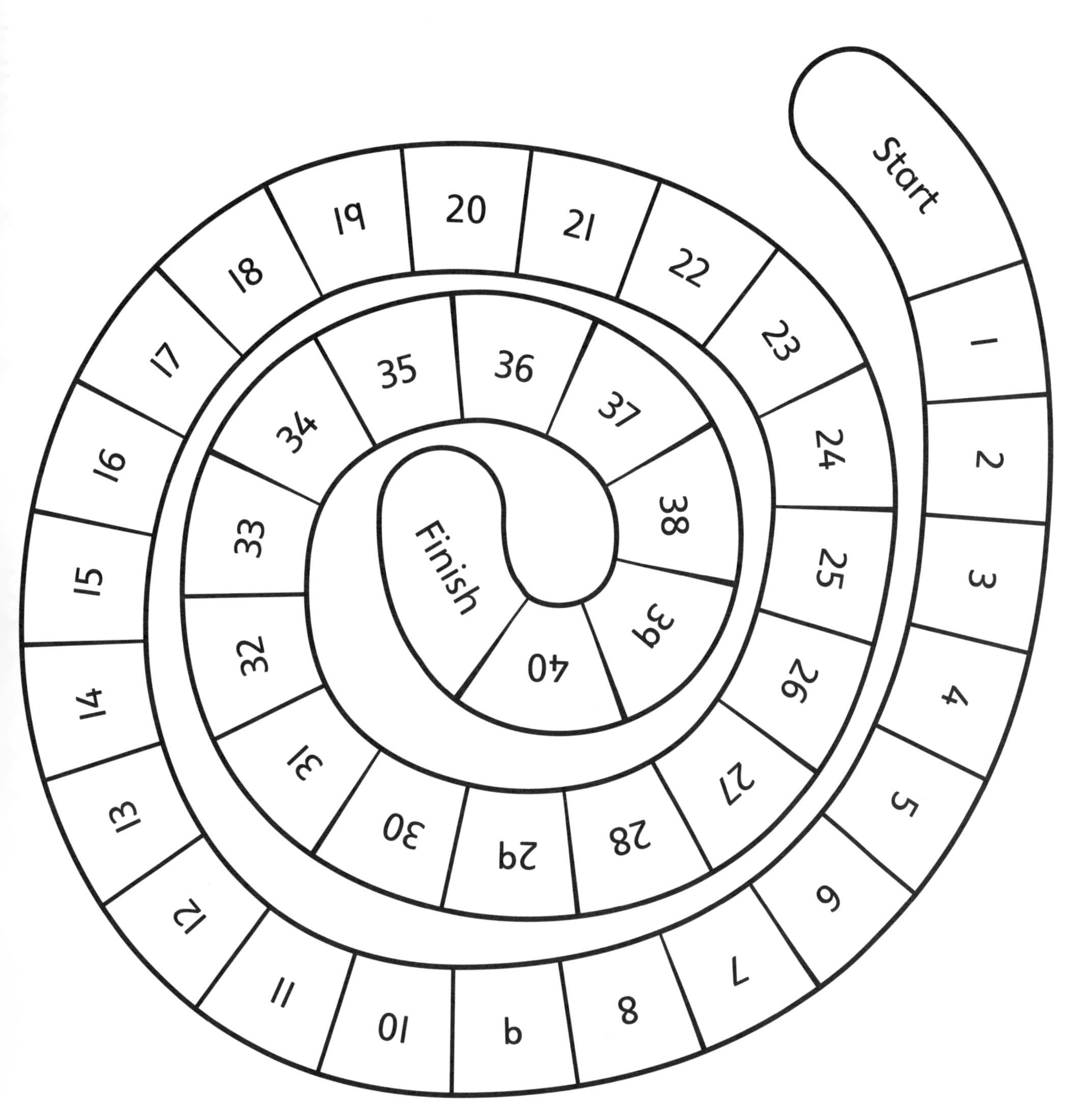

Rotating shapes 1

Rotate each of these shapes 90° clockwise around the point of origin.
What are the new coordinates of the corners of the shapes?

1

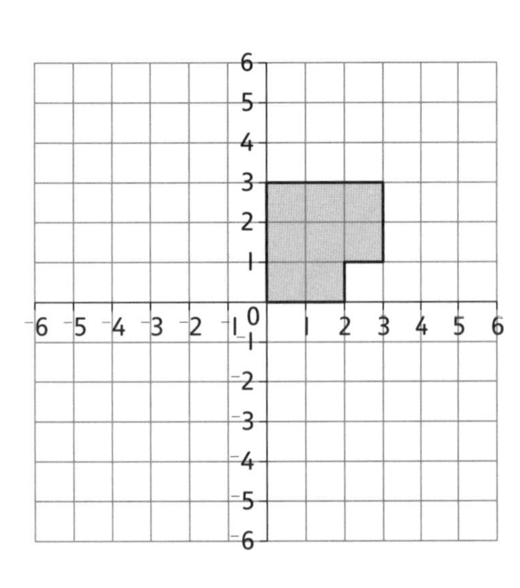

2

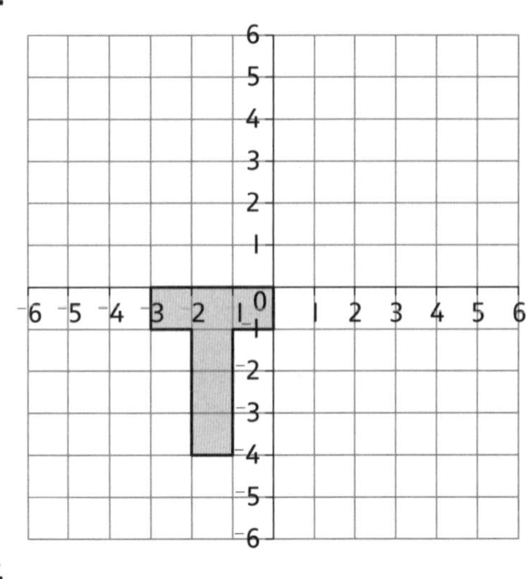

3

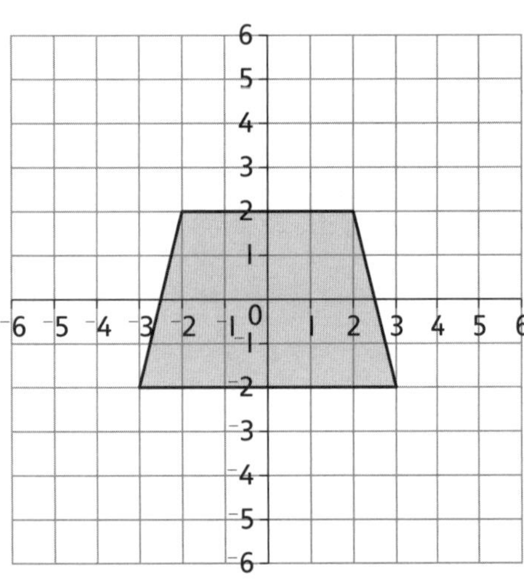

4

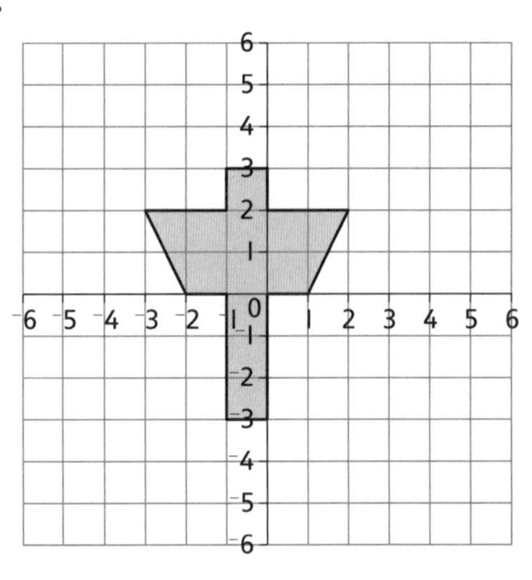

5

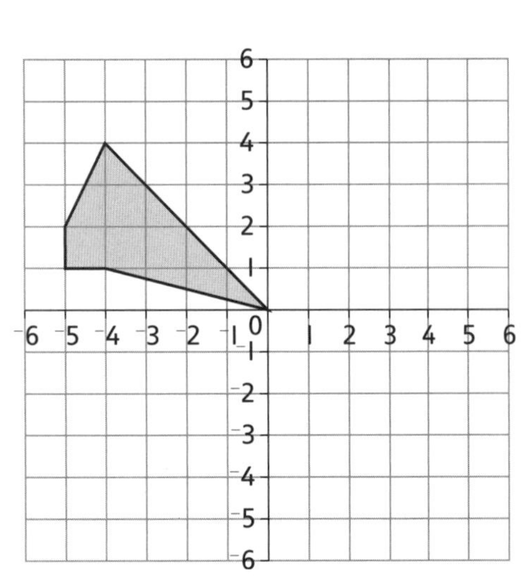

6

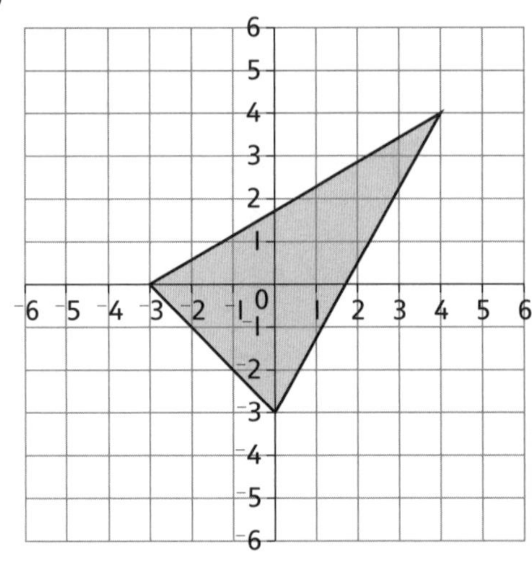

Rotating shapes 2

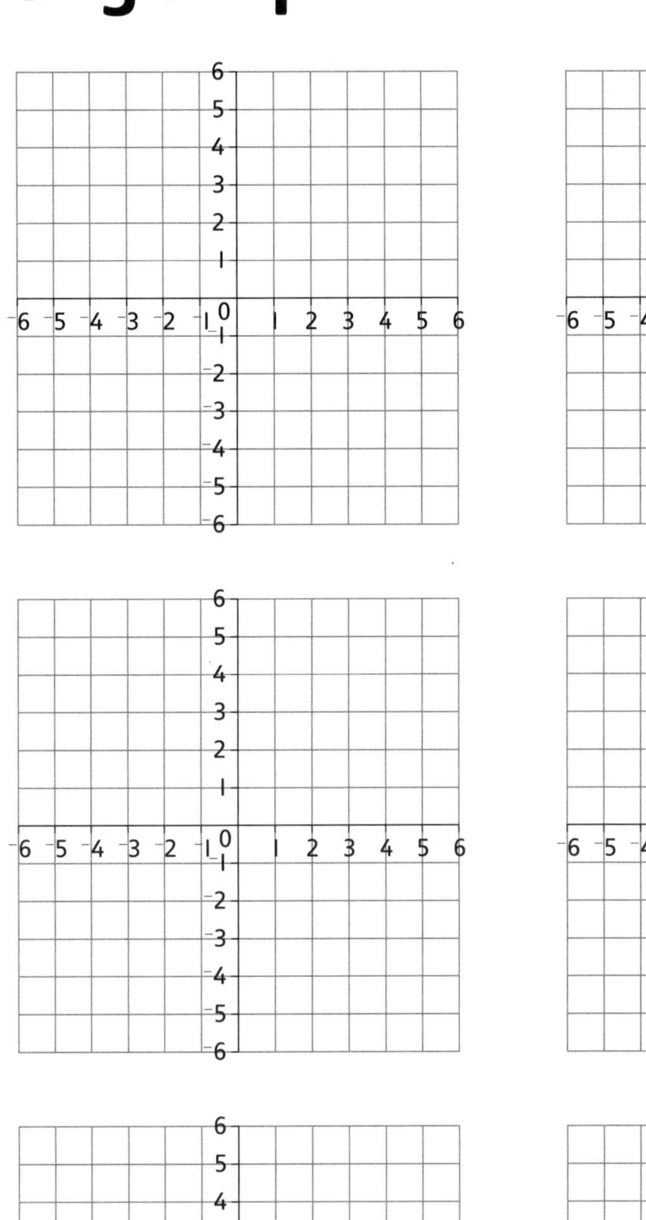

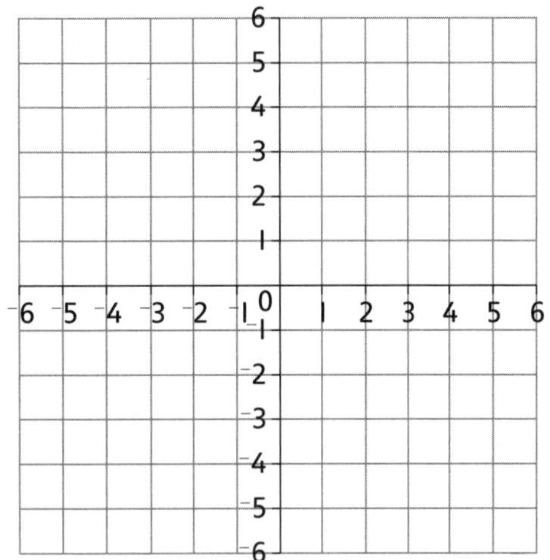

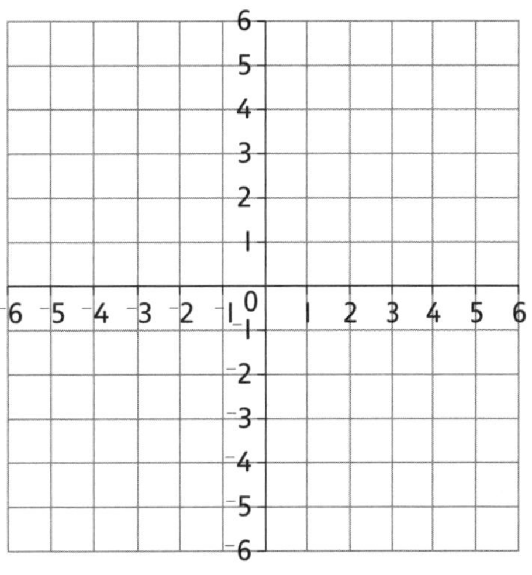

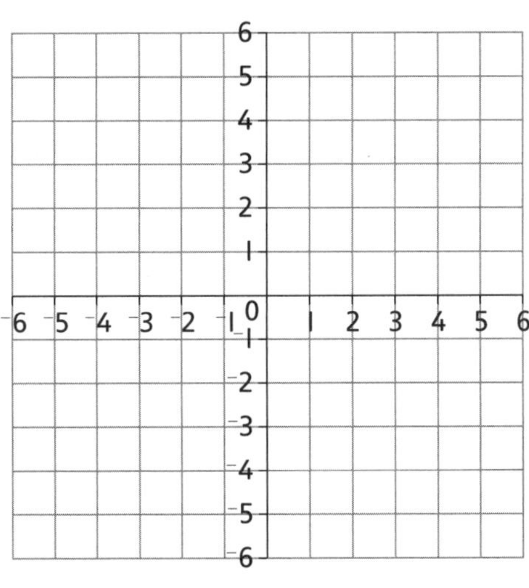

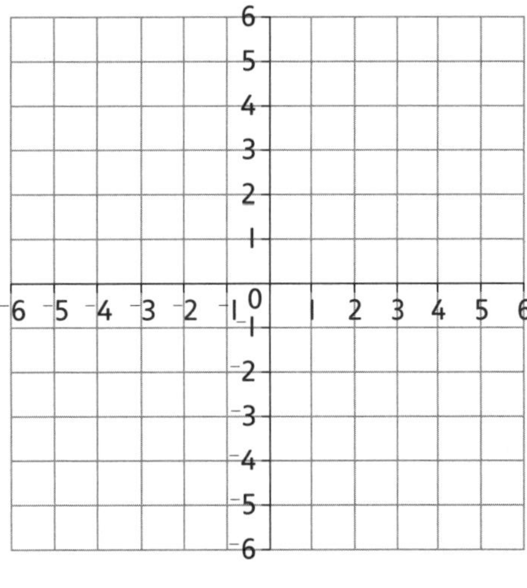

Walking speeds

Usain Bolt ran at 37·15 km/h in the 100 m Olympic final in Beijing.
Haile Gebrselassie holds the world marathon record over 41·92 km with a running speed of 20·32 km/h.
Alex Schwazer, the 50 km Olympic walking champion, walks at 13·8 km/h.

1 Time how long you take to walk 20 m, at your normal walking speed.

2 Complete the table for you and three others. Compare your speeds with the three athletes above.

Person	Time to walk 20 m	Speed in m/s	Speed in km/h
Me			
Person 1			
Person 2			
Person 3			

3 This table shows the time taken to walk 20 m in eight different cities. Calculate the walking speeds. Show the order of the speeds using the numbers 1–8 (1 = fastest, 8 = slowest).

City	Time to walk 20 m	Speed in km/h	Order
Blantyre, Malawi	35·1 s		
Singapore	11·7 s		
London, England	13·5 s		
Cairo, Egypt	15·8 s		
New York, USA	13·3 s		
Paris, France	14·1 s		
Dublin, Ireland	12·3 s		
Berne, Switzerland	19·3 s		

4 What is the difference in speed between the fastest walker and the slowest walker?

5 Add up the eight speeds and divide by 8 to find the mean speed. What does this average speed show you? How does your speed compare?

Maps

Map 1

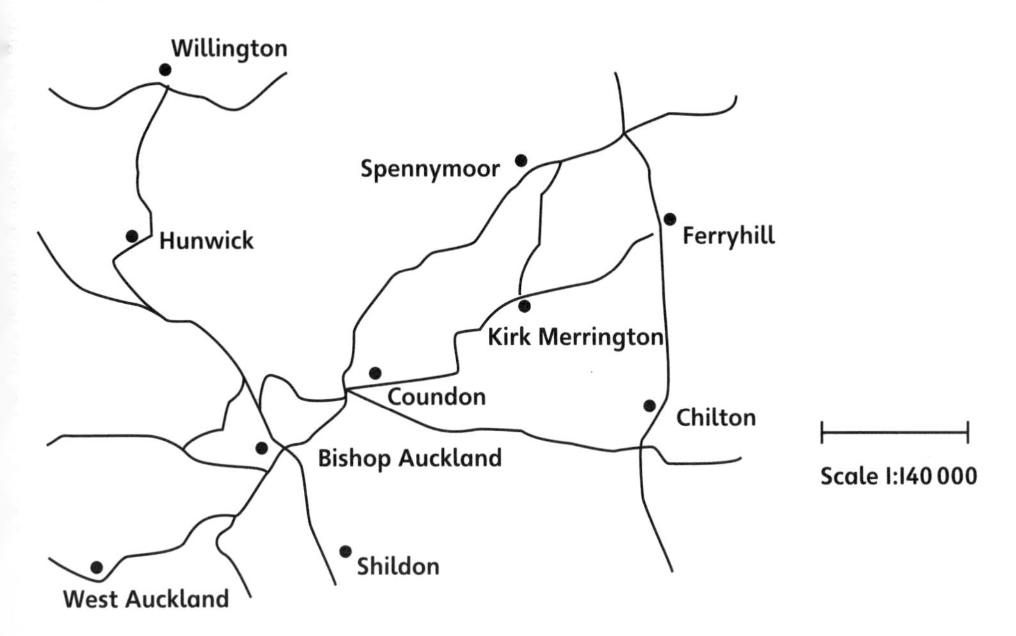

Map 2

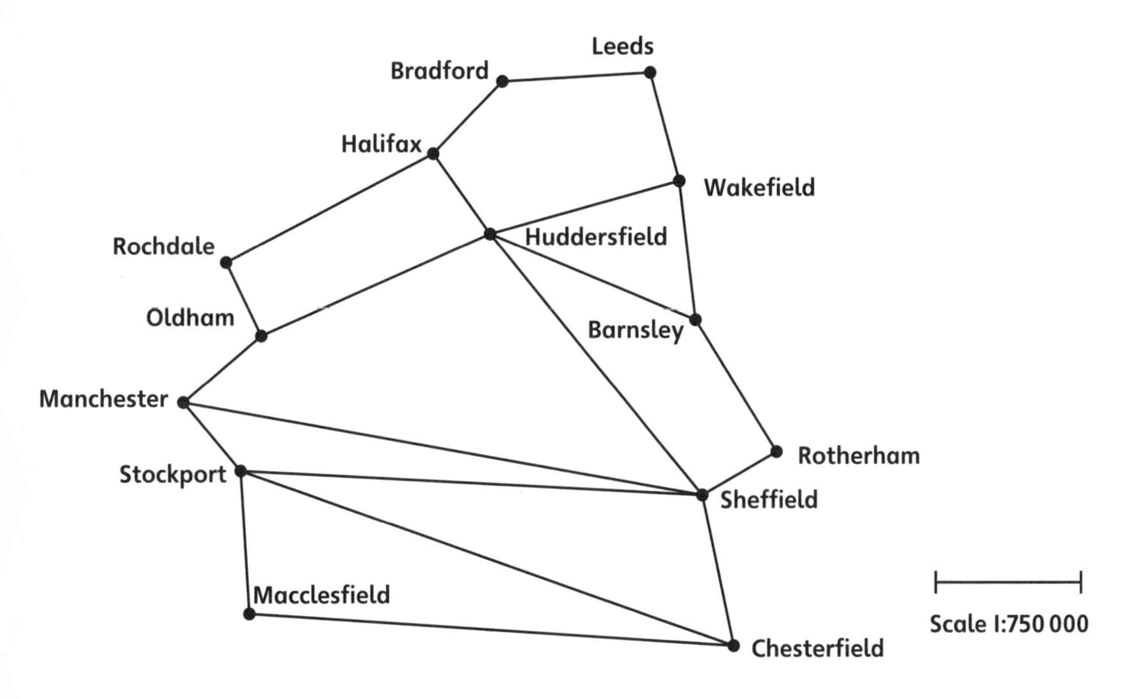

Three ratios

Bar of chocolate (20 pieces)

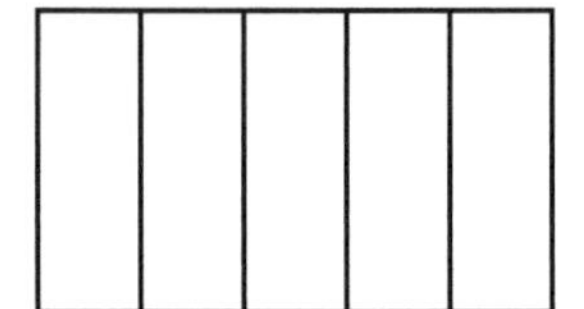
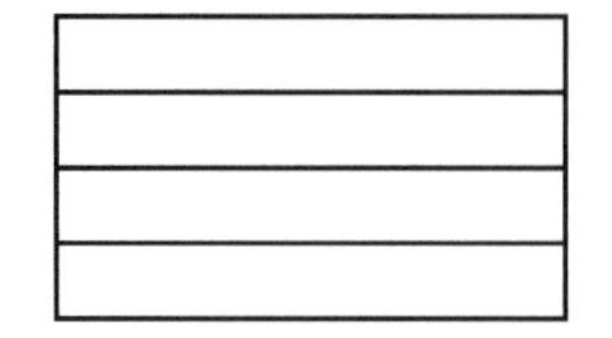
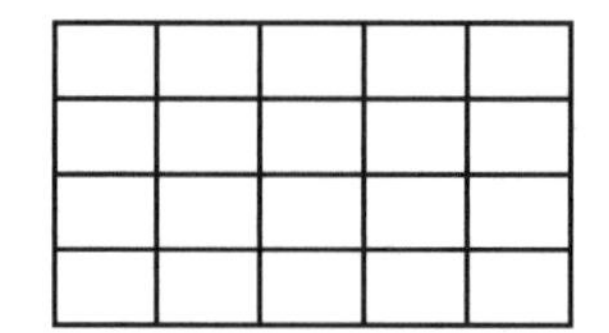

12 sandwiches

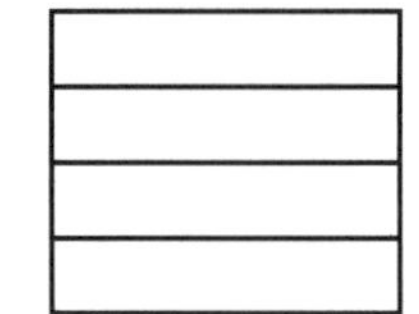
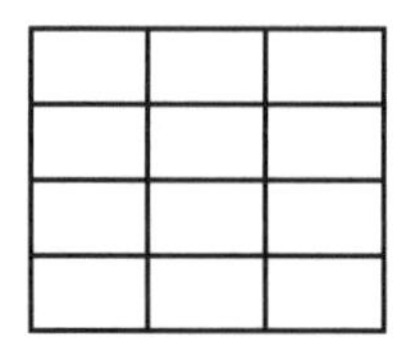

60 cheese straws

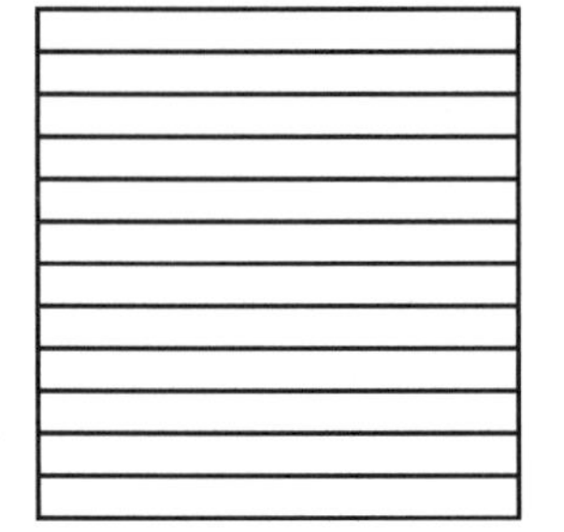
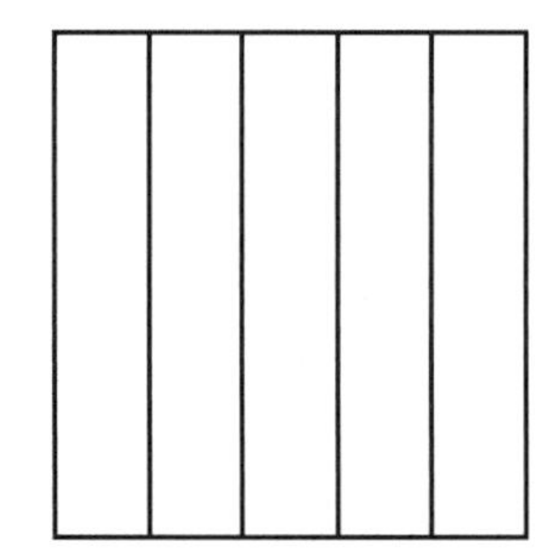
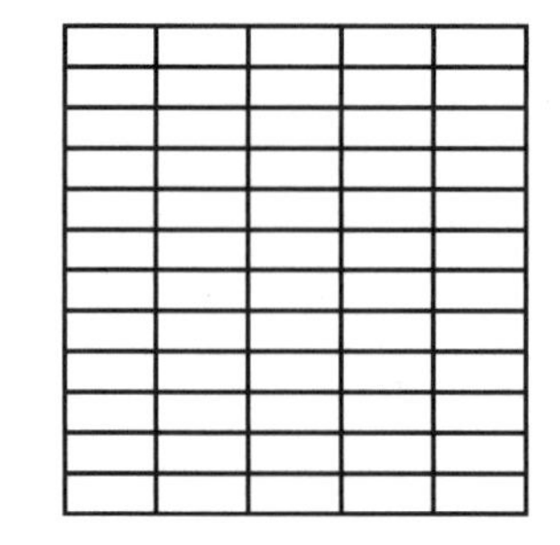

150 cl orange drink

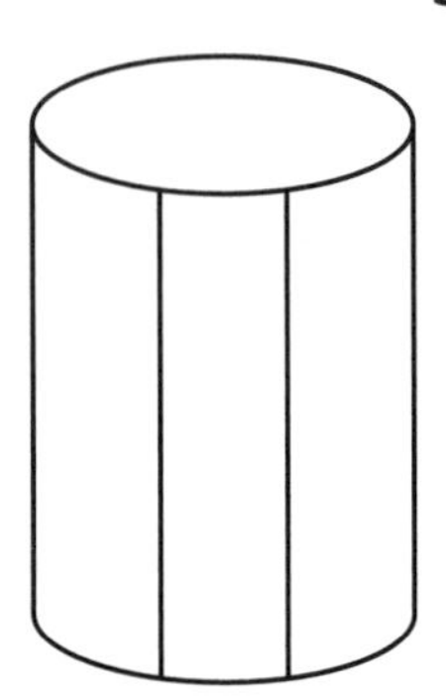
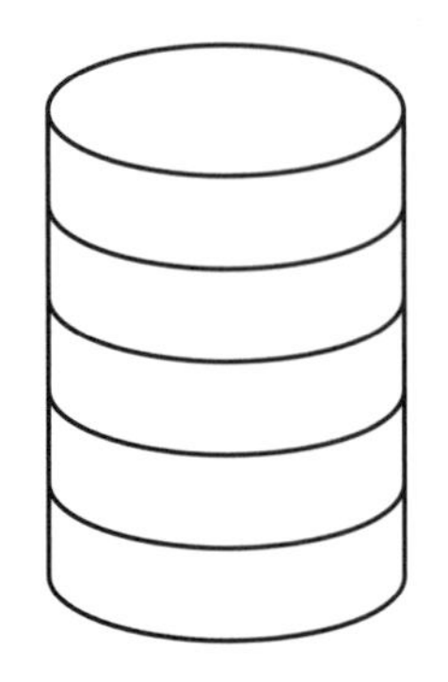
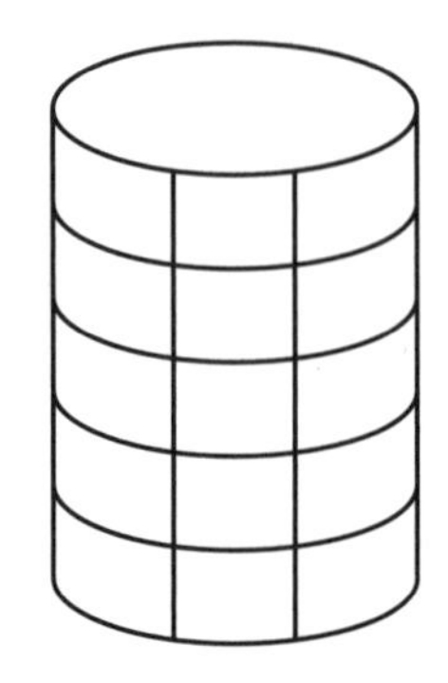

Number grids

1	2	3	4	5	6	7	8	9	10
11	12	13	14	15	16	17	18	19	20
21	22	23	24	25	26	27	28	29	30
31	32	33	34	35	36	37	38	39	40
41	42	43	44	45	46	47	48	49	50
51	52	53	54	55	56	57	58	59	60
61	62	63	64	65	66	67	68	69	70
71	72	73	74	75	76	77	78	79	80
81	82	83	84	85	86	87	88	89	90
91	92	93	94	95	96	97	98	99	100

1	2	3	4	5	6	7	8
9	10	11	12	13	14	15	16
17	18	19	20	21	22	23	24
25	26	27	28	29	30	31	32
33	34	35	36	37	38	39	40
41	42	43	44	45	46	47	48
49	50	51	52	53	54	55	56
57	58	59	60	61	62	63	64
65	66	67	68	69	70	71	72
73	74	75	76	77	78	79	80

Templates

Cross template

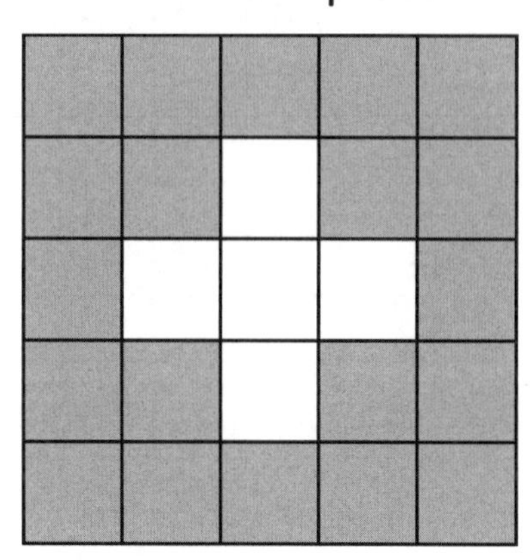

T templates

Short T

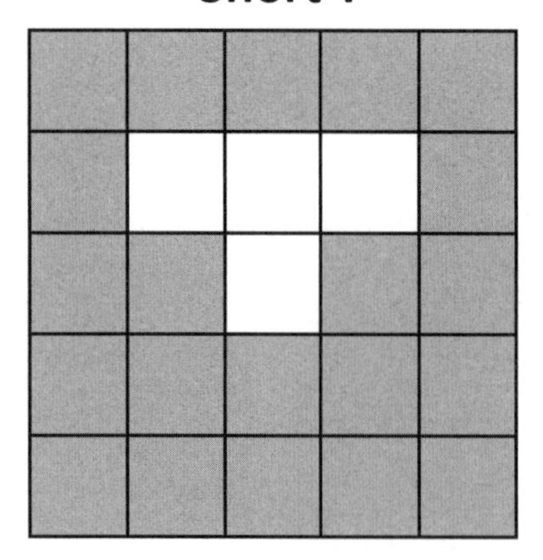

Long T

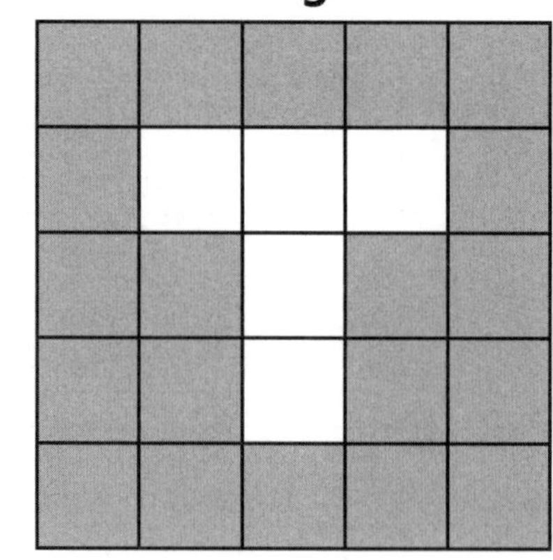

Recording tables (crosses)

Moving a cross

Cross number	Top number	Left number	Right number	Bottom number
12	2	11	13	22
13	3			
14				
15				
16				
34				

Cross totals

Cross number	Left + right	Top + bottom	Total of outer four numbers	Total of all five numbers
12				
13				
14				
15				
16				
28				

Recording tables (Ts)

Short T

T number	Number above T number	Left top number	Right top number	Total of all five numbers
12				
13				
14				
15				
25				
100				

Long T

T number	Number above T number	Middle top number	Left top number	Right top number	Total of all five numbers
12					
13					
14					
15					
25					
100					

Self-assessment sheet

	What I did to show this
I planned and completed my work in an organised way.	
I described patterns that I found.	
I made and tested predictions.	
I explained some of my findings, giving reasons.	
I wrote my conclusions looking back at my working.	
Other things I learned in this work.	

Domino products: 2 by 2 squares

1	2	3	4	5	6	7	8	9

Choose four digit cards at random. Place them in a 2 by 2 square.

8	3
2	4

The square contains four dominoes: two across and two down.

Find the product of each domino.

$8 \times 3 = 24$
$2 \times 4 = 8$
$8 \times 2 = 16$
$3 \times 4 = 12$

Add the products of the two 'across' dominoes. Across: $24 + 8 = 32$

Add the products of the two 'down' dominoes. Down: $16 + 12 = 28$

Find the overall total. Total: $32 + 28 = 60$

Smallest difference

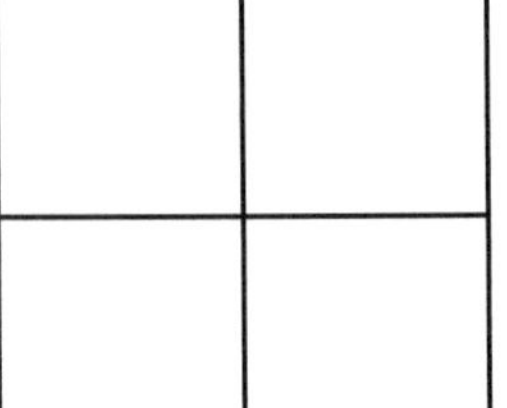

Across: ________

Down: ________

Total: ________

Largest difference

Across: ________

Down: ________

Total: ________

Maximum overall total

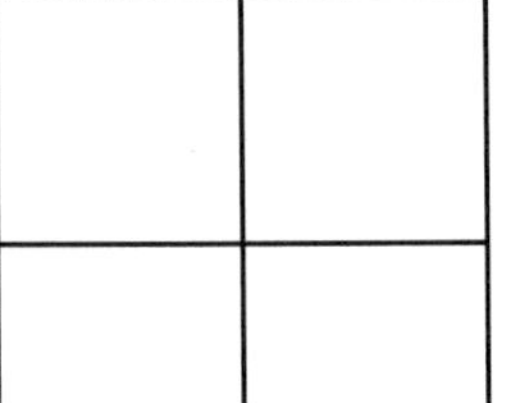

Across: ________

Down: ________

Total: ________

Minimum overall total

Across: ________

Down: ________

Total: ________

Domino products: 3 by 3 squares

Example

			Across products:	Down products:	Totals:
8	6	3	48 and 18	8 and 9	Across = 142
1	2	5	2 and 10	12 and 8	Down = 87
9	4	7	36 and 28	15 and 35	Overall = 229

Smallest difference

			Across products:	Down products:	Totals:
			______	______	Across = ______
			______	______	Down = ______
			______	______	Overall = ______

Largest difference

			Across products:	Down products:	Totals:
			______	______	Across = ______
			______	______	Down = ______
			______	______	Overall = ______

Maximum overall total

			Across products:	Down products:	Totals:
			______	______	Across = ______
			______	______	Down = ______
			______	______	Overall = ______

Minimum overall total

			Across products:	Down products:	Totals:
			______	______	Across = ______
			______	______	Down = ______
			______	______	Overall = ______

Polygons in squares: 8-point squares

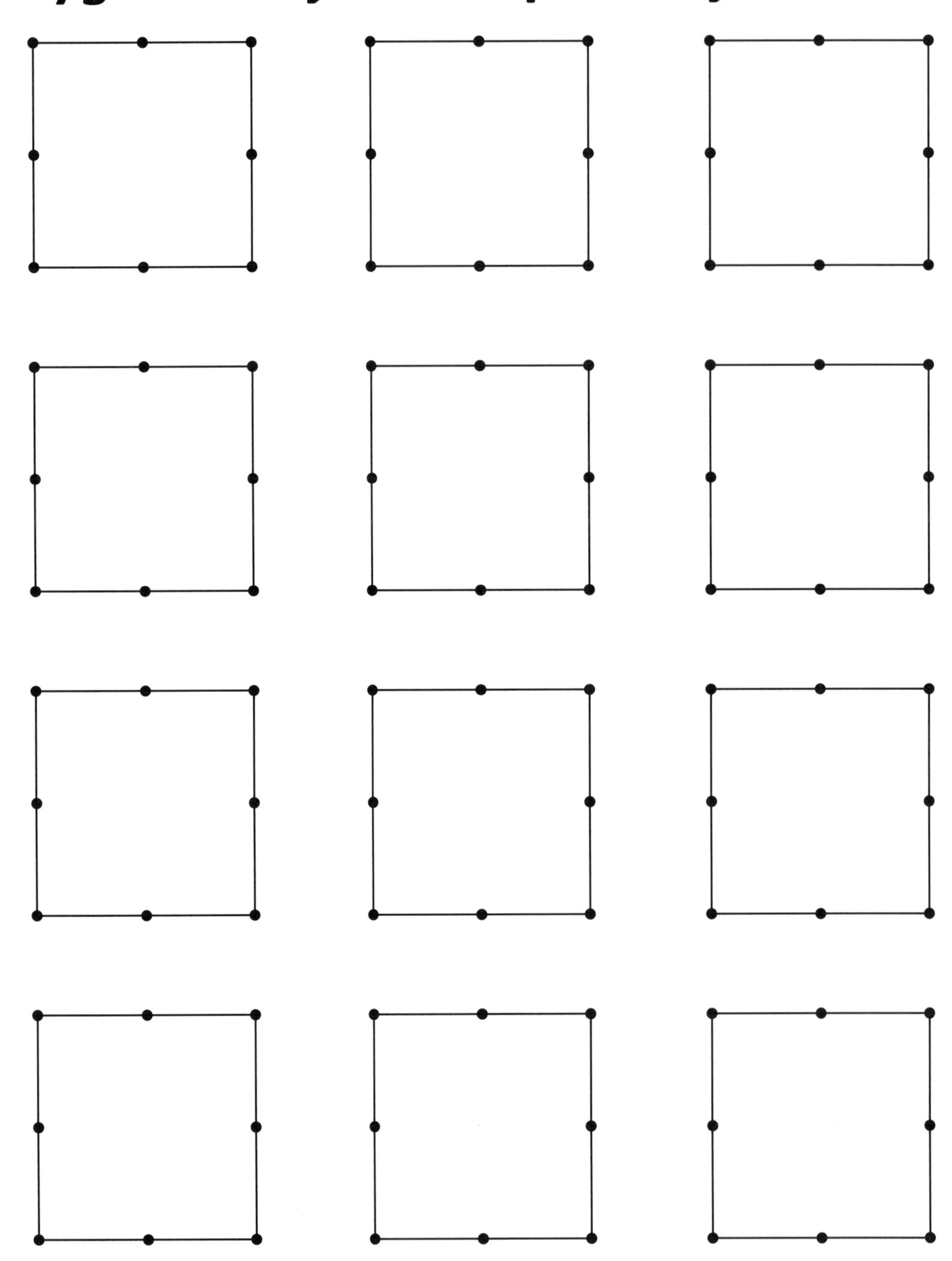

Polygons in squares: 12-point squares

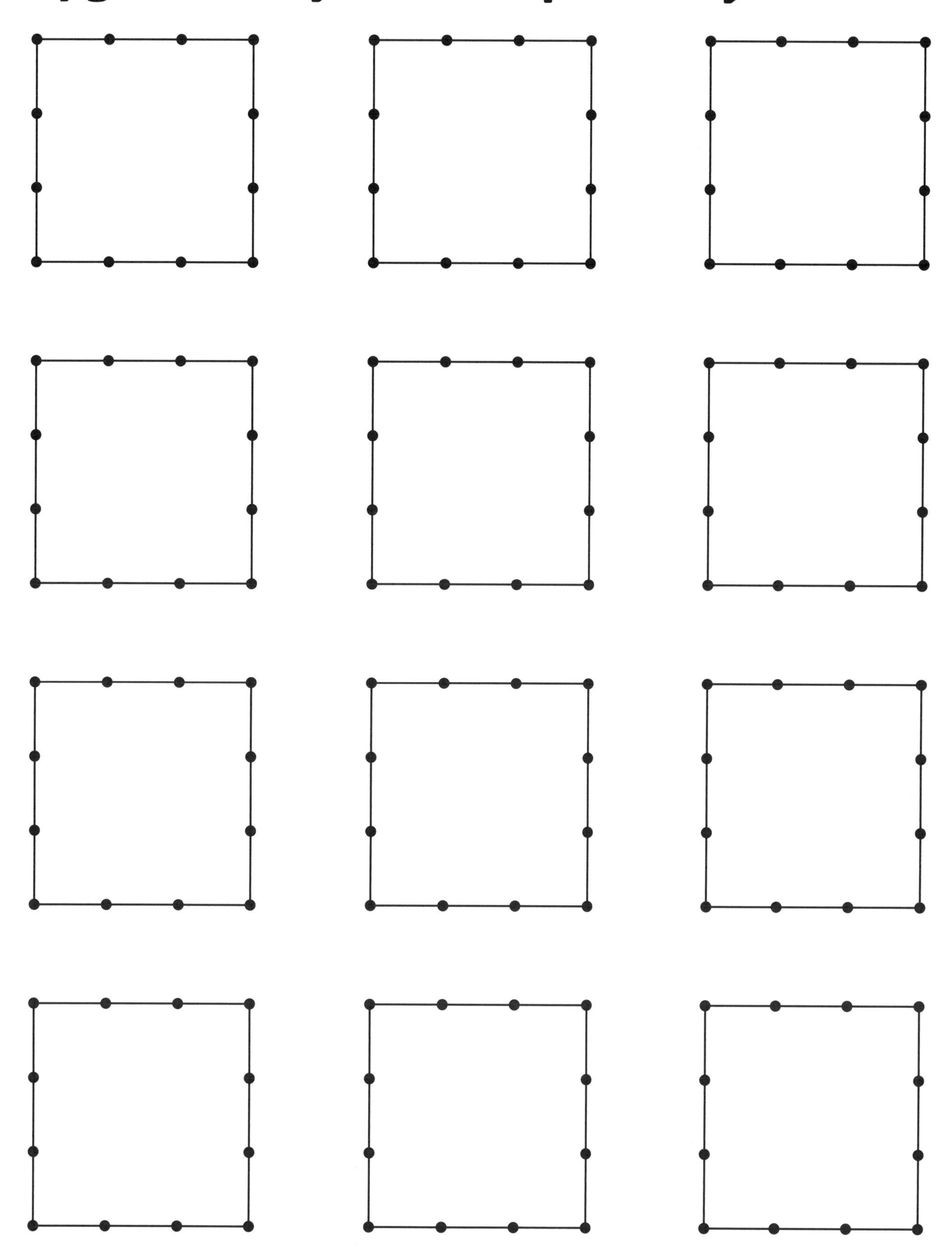

Polygons in squares: 16-point squares

Answers

AI

AI.I

PCM I

Value	Question 1 value of 1000 coins	Question 2 weight of 1000 coins	Question 3 height and value of 100 coins	Question 4 length of 10 coins, 10 000 coins, 1 million coins
£2	£2000	12 000 g = 12 kg	250 mm £200	284 mm 284 m 28·4 km
£1	£1000	9·5 kg	315 mm £100	225 mm 225 m 22·5 km
50p	£500	8 kg	178 mm £50	273 mm 273 m 27·3 km
20p	£200	5 kg	170 mm £20	214 mm 214 m 21·4 km
10p	£100	6·5 kg	185 mm £10	245 mm 245 m 24·5 km
5p	£50	3·3 kg	170 mm £5	180 mm 180 m 18·0 km
2p *	£20	7·1 kg	185 or 203 mm £2	259 mm 259 m 25·9 km
1p *	£10	3·6 kg	152 or 165 mm £1	203 mm 203 m 20·3 km

5. The boy is 1·45 m (1450 mm) tall and worth £1160. The girl weighs 49·2 kg (49 200 g) and is worth £8200.

Extra

For example for £2 coins
£166 per kg, £70 per linear metre (laid out) or £800 per metre (stacked)
Stacked coins is the best option.

Total value of all coins in circulation £3 349·83 million

AI.2

PCM 2

1. 200 g butter and 100 g sugar
2. 2000 g = 2 kg butter, 1000 g = 1 kg sugar, 3000 g = 3 kg flour
3. 150 g sugar and 450 g flour. She will make 30 biscuits.
4. 300 ml cream and 50 g onion
5. 4000 g = 4 kg vegetables, 500 g onion, 2500 ml = 2·5 litres stock and 3000 ml = 3 litres cream
6. 250 g onion, 1·25 litres stock and 1·5 litres cream. Serves 10 people.
7. 5%
8. 80 g butter, 100 g cheese and 20 g puree
9. 100 g flour, 40 g butter, 50 g cheese and 10 g puree
10. 1·2 kg butter, 1·5 kg cheese and 300 g puree. Makes 15 pizzas to serve 60 people.

Extra

For 10 people
500 g flour, 200 g butter, 250 g cheese and 50 g puree.

AI.3

PCM I

1. 10p coins worth £10
2. 20p coins worth £20
3. 2p coins worth £20
4. 5p coins worth £50
5. £1 coins worth £100
6. 1p coins worth £100

Extra

Total raised £300. Average £1·50 per child

AI.4

PCM 3

1. $6752 + 2356 = 9180$ wrong
   6752 + 2356 = 9180
   $2 + 7 \neq 0$ could be wrong
2. $9634 + 3826 = 13\,460$ correct
   9634 + 3826 = 13 460
   $4 + 1 = 5$ could be correct
3. $9234 - 3647 = 5767$ wrong
   9234 – 3647 = 5767
   $0 - 2 \neq 7$ could be wrong
4. $83\,746 - 2947 = 80\,799$ correct
   83 746 – 2947 = 80 799
   $1 - 4 \neq 6$
5. $683 \times 428 = 292\,324$ correct
   683 × 428 = 292 324
   $8 \times 5 = 4$ could be correct
6. $500 \times 4500 = 2\,250\,000$ correct
   500 × 4500 = 2 250 000
   $5 \times 0 = 0$ could be correct
7. $672 \div 24 = 28$ correct
   672 ÷ 24 = 28
   $6 \div 6 = 1$ could be correct
8. $525 \div 21 = 25$ correct
   525 ÷ 21 = 25
   $3 \div 3 \neq 7$ could be correct

Extra

This method is misleading when there are no 9s to strike out (as in question 8).

AI.5

PCM 4, 5

Job	New pay	Job	New pay
Window cleaning	£4·95	Bed making	£3·47
Car washing	£8·93	Cleaning	£5·25
Cat grooming	£5·72	Gardening	£6·45
Vacuuming	£3·06	Feeding the chickens	£6·55
Babysitting	£5·94	Dog walking	£8·24

AI.6

1. 245 full boxes; 0·5, $\frac{1}{2}$
2. $10\frac{1}{2}$ days
3. 8 cars
4. 8 tables per class; 56 tables all together
5. 12 minibuses with 6 spare seats
6. 43 packs of 5 with 3 left over; 53 packs of 4 with 0 left over; 27 packs of 8 with 4 left over.
7. 280 apples
8. £18·13; £160 – £145 = £15 change.
8. £503·50
10. 91 cars 44 more wheels needed.

Extra

£5·10 per hour
£51·00 for 10 hours
£127·50 for 25 hours

Minimum wage was £3·53 in 2009.
In 5 hours he earns £7·85 more than the minimum wage.
In 10 hours he earns £15·70 more than the minimum wage.
In 25 hours he earns £39·25 more than the minimum wage.

BI

BI.1

1. 1 and 2
2. 1 and 3
3. 2 and 4
4. 2, 3 and 4
5. 1, 2, 3 and 4
6. No (unless you use $0 + 1 = 1$ and $0 + 2 = 2$)
7. Yes
8. $3 + 6 = 9$ $6 + 9 = 15$ $9 + 12 = 21$
   $12 + 15 = 27$ always another number in the 3 × table, increasing by 6 each time
   $5 + 10 = 15$ $10 + 15 = 25$ $15 + 20 = 35$
   always another number in the 5 × table, increasing by 10 each time

Extra

The sum of three consecutive counting numbers always a multiple of 3.
The sum of three consecutive even numbers always a multiple of 3.
The sum of three consecutive odd numbers always a multiple of 3.

The sum of four consecutive counting numbers never a multiple of 4.
The sum of four consecutive even numbers always a multiple of 4.
The sum of four consecutive odd numbers always a multiple of 4.

The sum of five consecutive counting numbers always a multiple of 5.
The sum of five consecutive even numbers always a multiple of 5.
The sum of five consecutive odd numbers always a multiple of 5.

The sum of six consecutive counting numbers never a multiple of 6.
The sum of six consecutive even numbers always a multiple of 6.
The sum of six consecutive odd numbers always a multiple of 6.

The sum of seven consecutive counting numbers always a multiple of 7.
The sum of seven consecutive even numbers always a multiple of 7
The sum of seven consecutive odd numbers always a multiple of 7.

BI.2

1. 3
2. 1
3. 9
4. 4
5. 18
6. 9

7.

Shape	1	2	3	4	5	6	7	8	9	10
Triangular number	1	3	6	10	15	21	28	36	45	55
Number of triangles	1	4	9	16	25	36	49	64	81	100
Number of straws	3	9	18	30	45	63	84	108	135	165

8. Answers will vary. Children may recognise:
   - the number of triangles is the sequence of square numbers
   - the number of straws as 3 × triangular number or a sequence increasing by ascending multiples of 3.
9. Shape 20 has triangular number 210, number of triangles 400, number of straws 630.
   Shape 100 has triangular number 5050, number of triangles 10 000, number of straws 15 150.
10. Shape n has triangular number $\frac{1}{2}n(n + 1)$, number of triangles n^2, number of straws $\frac{3}{2}n(n + 1)$.

Extra

Shape	1	2	3	4	5	6	7	8	9	10
Triangular number	1	3	6	10	15	21	28	36	45	55
Number of diamonds	1	4	9	16	25	36	49	64	81	100
Number of straws	4	12	24	40	60	84	112	144	180	220

20th pattern triangular number 210, 400 diamonds and 840 straws

100th pattern triangular number 5050, 1000 diamonds and 20 200 straws

nth pattern has triangle number $\frac{1}{2}n(n + 1)$, number of diamonds n^2, number of straws $2n(n + 1)$

B1.3

PCM 6

1. 6
2. 17
3. 17
4. 36 = 17 + 19
5. 15 = 3 × 5
6. 39 = 3 × 13
7. 6 and 9
8. 3
9. 5
10. 3
11. 12
12. 30
13. 60
14. 42 = 6 × 7
    Total 300

Extra

Imaginary or complex numbers contain the number i, where $i^2 = -1$

For example $3 + 5i$, $7 - 8i$

B1.4

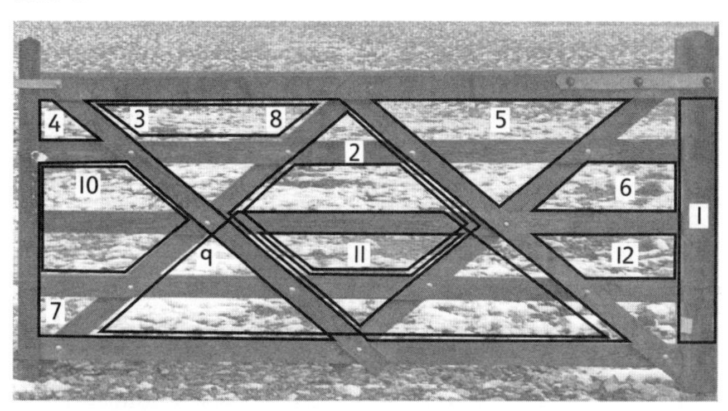

1. A rectangle
2. A rhombus
3. A parallelogram
4. A right angled triangle
5. An isosceles triangle
6. A small trapezium
7. A large trapezium
8. A small isosceles trapezium
9. A large isosceles trapezium
10. An irregular pentagon
11. An irregular hexagon
12. An irregular quadrilateral

B1.5

1. 90°, 34°, 56°
2. 60°, 60°, 60°,
3. 104°, 38°, 38°
4. 38°, 82°, 60°
5. (b) is impossible to construct.

BI.6

PCMs 8, 9 and 10

Pupils may link cards as shown

square, parallel perpendicular 4 sides all angles 90° right-angle	rectangle, parallel, perpendicular 4 sides all angles 90° right-angle	equilateral 3 sides all angles 60°	3 sides one angle 90° right-angle
square, parallel perpendicular 4 sides all angles 90° right-angle	rhombus parallel 4 sides	parallel, 4 sides	5 sides
6 sides parallel	1 side	cube 6 faces 8 vertices 12 edges parallel perpendicular Platonic	cuboid 6 faces 8 vertices 12 edges parallel perpendicular
cylinder 3 faces 2 parallel faces 2 edges	tetrahedron 4 faces 4 vertices 6 edges Platonic	dodecahedron 12 faces 20 vertices 30 edges Platonic each face has 5 sides	icosahedron 20 faces 12 vertices 30 edges Platonic equilateral

CI.1

1. ☻ = 5 children

1–10	
11–20	
21–30	
31–40	
41–50	
51–60	
61–70	
71–80	
81–90	
91–100	

2. Answers will vary, but should include comment that most children's results fall in the middle of the range of marks.
3. 51–60
4. 73·5% 13·5%
5. 44·5%, 92%
6. 79·5%, 71%
7.

1–20	21–40	41–60	61–80	81–100
14	39	79	52	16

8. 41–60
9. Answers will vary.

Extra

Answers will vary.

CI.2

PCMs 11 and 12

Monday

Lowest score 1
Highest score 20
Range 19

Scores grouped in 2s

score	frequency
1–2	2
3–4	1
5–6	6
7–8	14
9–10	14
11–12	17
13–14	10
15–16	8
17–18	6
19–20	2

Modal group from table: 11–12

Friday
Lowest score 1
Highest score 20
Range 19

Scores grouped in 2s

score	frequency
1–2	1
3–4	2
5–6	3
7–8	4
9–10	8
11–12	14
13–14	10
15–16	17
17–18	14
19–20	7

Modal group from table: 15–16

CI.3

Answers will vary.

CI.4

1. 1000
2. 100 000
3. 1 000 000
4.

Millimetres	Centimetres	Metres	Kilometres
1923	192·3	1·923	0·001 923
17 200	1720	17·2	0·0172
623 000	62 300	623	0·623
23 000 000	2 300 000	23 000	23
5620	562	5·62	0·005 62
4504	450·4	4·504	0·004 504
4 217 000	421 700	4217	4·217
7 200 000	720 000	7200	7·2
95 000	9500	95	0·095
78 000	7800	78	0·078

5. 2003 mm, 2·3 m, 235 cm
6. 0·6 km, 607 m, 67 000 cm
7. 0·09 km, 9009 cm, 99 000 mm
8. 29 000 mm, 7000 cm 207 m, 0·27 km

Extra

Answers will vary.

CI.5

1. 1 kg of bananas for 50p
   (1 lb for 25p equivalent to 1 kg for 55p)
2. 1 lb of oranges for 35p
   (1 lb for 55p equivalent to 1 kg for 77p)
3. 1 kg of tomatoes for £1·20
   (1 lb for 65p equivalent to 1 kg for £1·43)
4. 2 lb of grapes for £2·30
   (2 lb for £2·30 equivalent to 1 kg for £2·53)
5. 3 kg of potatoes for £3·60
   (5 lb for £2·80 equivalent to 3 kg for £3·70)
6. 2 kg of apples for £4·20
   (6 lb for £7 equivalent to 2 kg for £5·13)
7. 1·5 kg of cherries for £6·40
   (4 lb for £8 equivalent to 1·5 kg for £6·60)
8. 2 lb of carrots for 90p
   (2 lb for 90p equivalent to 3·5 kg for £3·47)

Extra

Answers will vary.

CI.6

1. 192 inches
2. 324 inches
3. 12 320 yards
4. 15 840 feet
5. 176 ounces
6. 448 pounds
7. 63 360 inches
8. 672 ounces
9. 7 feet 8 inches
10. 14 feet 5 inches
11. 9 lb 11 oz
12. 8 lb 5 oz
13. 12 stone 1 lb
14. 5 feet 5inches
15. 1 foot 6 inches
16. 7 lb 4 oz
17. 2 lb 12 oz
18. 3 stone 10 lb

Extra

Answers will vary.

DI.1

1. B 55° C 70° D 105° E 140°
   F 185° G 210° H 250° I 330°
2. B 305° C 290° D 255° E 220°
   F 175° G 150° H 110° I 30°
3. 50° (or 310° if children give the reflex angle instead)
4. 85°
5. 115°
6. 70°
7. 165°
8. 180°
9. 155°
10. 225°
11. 230°
12. 40°
13. 170°

Extra

Children's constructions.

DI.2

PCM 13

Kite 65°, 129°, 37°, 129°
Kite 113°, 97°, 53°, 97°
Parallelogram 56°, 124°, 56°, 124°
Parallelogram 76°, 104°, 76°, 104°
Trapezium 65°, 65°, 115°, 115°
Trapezium 117°, 63°, 63°, 117°

1. Kite: one pair of opposite angles will be equal
   Parallelogram: two pairs of opposite angles will be equal; consecutive angles add up to 180°
   Isosceles trapezium: opposite angles add up to 180°
2. Answers will vary.
3. a = 112°, b = 68°, c = 112°
   d = 112°, e = 99°
   f = g = 99°
   h = 139°, j = 139°, k = 41°

Children should know that angles inside a quadrilateral total 360°, and then use symmetry to calculate the missing angles.

Extra

Diagonals of a kite, rhombus and square all cross at 90°

DI.3

1. a = d = 50°, b = c = 130°
2. e = 68°, f = g = h = 112°
3. j = 59°, k = l = m = 121°
4. n = r = 119°, p = 58°, q = 61°
5. s = 55°, t = v = 125°, u = 105°
6. w = 141°, x = y = z = 129°

Extra

Three parallel lines with one line crossing: need 1 angle.
Three parallel lines with two lines crossing: need 2 angles (1 on each line).
Three parallel lines with three lines crossing: need 3 angles (1 on each line).

DI.4

PCMs 14 and 15

Game, no answers required.

DI.5

1. Answers will vary.
2. Answers are always a multiple of 9 equal to 9 times the difference between the digits.
3. Answers will vary.
4. Answers are always a multiple of 99 equal to 99 times the difference between the first and last digits.
5. Answers are always a multiple of 9 equal to (999 × the difference between the first and last digits) + (90 × the difference between the second and third digits)

Extra

Children will still find that all answers are multiples of 9.

DI.6

1. 1·402 millions   1 402 000
2. 1·557 millions   1 557 000
3. 0·055 millions   55 000
4. 0·929 millions   929 000
5. 0·931 millions   931 000
6. False. 16·756 millions all the rest 19·348 millions
7. False. 2·48 millions × 2 = 4·96 millions
8. True. 2·43 millions × 2 = 4·86 millions
9. False. 4·635 − 4·18 = 0·455 millions
10. False. 2·819 − 2·48 = 0·339 millions

Extra

Answers will vary.

EI.1

	start number	end digit number
1	1 2 3 4 5 6 7 8 9	1, 2, 4, 8, 6, 2, 4, 8, … 2, 4, 8, 6, 2, 4, … 3, 6, 2, 4, 8, 6, 2, … 4, 8, 6, 2, 4, 8, … 5, 0, 0, … 6, 2, 4, 8, 6, 2, 4, … 7, 4, 8, 6, 2, 4, 8, … 6, 2, 4, 8, 6, 2, 4, … 9, 8, 6, 2, 4, 8, 6, …
2	negative numbers	patterns the same but with negative numbers
3	2-digit numbers	same patterns as the corresponding single-digit number
4	Answers will vary.	

Extra

Answers will vary.
All sequences end with a loop 8 → 4 → 2 → 1 → 4 → 2 → 1, …
For example
23 → 26 → 13 → 16 → 8 → 4 → 2 → 1 → 4 → 2 → 1, …
97 → 100 → 50 → 25 → 28 → 14 → 7 → 10 → 5 → 8 → 4, …

EI.2

1. 2
2. 5
3. 7
4. 10
5. 129
6. 10111
7. 110110
8. 1011
9. 10100000
10. 11001000

Extra

64 digits in a byte (binary 1000000)
256 digits in a double word (100000000)

EI.3

1. 598
2. 592
3. 3250
4. 1078
5. 2322
6. 1156
7. 1485
8. 4968
9. 1860

Extra

2·4 × 1·2 = 2·88
46 × 3·2 = 147·2
66 × 7·8 = 514·8

EI.4

PCM 16

	fraction each	cost each
6 pizzas between 5 people	$1\frac{1}{5}$	£3
8 sausages between 6 people	$1\frac{1}{3}$	£0·33
12 cakes between 9 children	$1\frac{1}{3}$	£0·25
200 g of chocolate between 12 people	$16\frac{2}{3}$	£0·15
12 m of ribbon cut into 5 strips	$2\frac{2}{5}$	£0·60
10 apples between 7 children	$1\frac{3}{7}$	£0·70
20 sandwiches between 11 people	$1\frac{9}{11}$	£1·45
16 sweets between 5 people	$3\frac{1}{5}$	£0·13
9 cans between 8 people	$1\frac{1}{8}$	£0·46
£150 shared between 8 people	$18\frac{3}{4}$	£18·75

Extra

After 3 hours the tide dropped 1·2 m which is $\frac{1}{2}$ of the total tidal range. Low water is therefore 3·6 − 2·4 = 1·2 m

14:40: 2 h after high tide 3·0 m
17:40: 5 h after high tide 1·4 m

EI.5

PCM 17

1. $\frac{1}{2} > \frac{4}{9}$
2. $\frac{2}{5} > \frac{3}{8}$
3. $\frac{5}{8} > \frac{4}{7}$
4. $\frac{3}{10} > \frac{2}{9}$
5. $\frac{3}{10} > \frac{2}{7}$
6. $\frac{5}{6} > \frac{7}{10}$
7. $\frac{4}{9} > \frac{2}{5} > \frac{3}{8}$
8. $\frac{7}{10} > \frac{2}{3} > \frac{3}{5}$
9. $\frac{3}{4} > \frac{5}{9} > \frac{6}{11}$

Extra

Answers will vary.

EI.6

PCM 18

1. 1 m
2. 11 m
3.

Port	High water (m)	Low water (m)	Tidal range (m)	Water height 2 hours after low water (m)	Water height 3 hours after high water (m)
Belfast	6·0	3·7	**2·3**	**4·275**	**4·85**
Liverpool	9·5	0·8	**8·7**	**2·975**	5·15
Portland	2·0	0·2	**1·8**	0·65	**1·1**
London Bridge	6·8	0·8	**6·0**	2·3	**3·8**
Milford Haven	7·1	0·7	**6·4**	2·3	**3·9**
Barrow	9·4	**1·4**	8·0	3·4	**5·4**
Lerwick	**2·3**	0·7	1·6	**1·1**	1·5
Tyne	**5·4**	0·3	5·1	1·575	**2·85**
Avonmouth	**13·3**	1·5	11·8	**4·45**	7·4
Shoreham	6·3	**0·6**	5·7	**2·025**	3·45

A2

A2.1

PCM 19

Planet	Diameter (km)	To nearest 1000 km	Distance from Sun (millions of km)	To nearest 10 million km	How many times bigger or smaller than Earth	To nearest tenth	Time to travel around Sun (Earth days/ years)	To nearest 100 days
Mercury	4880	5000	57·9	60	0·38	0·4	87·96 days	100
Venus	12 104	12 000	108·2	110	0·95	1·0	224·68 days	200
Earth	12 756	13 000	149·6	150	1·00	1·0	365·26 days	400
Mars	6788	7000	228·0	230	0·53	0·5	686·98 days	700
Jupiter	142 740	143 000	778·4	780	11·19	11·2	11·68 years	4300
Saturn	120 034	120 000	1424·6	1420	9·41	9·4	29·46 years	10 800
Uranus	51 152	51 000	2873·5	2870	4·01	4·0	84·07 years	30 700
Neptune	49 620	50 000	4501·0	4500	3·89	3·9	164·81 years	60 200

Extra

In order of size:
Mercury, Mars, Venus, Earth, Neptune, Uranus, Saturn, Jupiter
In order of weight:
Mercury, Mars, Venus, Earth, Uranus, Neptune, Saturn, Jupiter

The order is similar except for Neptune and Uranus.

A2.2

PCM 21

1.

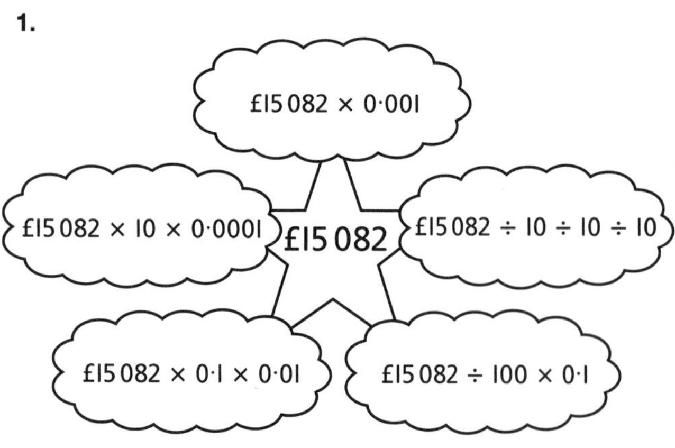

2. £15 082 × 0·1 ÷ 10 = £150·82 and
£15 082 × 10 ÷ 0·0001= £1 508 200 000
× 0·1 ÷ 10 is the same as dividing by 100
× 10 ÷ 0.0001 is the same as multiplying by 100 000

3. 4008 m

4. 130 km

Extra

Answers will vary.

A2.3

1.

1·05 kg	1·55 kg	1995 g	1505 g	1055 g
£9·78	£14·29	£18·18	£14·29	£10·23

2.

1·05 kg	1·55 kg	1995 g	1505 g	1055 g
£11·67	£16·67	£21·07	£16·67	£12·07

3. £66·77

4. £78·15

5. £11·38

Extra

1·05 kg 1055 g 1505 g 1·55 kg 1995 g
7·155 kg = 7155 g

A2.4

PCM 22

1. 6·1 6·7 7·23 7·61 8·04

2. 8·29 9·07 9·62 10·00 10·68

3. 1·00 2·25 2·75 3·50 4·50

- **a** 1·00 + 0·75 = 1·75
- **b** 2·25 + 0·75 = 3·00
- **c** 2·75 + 0·75 = 3·50
- **d** 3·50 + 0·75 = 4·25
- **e** 4·50 + 0·75 = 5·25

A2.5

PCMs 23 and 24

n	n^2	n^3	n^4	n^5	n^6	n^7
1	1	1	1	1	1	1
2	4	8	16	32	64	128
3	9	27	81	243	729	2187
4	**16**	**64**	**256**	**1024**	**4096**	**16 384**
5	25	125	625	3125	15 625	78 125
6	36	216	1296	7776	46 656	279 936
7	**49**	**343**	**2401**	**16 807**	117 649	823 543
8	64	512	4096	32 768	262 144	2 097 152
9	81	729	6561	59 049	531 441	4 782 969
10	100	1000	10 000	**100 000**	**1 000 000**	**10 000 000**
11	121	1331	14 641	161 051	1 771 561	19 487 171
12	144	1728	20 736	248 832	2 985 984	35 831 808
13	**169**	**2197**	28 561	371 293	4 826 809	62 748 517
14	**196**	**2744**	38 416	537 824	7 529 536	105 413 504
15	**225**	**3375**	50 625	759 375	11 390 625	170 859 375
16	**256**	**4096**	65 536	1 048 576	16 777 216	268 435 456
17	**289**	**4913**	83 521	1 419 857	24 137 569	410 338 673
18	**324**	**5832**	104 976	1 889 568	34 012 224	612 220 032
19	**361**	**6859**	130 321	2 476 099	47 045 881	893 871 739
20	**400**	**8000**	160 000	3 200 000	64 000 000	1 280 000 000

n	n^8	n^9	n^{10}
1	1	1	1
2	256	512	1024
3	6561	19 683	59 049
4	**65 536**	**262 144**	**1 048 576**
5	390 625	1 953 125	9 765 625
6	1 679 616	10 077 696	60 466 176
7	5 764 801	40 353 607	282 475 249
8	16 777 216	134 217 728	1 073 741 824
9	43 046 721	387 420 489	3 486 784 401
10	**100 000 000**	**1 000 000 000**	**10 000 000 000**

4. Children should notice the following patterns for ascending powers of n

n	Pattern of last digits n, n^2, n^3 etc.
1	1
2	2, 4, 8, 6, 2, 4, 8, …
3	3, 9, 7, 1, 3, 9, 7, …
4	4, 6, 4, 6, 4, …
5	5
6	6
7	7, 9, 3, 1, 7, 9, 3, …
8	8, 4, 2, 6, 8, 4, 2, …
9	9, 1, 9, 1, 9, 1, …
10	0
11	1
12	2, 4, 8, 6, 2, 4, 8, …
13	3, 9, 7, 1, 3, 9, 7, …
14	4, 6, 4, 6, 4, …
15	5
16	6
17	7, 9, 3, 1, 7, 9, 3, …
18	4, 2, 6, 8, 4, 2, …
19	1, 9, 1, 9, 1, …
20	0

5. All numbers with a 5 units digit have 5 units digit for all powers.
All numbers with a 0 units digit have 0 units digit for all powers.

6. Rows 4 and 14, 6 and 16, 9 and 19 all show the same pattern, respectively.

A2

7. Rows 5 and 15, 6 and 16 have the same units digit (5 and 6) for all powers.
8. Row 2: units digits are all even numbers, and follow the sequence 2, 4, 8, 6, 2, …. Row 20: units digits are all 0.
9. Rows 21 and 31 would always end in 1.
10.

n	Last digits n^{11}, n^{12}
1	1, 1
2	8, 6
3	7, 1
4	4, 6
5	5, 5
6	6, 6
7	3, 1
8	2, 6
9	9, 1
10	0, 0
11	1, 1
12	8, 6
13	7, 1
14	4, 6
15	5, 5
16	6, 6
17	3, 1
18	2, 6
19	9, 1
20	0, 0

11. Pattern 1, 6, 1, 6, …
12. Answers will vary.

A2.6

1. 3
2. 5, 7
3.

Number of horses	Number of fence strips	Number of fasteners
1	3	3
2	5	4
3	7	5
4	9	6
5	11	7
6	13	8
7	15	9
8	17	10
9	19	11
10	21	12

4. 12 horses need 25 strips; 20 horses need 41 strips; n horses need $2n + 1$ strips.
5. 25 strips makes 12 paddocks. He needs 14 fasteners.
6. 10 paddocks
7. No, 39 strips will give him 19 paddocks.

PCM 25

Extra

n	Digital root	n^2	Digital root	n^3	Digital root	n^4	Digital root	n^5	Digital root
1	1	1	1	1	1	1	1	1	1
2	2	4	4	8	8	16	7	32	5
3	3	9	9	27	9	81	9	243	9
4	4	16	7	64	1	256	4	1024	7
5	5	25	7	125	8	625	4	3125	2
6	6	36	9	216	9	1296	9	7776	9
7	7	49	4	343	1	2401	7	16 807	4
8	8	64	1	512	8	4096	1	32 768	8
9	9	81	9	729	9	6561	9	59 049	9
10	1	100	1	1000	1	10 000	1	100 000	1
11	2	121	4	1331	8	14 641	7	161 051	5
12	3	144	9	1728	9	20 736	9	248 832	9
13	4	169	7	2197	1	28 561	4	371 293	7
14	5	196	7	2744	8	38 416	4	537 824	2
15	6	225	9	3375	9	50 625	9	759 375	9
16	7	256	4	4096	1	65 536	7	1 048 576	4
17	8	289	1	4913	8	83 521	1	1 419 857	8
18	9	324	9	5832	9	104 976	9	1 889 568	9
19	1	361	1	6859	1	130 321	1	2 476 099	1
20	2	400	4	8000	8	160 000	7	3 200 000	5

Extra

Square paddocks

Number of horses	Number of fence strips	Number of fasteners
1	4	4
2	7	6
3	10	8
4	13	10
5	16	12
6	19	14
7	22	16
8	25	18
9	28	20
10	31	22

n horses need $3n + 1$ strips and $2n + 2$ fasteners.

B2

B2.1

1. $(48 \div 8) + 4 = 10$ brackets not essential
2. $48 \div (8 + 4) = 4$
3. $(23 + 46) \div 23 = 3$
4. $23 + (46 \div 23) = 25$ brackets not essential
5. $(36 \div 9) - 3 = 1$ brackets not essential
6. $36 \div (9 - 3) = 6$
7. $(25 - 19 + 45) \div 3 = 17$
8. $25 - 19 + (45 \div 3) = 21$ brackets not essential
9. $(30 + 20) \div 10 = 5$
10. $30 - (20 \div 10) = 28$ brackets not essential
11. $28 - (7 \div 7) = 27$ brackets not essential
12. $(28 - 7) \div 7 = 3$
13. $140 \div (7 + 13) = 7$
14. $(140 \div 7) + 13 = 33$ brackets not essential
15. $(36 + 36) \div 9 \times 20 = 160$
16. $(36 + (36 \div 9)) \times 20 = 800$ internal brackets not essential
17. $(38 \times 34) - 22 = 1270$ brackets not essential
18. $38 \times (34 - 22) = 456$
19. $(48 \div 4) + 44 = 56$ brackets not essential
20. $48 \div (4 + 44) = 1$

Extra

Questions marked 'brackets not essential' will give correct answers without brackets on 'scientific' calculators; basic calculators may need brackets in all cases.

B2.2

1. Silver, silver, silver, none, none
2. Gold, gold, gold, gold, gold
3. 27 395, 8354, 11 060, 15 274, 3751

Extra

Answers will vary.

B2.3

1. 3·81
2. 6·45
3. 9·10
4. 10·309
5. 4·717
6. 8·205
7. 2·571
8. 2·105
9. 10·342

Extra

Answers will vary.

B2.4

PCM 26

1.

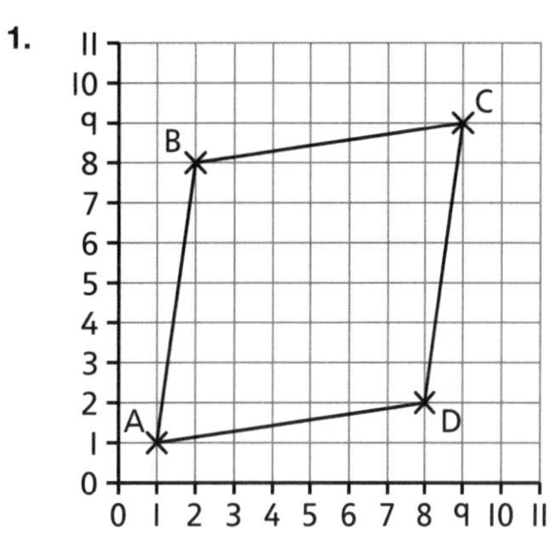

2. A (1,1) B (2,8) C (9,9) D (8, 2)
3. Parallelogram
4.

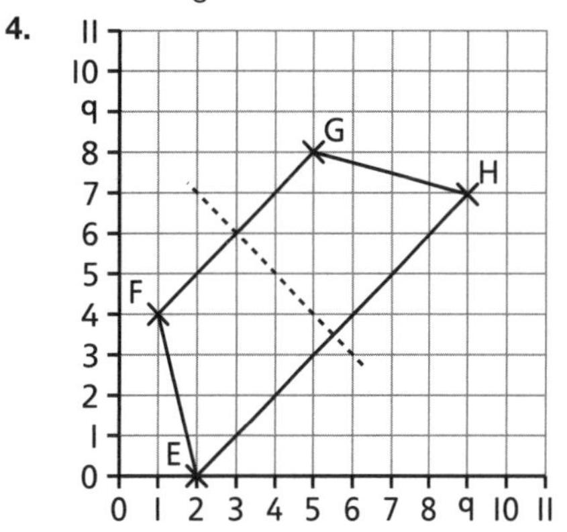

5. E (2,0) F (1,4) G (5,8) H (9,7)
6. 1 line of symmetry through (2,7) and (6,3)
7.

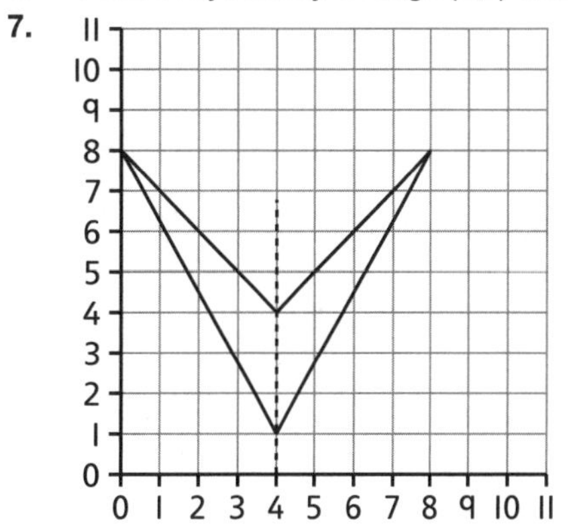

8. Arrowhead, concave kite, or delta
9. One line of symmetry through (4,1) and (4,4)

10.

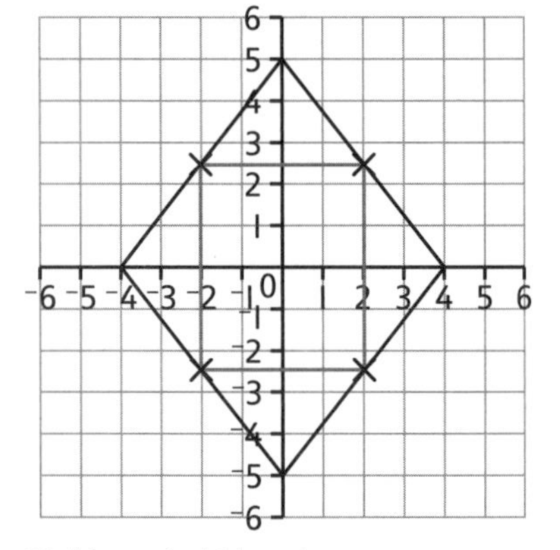

11. Right-angled triangle
12. See diagram
13. Rhombus
14. See diagram

B2.5

1. Right
2. Top
3. Front
4. a, e, f
5. b

Extra

Answers will vary.

B2.6

For example:

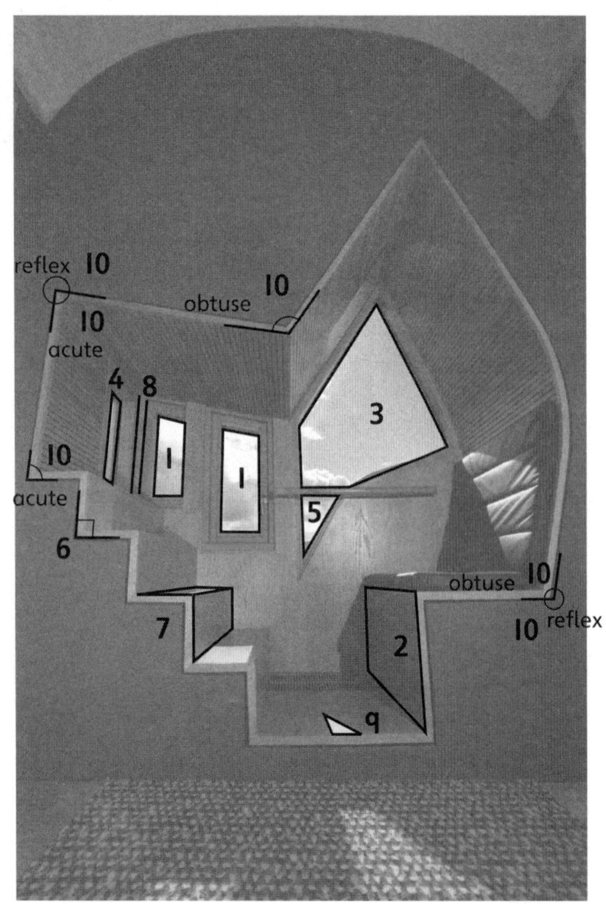

Extra

Answers will vary.

C2

C2.1

1. 400 cm² 423 cm² 558 cm² 329 cm²
The area of each shape can be calculated by adding individual component shapes, or by subtracting 'blank' shapes from the complete rectangle

Extra

Answers will vary.

C2.2

	Surface area (cm²)	Volume (cm³)
1	228	216
2	318	378
3	290	300
4	332	240
5	742	1274
6	498	702

Extra

6cm cube: surface area = 216 cm²; volume = 216 cm³

Cubes smaller than 6 cm have surface area larger than volume, cubes larger than 6 cm have surface area smaller than volume.

C2.3

A 224 cm²
B 129.5 cm²
C 362 cm²
D 755·5 cm²
E 234 cm²

Extra

Answers will vary.

C2.4

1.

	Mon	Tue	Wed	Thu	Fri
Mean (°C)	14·0	17·625	18·875	17·0	16·875
Mode (°C)	15	18	19	15 and 20	17
Median (°C)	14·5	18	19	15·5	17
Range (°C)	7	5	6	10	4

2. Highest mean — Wednesday
Highest mode — Thursday
Highest median — Wednesday
Greatest range — Thursday

Lowest mean — Monday
Lowest mode — Monday and Thursday
Lowest median — Monday
Smallest range — Friday

3. Mean — 18·4
Mode — 19 (no change)
Median — 19 (no change)
Range — 8

Extra

City	Mean (°C)	Mode (°C)	Median (°C)
Exeter	20	none	20
London	18·6	none	19
Birmingham	16·6	none	17
Cardiff	17·6	18	18
Manchester	16·4	19	16
Sheffield	16·0	none	17
Belfast	16·0	16	16
Glasgow	13·8	15	15

Highest mean: Exeter
Highest mode: Manchester
Highest median: Exeter

Lowest mean: Glasgow
Lowest mode: Glasgow
Lowest median: Glasgow

C2.5

PCM 28

Data may have slight differences depending on how children decide to deal with numbers, abbreviations and apostrophes, but the trends will be the same.

Raw data

Word length	Frequency article 1	Frequency article 2
1	2	2
2	26	13
3	32	17
4	31	16
5	29	13
6	18	10
7	16	5
8	10	2
9	7	1
10	4	0
11	1	0
12	3	1
13	1	0
14	0	0
15	1	0
Mean	5.0	4.3
Median	4	4
Mode	3	3

Graphs will vary, for example bar graph of raw data

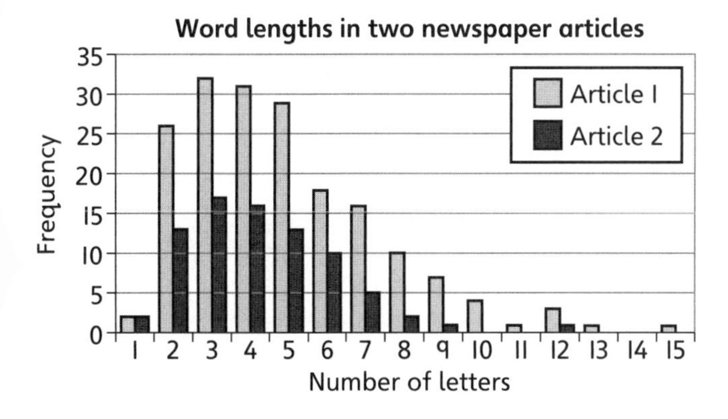

C2.6

1. 13 cm
2. 50 cm
3. 30 cm
4. 18 cm
5. 4 inches
6. 20 inches
7. 14 inches
8. 9 inches
9. 12·7 cm; 50·8 cm; 30·48 cm; 17·78 cm;
   3·94 in; 19·69 in; 13·78 in; 9·06 in
10. Answers will vary.
11. Answers will vary.
12. Children's own graph showing a straight line from (0,0) through (5 miles, 8 km). Children may put miles/km on either axis.

Extra

Answers will vary.

D2

D2.1

+	1·5	3·7	0·52	10·37	1·7	16·44	7·1	5·012
2·09	3·59	5·79	2·61	12·46	3·79	18·53	9·19	7·102
7·1	8·6	10·8	7·62	17·47	8·8	23·54	14·2	12·112
3·2	4·7	6·9	3·72	13·57	4·9	19·64	10·3	8·212
8.92	10·42	12·62	9·44	19·29	10·62	25·36	16·02	13·932
0.94	2·44	4·64	1·46	11·31	2·64	17·38	8·04	5·952
6.69	8·19	10·39	7·21	17·06	8·39	23·13	13·79	11·702
7.72	9·22	11·42	8·24	18·09	9·42	24·16	14·82	12·732
6.098	7·598	9·798	6·618	16·468	7·798	22·538	13·198	11·11

3. Largest column total: 174·278 in column16·44
4. Largest row total: 117·702 in row 8·92

Extra

8 × (sum head of columns) + 8 × (sum of head of rows)
8 × 46·342 + 8 × 42·758 = 712·8

D2.2

PCM 29

1.

Menu A	Menu B	Menu C	Menu D
£5 £6 £10 £12 £2 £3 £3 £1 £1	£6 £5 £10 £13 £12 £3 £2 × 2 £3 £3 £2 £2	£6 £6 £8 £10 £3 £3 × 2 £1 × 2	£6 £9 £13 £13 £12 £2 × 3 £1 × 2 £3
£43	£63	£41	£64

2.

Menu A	Menu B	Menu C	Menu D
£4·95 £5·50 £9·65 £11·95 £1·90 £2·55 £3·20 £1·25 £0·95	£5·50 £4·95 £9·95 £12·95 £11·95 £2·50 £1·90 × 2 £2·75 £2·95 £2·20 £2·25	£5·50 £5·50 £7·50 £9·50 £2·95 £2·75 × 2 £1·30 × 2	£5·50 £8·95 £12·95 £12·95 £11·95 £1·90 × 3 £1·25 × 2 £2·70
£41·90	£61·75	£39·05	£63·20

3. Answers will vary.

Extra

Menu A	Menu B	Menu C	Menu D
£37·71	£55·58	£35·15	£56·88

D2.3

PCM 30

1. Top number is 1626
2. Largest top number is 2068 (two smallest numbers on the outside)

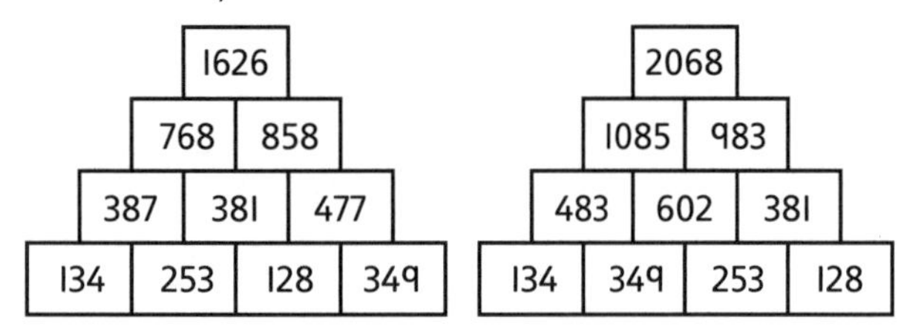

3. Largest number is 1981
4. Smallest number is 1447

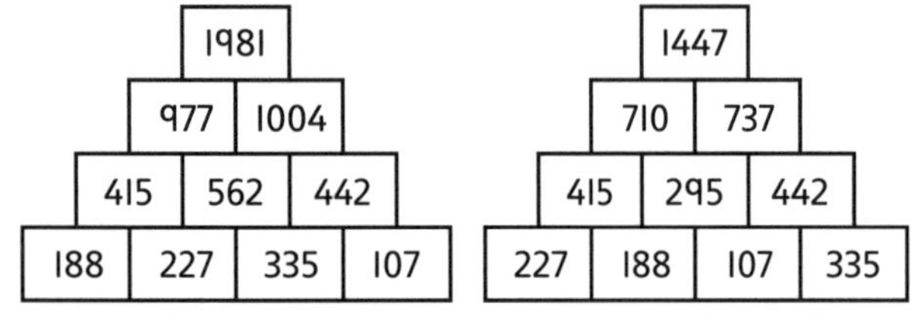

5. Smallest numbers on outside, largest number in the centre

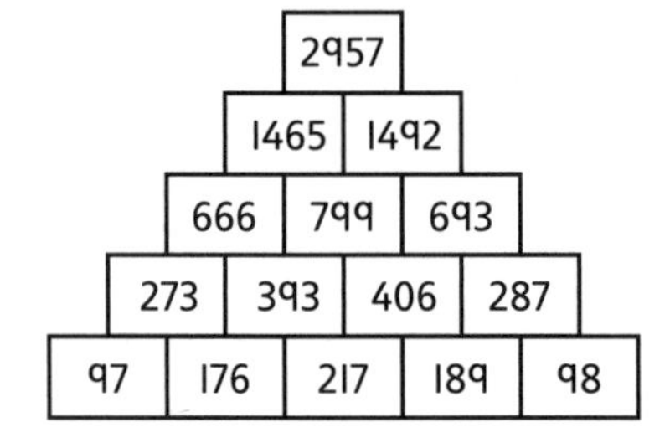

D2.4

1.

Number	Square root
1	1
4	2
9	3
16	4
25	5
36	6
49	7
64	8
81	9
100	10
121	11
144	12
169	13
196	14
225	15

2. 4·690
3. 8·660
4. 10·583
5. 2·449
6. 14·560

Extra

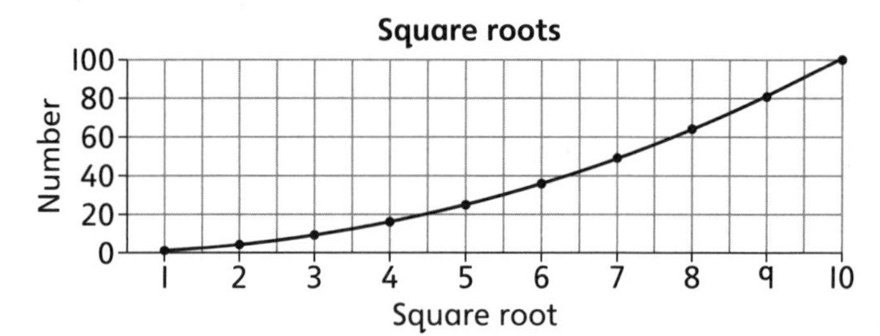

D2.5

1. 5 × (3 + 8) = 55 > (5 × 3) + 8 = 23
2. 40 ÷ (10 − 2) = 5 > (40 ÷ 10) − 2 = 2
3. 8 × (23 − 2) = 168 < (8 × 23) − 2 = 182
4. 9 + (17 × 3) = 60 < (9 + 17) × 3 = 78
5. 7 × (6 − 3) = 21 < (7 × 6) − 3 = 39

Answers will vary but may include:

6. (12 × 6) ÷ 3 + 9 = 33 12 × (6 ÷ 3) + 9 = 33
   12 × 6 ÷ (3 + 9) = 6
7. (11 + 3) × 4 + 7 = 63 11 + (3 × 4) + 7 = 30
   11 + 3 × (4 + 7) = 44 (11 + 3) × (4 + 7) = 154
8. (8 × 9) − (3 × 5) = 57 8 × (9 − 3) × 5 = 240
   8 × (9 − 3 × 5) = ⁻48
9. (52 ÷ 4) + (9 × 5) = 58 52 ÷ (4 + 9) × 5 = 20
   52 ÷ (4 + 9 × 5) = $\frac{52}{49}$
10. 21 + (35 × 6) − 2 = 229 (21 + 35) × 6 − 2 = 334

Extra

52 × (26 + 10) × 13 = 24 336
(10 − 52) × 26 × 13 = ⁻14 196

D2.6

1. Sequence B: 7, 12, 17 Sequence C: 10, 17, 24
2. Sequence A: 13, 16 Sequence B: 22, 27
   Sequence C: 31, 38

3.

	1st pattern	2nd pattern	3rd pattern	4th pattern	5th pattern
Sequence A	4	7	10	13	16
Sequence B	7	12	17	22	27
Sequence C	10	17	24	31	38

4. Sequence A: 31 Sequence B: 52 Sequence C: 73
   Answers will vary but may include some variation of the rules:
   Sequence A: $3n + 1$; Sequence B: $5n + 2$;
   Sequence C: $7n + 3$.

Extra

	1st pattern	2nd pattern	3rd pattern	4th pattern	5th pattern
Sequence D	13	22	31	40	49
Sequence E	16	27	38	49	60

E2

E2.1

1. 18 315
2. 129 600
3. 118 840
4. No. Total sales (each rounded to nearest 1000) = 1 176 000.
5. Yes
6. Yes. Mean price is £6·09
7. £155 838·45
8. No. *Hillside* has the highest value (see table)
9. See table
10. Yes. Total value (each rounded to nearest 1000) = £6 617 000

Position	Title	Total value of sales for the year (£)
1	*Hillside*	1 123 074·40
2	*New Ends*	836 500·00
3	*Wet Weekend*	773 185·00
4	*Down Down*	763 934·65
5	*Surprise!*	758 979·00
6	*Sky Blue*	697 120·00
7	*Tony's Tall Tale*	545 612·55
8	*Mountain Track*	451 200·00
9	*Madge and Mike*	364 285·35
10	*Two Together*	302 812·25

Extra

Total reduction
129 600 × £1 = £129 600

Title	Reduction (£)
Tony's Tall Tale	24 235
New Ends	21 450
Surprise!	19 470
Mountain Track	16 455
Wet Weekend	11 215
Hillside	9070
Down Down	8695
Two Together	6985
Sky Blue	6105
Madge and Mike	5920

E2.2

1.

Saturated fat (g)	8	40%

2.

Calories (kcal)	80	4%

3.

Calories (kcal)	160	8%
Fat (g)	3·6	5%

4.

Calories (kcal)	193	10%
Fat (g)	17·9	26%

5.

Calories (kcal)	49	2%

6.

Calories (kcal)	319	16%
Sugar (g)	9	10%

7.

Calories (kcal)	120	6%
Salt (g)	0·5	8%

8.

Calories (kcal)	100	5%
Fat (g)	6·1	9%

Extra

Answers will vary.

E2.3

PCM 31

1. Car E, $\frac{7}{10}$
2. See table
3. Car D, 90 litres
4. Car D, 56·25 litres
5. See table
6. See table
7. £156·71
8. 379 litres
9. Car E, 19·2 km per litre
10. Car E, 739·2 km

Figures may vary slightly due to cumulative effects of rounding.

Car	Proportion empty	Capacity of tank (litres/gall)	Amount in tank (litres/gall)	Fuel need to fill up (litres/gall)	Cost to fill (£)	Consumption (km per litre)	Distance travelled (km)	Distance on a full tank (km)
A	$\frac{1}{2}$	75 16·7	37·5 8·3	37·5 8·3	31·88	11·2	420	840
B	0·75	60 13·3	15 3·3	45 10	38·25	12·4	186	744
C	$\frac{2}{3}$	45 10	15 3·3	30 6·7	25·50	16	240	720
D	$\frac{3}{8}$	90 20	56·25 12·5	33·75 7·5	28·69	5	281·25	450
E	$\frac{3}{10}$	55 12·2	38·5 8·6	16·5 3·7	14·03	19·2	739·2	1056
F	40%	54 12	32·4 7·2	21·6 4·8	18·36	12·4	401·76	669·6

Extra

See table.
Total distance travelled by all cars 4480 km = 2800 miles (rounded to nearest km/mile).

E2.4

1. a £11·95 b $\frac{1}{2}$
   c 0·50 d £35·98
   e Every 2 months f $\frac{1}{6}$
   g 0·33 h £42·15
   i monthly j £4·35
   k $\frac{1}{52}$ l 0·02
   m £47·84 n Fortnightly
   o £1·75 p $\frac{1}{13}$
   q £51·87
2. Sadie
3. Answers will vary.
4. 118

Extra

Baljit	92p/week
Ricky	69p/week
Louisa	79p/week
Jamal	81p/week
Sadie	£1/week
Kezia	92p/week
Jonah	88p/week
Marta	£1/week

E2.5

Answers will vary.

E2.6

1. Josh is wrong. 16 ÷ 4 = 4 with no remainder.
   Samir is correct for all square numbers.
2. Alina is correct for all square numbers.
   Leila is correct for all square numbers.

Extra

Answers will vary but children should notice that the square numbers only ever have units digits of 0, 1, 4, 9, 6, and 5.

A3

A3.1

PCM 36

Plane	Cruising height in feet	Cruising height in metres	Ground temperature at sea level	Approximate temperature outside plane (nearest °C)
A	12 000	3660	5°C	$^-$19°C
B	20 000	6100	5°C	$^-$35°C
C	22 000	6710	0°C	$^-$44°C
D	38 000	11 590	10°C	$^-$65°C
E	43 000	13 115	0°C	$^-$85°C
F	48 000	14 640	10°C	$^-$85°C
G	70 000	21 350	20°C	$^-$119°C

Mountain	Height in feet	Height in metres	Approximate temperature at summit (nearest 0·5°C)
Mount Everest	29 028	8853	$^-$57·5°C
K2	28 251	8617	$^-$56·0°C
Annapurna I	26 545	8096	$^-$52·5°C
Chimborazo	20 564	6272	$^-$40·5°C
Mount McKinley	20 321	6198	$^-$40·5°C
Mount Kilimanjaro	19 340	5899	$^-$38·5°C
Mount Ararat	16 853	5140	$^-$33·5°C
Mount Fuji	12 388	3778	$^-$24·5°C
Ben Nevis	4409	1345	$^-$8·5°C

Extra

21 290 m balloon record
15 460 m glider record

A3.2

1. £23
2. £17·25 £17·63
3. £43·70 £44·65
4. £20·13 £20·56
5. £458·85 £468·83
6. £316·25 £323·13
7. £1148·85 £1173·83
8. £136·85 £139·83
9. £7532·50 £7696·25
10. £91·99 £93·99

Extra

1. 50p
2. 38p
3. 95p
4. 43p
5. £9·98
6. £6·88
7. £24·98
8. £2·98
9. £163·75
10. £2

Total saving: £212·83 (212·81 without rounding)
If VAT fell to 12·5% from 17·5% the saving would be £425·62
If VAT fell to 12·5% from 15% the saving would be £212·81

A3.3

Answers rounded to 3 significant figures where appropriate

1. 1·552 m 1·55 m
2. 144·275 cm 144 cm
3. 1·94025 m 1·94 m
4. 1343·25 mm 1340 mm
5. 134·201 m 134 m
6. 227·3405 m 227 m
7. 156·234 m 156 m
8. 155·73325 m 156 m
9. 52 cm
10. 67·5 cm
11. 0·351 m
12. 37·8 cm

Extra

65 cm → 71·5 cm
75 cm → 78·75 cm
0·45 m → 0·675 m
54 cm → 67·5 cm

A3.4

1.

×	50	2
6	300	12

Answer: £312

2.

×	80	7
60	4800	420
5	400	35

Answer: £56·55

3.

×	70	9
40	2800	360
7	490	63

Answer: £37·13

4.

×	50	6
30	1500	180
6	300	36

Answer: £2016

5.

×	100	10	2
10	1000	100	20
2	200	20	4

Answer: £1344

6.

×	300	80	5
20	6000	1600	100
5	1500	400	25

Answer: 9625 minutes

7.

×	4	0·5
10	40	5
5	20	2·5

Answer: £67·50

8.

×	8	0·9	0·08
20	160	18	1·6
3	24	2·7	0·24

Answer: £206·54

Extra

1. £62·00
2. £169·65
3. £4·70
4. £180·00

A3.5

PCM 37

Hotel	Total self-catering	Total hotel	Total SC 4 adults, 4children	Total hotel 4 adults, 4children
Sunny Beach	£2676	£2504	£3886	£3542
Kos View	£2690	£2840	£3780	£4080
Stelios Bay	£2683	£2625	£3721	£3605
Arta Apartments	£2714	Not available	£3712	Not available

1. Cheapest Sunny Beach – hotel
2. Cheapest Sunny Beach – hotel
3.

Item	Cost for one child	Cost for one adult	Cost for 2 adults and 4 children	Cost for 4 adults and 4 children
3 pairs of shorts	£11·97	£26·97	£101·82	£155·76
5 T-shirts	£9·90	£20·00	£79·60	£119·60
2 swimsuits	£13·00	£29·98	£111·96	£171·92
1 pair of beach shoes	£3·00	£5·00	£22·00	£32·00
1 pair of trousers	£5·25	£12·00	£45·00	£69·00
4 shirts	£17·40	£31·80	£133·20	£196·80
1 suitcase	£22·00	£37·00	£162·00	£236·00
1 beach ball	£2·97	£2·97	£17·82	£23·76
7 sets of underwear	£34·93	£55·93	£251·58	£363·44
1 pair of shoes	£6·00	£11·00	£46·00	£68·00
2 books	£3·96	£7·96	£31·76	£47·68
1 magazine	£0·99	£2·95	£9·86	£15·76
1 wash bag	£1·00	£2·99	£9·98	£15·96
1 sunhat	£2·00	£4·50	£17·00	£26·00
1 beach towel	£5·80	£5·80	£34·80	£46·40
1 beach bag	£2·50	£7·30	£24·60	£39·20
2 pairs of sunglasses	£9·98	£36·00	£111·92	£183·92
1 bottle of sun-block	£3·99	£3·99	£23·94	£31·92
1 bottle of after-sun	£3·99	£3·99	£23·94	£31·92
1 camera	£5·75	£5·75	£34·50	£46·00
Grand totals			£1293·28	£1921·04

Extra

Answers will vary.

A3.6

PCM 38

1. For any 2-digit number AB: AB × 101 = ABAB;
   54 × 101 = 4545
2. For any 2-digit number AB: AB × 101 = ABAB
3. For any 2-digit number AB: AB × 1001 = AB 0AB
   For any 2-digit number AB: AB × 10 001 = AB0 0AB
   For any 2-digit number AB: AB × 100 001 = A B00 0AB
4. For any 3-digit number ABC:
   ABC × 1001 = ABC ABC
   For any 3-digit number ABC:
   ABC × 10 001 = A BC0 ABC
   For any 3-digit number ABC:
   ABC × 100 001 = AB C00 ABC
5. For any 4-digit number ABCD:
   ABCD × 10 001 = AB CDA BCD
   For any 4-digit number ABCD:
   ABCD × 100 001 = ABC D0A BCD
6. For any 5-digit number ABCDE:
   ABCDE × 100 001 = A BCD EAB CDE
7. Answers will vary.
8. Answers will vary.

B3

B3.1

1.

Car	£6525·00
Bicycle	£75·75
Trainers	£63·00
Computer game	£7·25
TV	£480·00
Cinema Ticket	£5·29
CD	£17·90
Mobile phone	£101·05
MP3 player	£50·05
Bus fare	£1·35

2. Total cost £7326·64

Extra

Answers will vary, but could include:
240 old pennies = £1 so 2·4 old pennies = 1p
20 shillings = £1
£sd abbreviations
3 shillings and 6 old pence as 15/6, 'fifteen and six'

B3.2

PCMs 39, 40 and 41

City	Distance travelled (km)	Time travelling hh:mm	Attendance	Ticket price	Total cost
Glasgow			12 500	£32·50	£406 250
Newcastle	244	2:53	11 000	£32·50	£357 500
Sheffield	215	2:24	12 500	£32·50	£406 250
Manchester	62	7:34	19 000	£35·00	£665 000
Liverpool	55	0:49	10 600	£32·50	£344 500
Bournemouth	424	4:34	6500	£32·50	£211 250
Brighton	152	2:11	4500	£32·50	£146 250
London	85	1:30	23 000	£35·00	£805 000
Plymouth	383	4:09	2500	£32·50	£81 250
Nottingham	408	4:22	9300	£32·50	£302 250
Cardiff	270	2:59	5500	£32·50	£178 750
Birmingham	200	2:08	14 000	£35·00	£490 000
Total	2498	35:33			£4 394 250

1. 2498 km
2. 35 h 33 min
3. 29 days including first and last
4. 17 days
5. 130 900
6. see table
7. £4 394 250
8. No. Expenses (wages, transport and accommodation) will have to be paid first.

Extra

Answers will vary.

B3.3

1. For example 693 − 396 = 297
2. 792 − 279 = 495   594 − 495 = 99
   99 − 99 = 0
3. **532** − 235 = 297   792 − 297 = 495
   594 − 495 = 99   99 − 99 = 0

   761 − 167 = 594   594 − 495 = 99   99 − 99 = 0

   928 − **829** = 99   99 − 99 = 0

   503 − 305 = 198   891 − 198 = 693
   693 − 396 = 297

   792 − 279 = 495   594 − 495 = 99
   99 − 99 = 0
   All number chains end at 99.
4. For example 5431 − 1345 = 4086
5. 6804 − 4086 = 2718   8172 − 2718 = 5454
   5454 − 4545 = 909   909 − 909 = 0
6. **4152** − 2514 = 1638   8361 − 1638 = 6723
   6723 − 3276 = 3447   7443 − 3447 = 3996
   6993 − 3996 = 2997   7992 − 2997 = 4995
   5994 − 4995 = 999   999 − 999 = 0

   6375 − 5736 = 639   936 − 639 = 297
   792 − 297 = 495   594 − 495 = 99
   99 − 99 = 0

   7856 − 6587 = 1269   9621 − 1269 = 8352
   8352 − 2538 = 5814   5814 − 4185 = 1629
   9261 − 1629 = 7632   7632 − 2367 = 5265
   5625 − 5265 = 360   360 − 063 = 297
   792 − 297 = 495   594 − 495 = 99
   99 − 99 = 0

7. 6472 − 2746 = 3726 6273 − 3726 = 2547
7452 − 2547 = 4905 5094 − 4905 = 189
981 − 189 = 792 792 − 297 = 495
594 − 495 = 99 99 − 99 = 0

Extra

63·2 − 2·36 = 60·84 60·84 − 48·06 = 12·78
87·21 −12·78 = 74·43 74·43 − 34·47 = 39·96
69·93 − 39·96 = 29·97 79·92 − 29·97 = 49·95
59·94 − 49·95 = 9·99 99·9 − 9·99 = 89·91
89·91 − 19·98 = 69·93 stuck in a loop

87·9 − 9·79 = 78·12 78·12 − 21·87 = 56·25
56·25 − 52·65 = 3·6 6·3 − 3·6 = 2·7
7·2 − 2·7 = 4·5 5·4 − 4·5 = 0·9
9·0 − 0·9 = 8·1 8·1 − 1·8 = 6·3
stuck in a loop

95·6 − 6·59 = 89·01 89·01 − 10·98 = 78·03
78·03 − 30·87 = 47·16 61·74 − 47·16 = 14·58
85·41 − 14·58 = 70·83 70·83 − 38·07 = 32·76
67·23 − 32·76 = 34·47 74·43 − 34·47 = 39·96
69·93 − 39·96 = 29·97 79·92 − 29·97 = 49·95
59·94 − 49·95 = 9·99 99·9 − 9·99 = 89·91
89·91 − 19·98 = 69·93 stuck in a loop

91·82 − 28·19 = 63·63 63·63 − 36·36 = 27·27
72·72 − 27·27 = 45·45 54·54 − 45·45 = 9·09
90·9 − 9·09 = 81·81 81·18 − 18·18 = 63·63
stuck in a loop

B3.4

PCM 42

1. One table

Item	Size	Number	Cost
Plywood	2440 mm × w 1220 mm × d 9 mm	1	£12·88
Wooden strip	2100 mm × w 10 mm × d 10 mm	1	£1·43
Wooden plank	1750 mm × w 200 mm × d 18 mm	1	£11·98
Wooden post	3100 mm × w 44 mm × d 44 mm	1	£4·68
Additional materials	Assorted	1	£1·00

One table costs £31.97

Five tables

Item	Size	Number	Cost
Plywood	2440 mm × w 1220 mm × d 9 mm	1	£12·88
Wooden strip	2100 mm × w 10 mm × d 10 mm	4	£5·72
Wooden plank	1750 mm × w 200 mm × d 18 mm	2	£23·96
Wooden post	3100 mm × w 44 mm × d 44 mm	3	£14·04
Additional materials	Assorted	5	£5·00

Five tables cost £61·60 or £12·32 each

Extra

Answers will vary
For example for one table

Item			
Plywood	Area bought 2976800 mm^2	Area used 322 500 mm^2	Area left 2 654 300 mm^2
Wooden strip	Length bought 2100 mm	Length used 1320 mm	Length left 780 mm
Wooden plank	Area bought 350000 mm^2	Area used 40 000 mm^2	Area left 310 000 mm^2
Wooden post	Length bought 3100 mm	Length used 1500 mm	Length left 1600 mm

B3.5

Apple 100 ml Banana 175 ml Lemon 75 ml
Mango 250 ml Melon 500 ml Orange 150 ml
Pear 125 ml Pineapple 400 ml Strawberry 15 ml
Tomato 50 ml

Extra

1840 ml

B3.6

All rounded to 2 dp

City	Distance travelled (km)	fuel used gallons	fuel used litres
Glasgow			
Newcastle	244	5·08	22·86
Sheffield	215	4·48	20·16
Manchester	62	1·29	5·81
Liverpool	55	1·15	5·18
Bournemouth	424	8·83	39·74
Brighton	152	3·17	14·27
London	85	1·77	7·97
Plymouth	383	7·98	35·91
Nottingham	408	8·5	38·25
Cardiff	270	5·63	25·34
Birmingham	200	4·17	18·77
Total	2498	52·05	234·26

1. See table
2. See table
3. £199·11
4. 89p left over

C3

C3.1

Answers will vary.

C3.2

PCMs 44 and 45

1. Answers will vary.
2. No
3. Answers will vary.
4. Answers will vary. Since the mean score on throwing a dice is 3.5 then the fairest would be for player A to move 3, 4, 3, 4 alternately.

C3.3

1. Oranges 9; apples 12; cherries 3; plums 6; bananas 6
2.

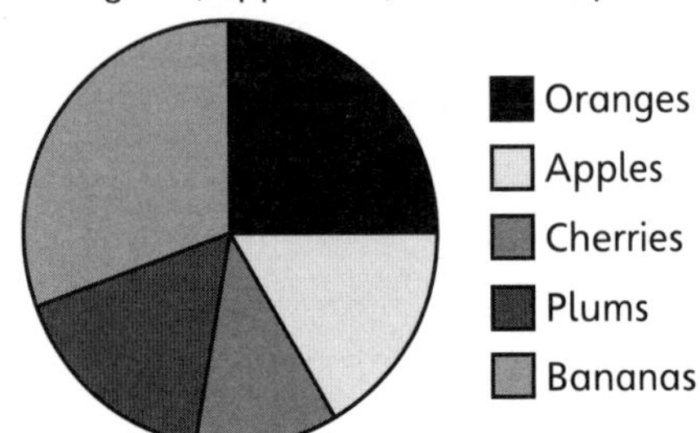

3. The slice for apples is smaller because it is a smaller proportion of a larger group of children.
4. In both cases $\frac{1}{4}$ of the children likes oranges.
5. Answers will vary.

C3.4

1. Largest area: 99 m^2

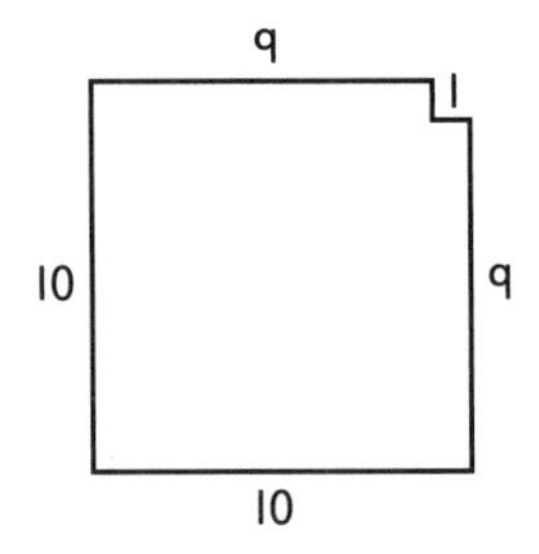

2. Largest area: 624 m^2

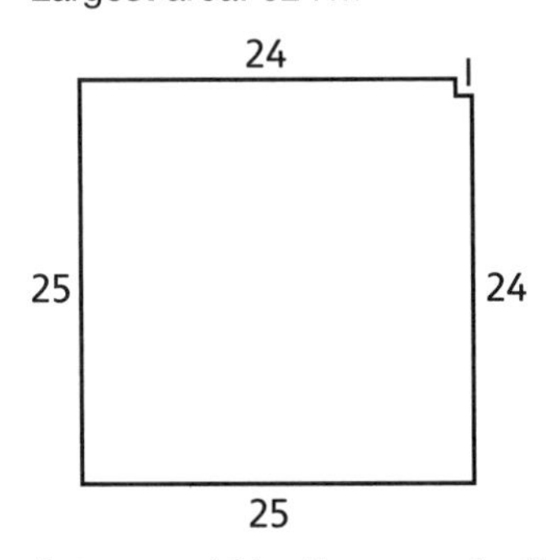

3. Areas would be the same for T shapes that are the same width.

Extra

For example:

E shape maximum 79 m^2 (9 × 9 with 2 × 1 m^2 'cut-outs')

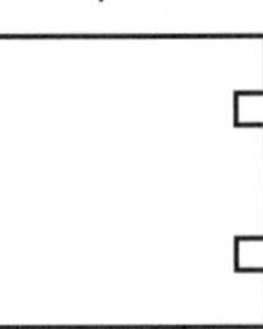

F shape maximum 88 m^2 (10 × 9 with 2 × 1 m^2 'cut-outs')

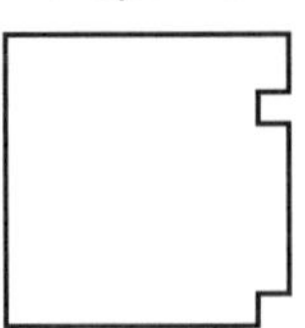

C3.5

1.

	Gets up	Shopping	Lunch	Football	Bath	Dinner	Bed
Los Angeles	00:30	02:45	05:15	07:20–08:45	10:00	11:30	13:45
Washington	03:30	05:45	08:15	10:20–11:45	13:00	14:30	16:45
Buenos Aires	04:30	06:45	09:15	11:20–12:45	14:00	15:30	17:45
Manchester	08:30	10:45	13:15	15:20–16:45	18:00	19:30	21:45
Baghdad	10:30	12:45	15:15	17:20–18:45	20:00	21:30	23:45
Hong Kong	15:30	17:45	20:15	22:20–23:45	01:00	02:30	04:45
Sydney	17:30	19:45	22:15	00:20–01:45	03:00	04:30	06:45

2. 12:34
3. 12:12 (the next day)
4. Answers will vary.

Extra

	Gets up	Shopping	Lunch	Football	Bath	Dinner	Bed
Caracas	01:00	03:15	05:45	07:50–09:15	10:30	12:00	14:15
Manchester	08:30	10:45	13:15	15:20–16:45	18:00	19:30	21:45
Mumbai	14:00	16:15	18:45	20:50–22:15	23:30	01:00	03:15
Darwin	18:00	20:15	22:45	00:50–02:15	03:30	05:00	07:15

C3.6

Answers will vary.

Extra

Answers will vary but may include 10 months in a year or 10 days in a week (but not both because 365.25 days in a year is fixed).

D3

D3.1

1 Mirror

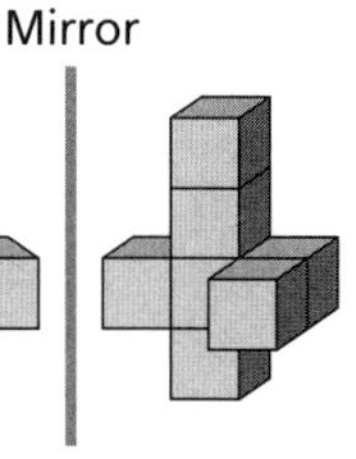

2 Mirror

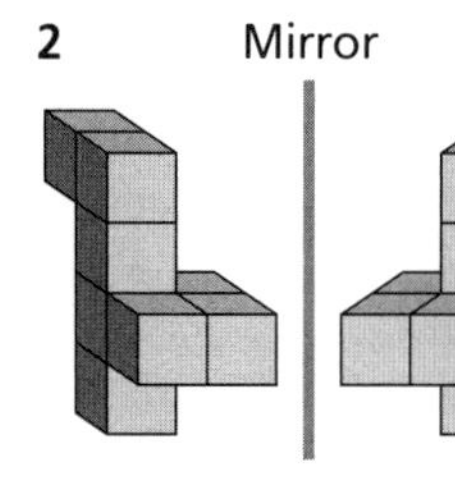

3 Mirror

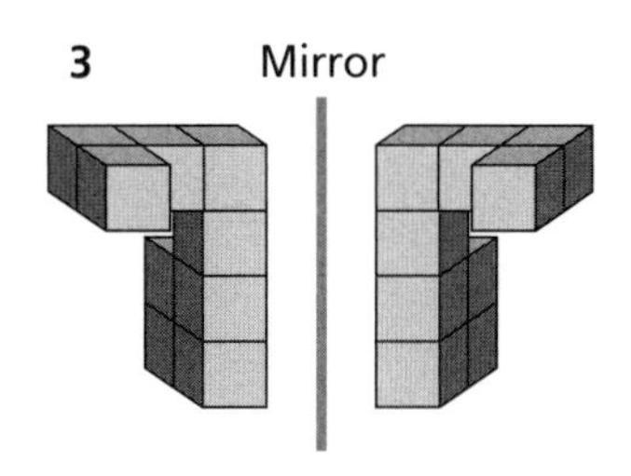

4 Mirror

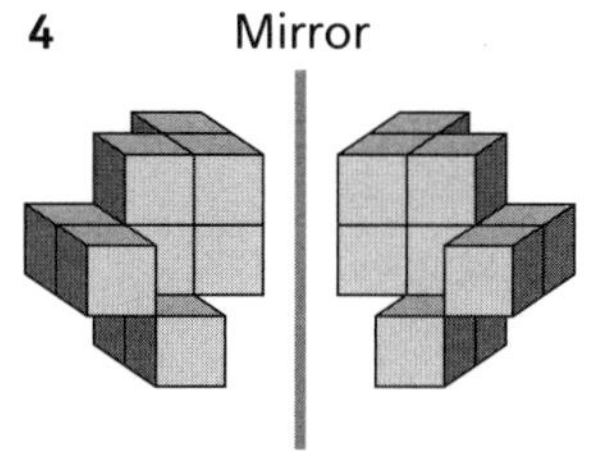

5 Mirror

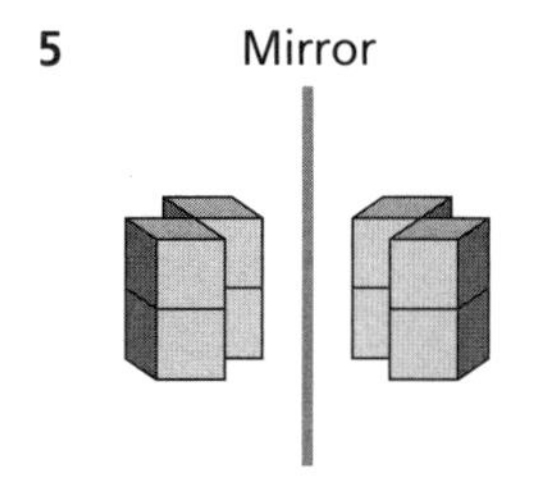

6 Mirror

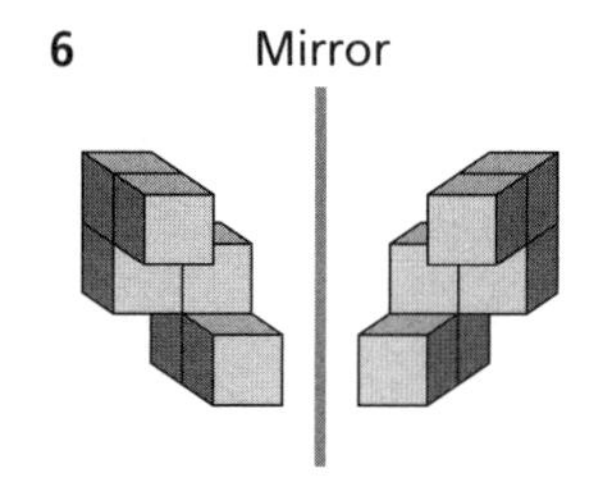

D3.2

PCMS 46 AND 47

1. (0,0)(3,0)(3,$^-$3)(1,$^-$3)(1,$^-$2)(0,$^-$2)
2. (0,0)(0,3)($^-$1,3)($^-$1,2)($^-$4,2)($^-$4,1)($^-$1,1)($^-$1,0)
3. (2,2)(2,$^-$2)($^-$2,$^-$3)($^-$2,3)
4. (0,0)($^-$3,0)($^-$3,1)(0,1)(0,2)(2,3)(2,1)(3,1)(3,0)(2,0)(2,$^-$2)(0,$^-$1)
5. (0,0)(4,4)(2,5)(1,5)(1,4)
6. (4,$^-$4)($^-$3,0)(0,3)

D3.3

Answers will vary.

D3.4

1. 21
2. 19
3. 36
4. 62
5. 35
6. See answers 1–5.
7. Answers will vary but must be multiples of 26 between 598 and 1014.
8. Answers will vary but must be multiples of 51 between 1173 and 1989.
9. Answers will vary but must be multiples of 62 between 1426 and 2418.
10. Answers will vary but must be multiples of 67 between 1541 and 2613.
11. Answers will vary but must be multiples of 83 between 1909 and 3237.

Extra

Answers will vary.

D3.5

Answers will vary.

D3.6

1. 5·39
2. 3·24
3. 3·54
4. 6·26
5. Eight people pay more. 94·75 ÷ 8 = £11.84
152.80 ÷ 13 = £11·75
6. Twelve people pay more. 106·50 ÷ 12 = £8·88
128·65 ÷ 15 = £8·58
7. Twenty-two people pay more 251·45 ÷ 16 = £15·72
346·05 ÷ 22 = £15·73

Extra

Answers will vary.

E3.1

1. Answers will vary. Using ratio of heights it might cost £22 800 000.
2. 1·00 m
3. 5·4 m   2·7 m
4. $\frac{1}{10}$
5. 2·5 times
6. 7·2 tonnes
7. 2·7 m
8. 42 tonnes

Extra

50 cm

$\frac{1}{324}$

E3.2

PCM 48

2.

Person	Time to walk 20 m	Speed in m/s	Speed in km/h
Me	Answers will vary		
Bolt	1·94	10·32	37·15
Gebrselassie	3·55	5·64	20·32
Schwazer	5·22	3·83	13·8

3.

City	Time to walk 20 m	Speed in km/h	Order
Blantyre, Malawi	35·1	2·05	8
Singapore	11·7	6·15	1
London, England	13·5	5·33	4
Cairo, Egypt	15·8	4·56	6
New York, USA	13·3	5·41	3
Paris, France	14·1	5·11	5
Dublin, Ireland	12·3	5·85	2
Berne, Switzerland	19·3	3·73	7

4. 4·1 km/h
5. 4·78 km/h

E3.3

PCM 49

1. 4 km
2. 3 km
3. 3 km
4. 8 km
5. Via Wakefield 89·25 km. Via Halifax 90 km. The shortest route is via Wakefield.
6. Via Stockport and Sheffield 81 km. Via Sheffield 78·75 km. Via Stockport 72·75 km. The shortest route is via Stockport, without going through Sheffield.

Extra

Answers will vary.

E3.4

PCM 50

1. 8
2. 5
3. $\frac{7}{20}$
4. 8 : 5 : 7
5. $\frac{5}{12}$
6. Jaz 4; Amit 3; Ellie 5
7. 4 : 3 : 5
8. $\frac{5}{12}$
9. Amit 10; Jaz 25; Ellie 25
10. 2 : 5 : 5
11. $\frac{4}{15}$
12. Ellie 50 cl; Jaz 60 cl; Amit 40 cl
13. 5 : 6 : 4

Extra

18 sweets $\frac{1}{3}, \frac{1}{6}, \frac{1}{2}$ 6 : 3 : 9 or 2 : 1 : 3

30 marshmallows $\frac{3}{10}, \frac{1}{3}, \frac{11}{30}$ 9 : 10 : 11

E3.5

1. There is one more way to arrange three dominoes. In total there are three ways to arrange three dominoes.

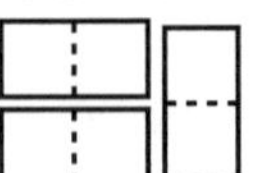

2. There are five ways to arrange four dominoes
3. There are eight ways to arrange five dominoes
4.

Number of dominoes	1	2	3	4	5	6	7
Number of arrangements	1	2	3	5	8	13	21

5. Each number is the sum of the two previous numbers. Nine dominoes would have 55 arrangements.

Extra

Number of dominoes	Maximum score	Minimum score
2	23	1
3	33	3
4	43	5
5	52	8
6	61	11

E3.6

1. My PIN is the sum of the first 11 prime numbers, multiplied by 10.
   1600
2. My PIN is two 2-digit square numbers.
   8164
3. My PIN is a cubed number.
   1331
4. The first two digits of my PIN are the sum of all the factors of 24. The second two digits are the sum of all the factors of 36.
   6091
5. The prime factors of my PIN are the first four odd prime numbers.
   1155
6. My PIN is a square number.
   2500
7. My PIN is the first four prime numbers in reverse.
   7532

E3

8. My PIN is the sum of the first 15 square numbers.
   1240
9. My PIN is the first 4-digit prime number.
   1009
10. My PIN is two 2-digit prime numbers, less than 30.
   2327

Extra

Answers will vary.

Part of Pearson

Ginn is an imprint of Pearson Education Limited, a company incorporated in England and Wales, having its registered office at Edinburgh Gate, Harlow, Essex, CM20 2JE. Registered company number: 872828

www.pearsonschools.co.uk

Ginn is a registered trademark of Pearson Education Limited

First published 2009

13 12 11 10
10 9 8 7 6 5 4 3

British Library Cataloguing in Publication Data
A catalogue record for this book is available from the British Library

ISBN 978 0 602 57777 3

Typeset by Tech-Set Ltd, Gateshead
Cover photo/illustration © Per José Karlén
Printed in Britain by Ashford Colour Press

Acknowledgements
Every effort has been made to contact copyright holders of material reproduced in this book. Any omissions will be rectified in subsequent printings if notice is given to the publishers.

Authors

Jon Kurta is currently Primary Strategy Manager in Camden. He has previously worked as a primary teacher and maths subject leader, a numeracy consultant and a lecturer in Initial Teacher Education.

Carol Richardson is a freelance consultant in primary mathematics. She has worked as a class teacher and subject leader across Key Stages 1 to 4. She has also been a Numeracy Consultant in Somerset, where her role included working with the Gifted and Talented Adviser to support teachers in this area.